The Pageant of Literature

MODERN ENGLISH WRITERS

CATHOLIC **CED** EDUCATION DIVISION

New York THE MACMILLAN COMPANY

820

M

The Macmillan Company, New York
Brett-Macmillan, Ltd., Galt, Ontario
Printed in the United States of America

7C

For permission to use material in this book, grateful acknowledgment is made to the following:

George Allen & Unwin, Ltd.: For *Riders to the Sea* by John Millington Synge.

J. M. Dent & Sons, Ltd.: For "The Secret Sharer" by Joseph Conrad.

Devin-Adair Co. and Curtis Brown, Ltd.: For "The Fur Coat" from *The Man Who Invented Sin* by Sean O'Faolain. Copyright 1948 by The Devin-Adair Company of New York.

Dodd, Mead & Co., McClelland & Stewart, Ltd., and Sidgwick & Jackson, Ltd.: For "The Soldier," "The Great Lover," and "Dining-Room Tea" from *The Collected Poems of Rupert Brooke.* Copyright 1915 by Dodd, Mead & Company, Inc.; copyright 1943 by Edward Marsh.

Doubleday & Co. and A. P. Watt & Son: For "Mandalay" and "Fuzzy-Wuzzy" from *Departmental Ditties and Ballads & Barrack-Room Ballads* by Rudyard Kipling; "Recessional" from *The Five Nations* by Rudyard Kipling; "Miss Youghal's Sais" from *Plain Tales from the Hills* by Rudyard Kipling. Reprinted by permission of Mrs. George Bambridge and Doubleday & Company, Inc. For "The Verger" from *Cosmopolitans* by W. Somerset Maugham. Copyright 1929 by W. Somerset Maugham. Reprinted by permission of Doubleday & Company, Inc., William Heinemann, Ltd., A. P. Watt & Son, and the author.

E. P. Dutton & Co. and William Heinemann, Ltd.: For "The Crime" from *And Even Now* by Max Beerbohm. Copyright 1921, by E. P. Dutton & Company, Inc. Renewal, 1949, by Max Beerbohm. Reprinted by permission of the publishers.

Harcourt, Brace and World, Inc.: For "The New Dress" from *A Haunted House and Other Stories* by Virginia Woolf. Copyright, 1927, by Events Publishing Company. Reprinted by permission of Harcourt, Brace and World, Inc. and The Hogarth Press. For "David Copperfield" from *The Moment and Other Essays* by Virginia Woolf. Copyright, 1948, by Harcourt, Brace and Company, Inc. Reprinted with their permission and The Hogarth Press. For "Shooting an Elephant" from *Shooting an Elephant and Other Essays* by George Orwell. Copyright, 1945, 1946, 1949, 1950, by Sonia Brownell Orwell. Reprinted by permission of Harcourt, Brace and World, Inc. and Martin Secker & Warburg, Ltd. For "The United States" from *Two Cheers for Democracy* by E. M. Forster. Copyright, 1947, by E. M. Forster. Reprinted by permission of Harcourt, Brace and World, Inc.

Holt, Rinehart and Winston, Inc.: For "To an Athlete Dying Young," "When I Was One-and-Twenty," "1887," "The First of May," "Bredon Hill" from *Collected Poems of A. E. Housman* by A. E. Housman, published by Holt, Rinehart and Winston, Inc. Copyright 1940 by Henry Holt & Co., Inc. Also reprinted by permission of The Society of Authors as the literary representatives of the Estate of the late A. E. Housman and Messrs. Jonathan Cape, Ltd., publishers of A. E. Housman's *Collected Poems.*

Houghton Mifflin Co.: For "The Graf Spee" from *The Gathering Storm* by Winston Churchill. Copyright, 1948. Reprinted by permission of Houghton Mifflin Company and Cassell & Company, Ltd.

Alfred A. Knopf, Inc.: For "Her First Ball" from *The Short Stories of Katherine Mansfield* by Katherine Mansfield. Copyright, 1922, 1937 by Alfred A. Knopf, Inc. Reprinted by permission of Alfred A. Knopf, Inc. and The Society of Authors as the literary representative of the Estate of the late Miss Katherine Mansfield. For "A Queer Heart" from *Look at All Those Roses* by Elizabeth Bowen. Copyright, 1941, by Elizabeth Bowen. Reprinted by permission of Alfred A. Knopf, Inc. and Curtis Brown, Ltd.

Little, Brown & Co.: For *The Barretts of Wimpole Street* by Rudolf Besier. Copyright, 1930, by Rudolf Besier. Reprinted by permission of Little, Brown & Company and Victor Gollancz, Ltd.

The Macmillan Company: For "A Prayer for My Daughter" from *Collected Poems* by W. B. Yeats. Copyright, 1924, by The Macmillan Company. For "The Wild Swans at Coole" from *Collected Poems* by W. B. Yeats. Copyright, 1919, renewed 1946, by The Macmillan Company. For "The Lamentation of the Old Pensioner," "When You Are Old," "The Cap and Bells," "The Lake Isle of Innesfree" from *Collected Poems* by W. B. Yeats. Copyright, 1906, renewed 1934, by The Macmillan Company. For "For Anne Gregory" from *Collected Poems* by W. B. Yeats. Copyright, 1933, by The Macmillan Company. For "Sailing to Byzantium" from *Collected Poems* by W. B. Yeats. Copyright, 1928, by The Macmillan Company. Reprinted with their permission and that of A. P. Watt & Son. For "Cargoes," "Spanish Waters," "The West Wind," "Truth" from *Poems* by John Masefield. Copyright, 1912, renewed 1940, by The Macmillan Company. For "On Growing Old" from *Poems* by John Masefield. Copyright, 1920, by John Masefield, renewed 1948. Reprinted with the permission of The Macmillan Company, The Society of Authors, and Dr. John Masefield, D.M. For "Autumn," "St. Peter," "Pilgrimage," "After the Annunciation" from *Poems* by Eileen Duggan. Copyright, 1939, by The Macmillan Company and reprinted with their permission and that of George Allen & Unwin Ltd.

New Directions: For "Strange Meeting," "The Send-off," "Apologia Pro Poemate Meo" from *The Poems of Wilfred Owen* by Wilfred Owen. All rights reserved. Reprinted by permission of New Directions and Chatto & Windus, Ltd. For "Fern Hill," "Poem in October," "The Force That Through the Green Fuse," "Author's Prologue," "Do Not Go Gentle into That Good Night," "The Hand That Signed the Paper" from *The Collected Poems of Dylan Thomas* by Dylan Thomas. Copyright, 1939, 1942, 1946 by New Directions. Copyright, 1952, 1953, by Dylan Thomas. Reprinted by permission of New Directions and J. M. Dent & Sons, Ltd.

Hesketh Pearson: For "The Drama" from *Bernard Shaw: His Life and Personality* by Hesketh Pearson. Reprinted by permission of the author and Methuen & Co. Ltd.

A. D. Peters: For "Henry V" from *A Conversation with Cats and Others* by Hilaire Belloc. Reprinted by permission of the publishers.

Random House, Inc.: For "Oh Young Men, Oh Young Comrades" and "The Express." Copyright, 1934, by The Modern Library, Inc. Reprinted from *Collected Poems 1928–1953*, by Stephen Spender. For "Ultima Ratio Regum" and

"The Barn." Copyright, 1942, by Stephen Spender. Reprinted from *Collected Poems 1928–1953*, by Stephen Spender. For "The Journey." Copyright, 1942, by Stephen Spender. Reprinted from *Ruins and Visions: Poems 1934–1942*, by Stephen Spender. All reprinted by permission of Random House, Inc. and Faber and Faber, Ltd.

Charles Scribner's Sons: For "Quality" from *The Inn of Tranquillity* by John Galsworthy. Copyright, 1912, Charles Scribner's Sons; renewal copyright 1940. Reprinted with permission of Charles Scribner's Sons and William Heinemann, Ltd. For "The Old Lady Shows Her Medals" by James M. Barrie from *The Plays of James M. Barrie*. Copyright, 1918, James M. Barrie; renewal copyright, 1946, Cynthia Asquith. Reprinted with the permission of Charles Scribner's Sons and Hodder & Stoughton, Ltd. For performing rights, permission must be obtained from Samuel French, Inc.

Sheed & Ward, Inc.: For "The Fear of the Past" from *What's Wrong with the World* by G. K. Chesterton. Copyright and published by Sheed & Ward, Inc., New York and with the permission of Miss Dorothy Collins and A. P. Watt & Son.

The Society of Authors: For "The Listeners," "Once," "Scholars," "A Dull Boy," "The Rapids," "The Burning-Glass" by Walter de la Mare. Reprinted by permission of the Literary Trustees of Walter de la Mare and The Society of Authors as their representative.

Vanguard Press: For "Aubade," "En Famille," "Mariner Man," "The Little Ghost Who Died for Love" from *The Collected Poems of Edith Sitwell*. Copyright, 1949, 1954, by Edith Sitwell. Reprinted by permission of the publisher, Vanguard Press, and David Higham Associates, Ltd.

The Viking Press: For "Aftermath" and "Everyone Sang" from *Collected Poems* by Siegfried Sassoon. Copyright, 1920, by E. P. Dutton & Company, 1948 by Siegfried Sassoon. For "Dreamers" from *Collected Poems* by Siegfried Sassoon. Copyright, 1918, by E. P. Dutton & Company, 1946 by Siegfried Sassoon. All reprinted by permission of The Viking Press, Inc. and the author. For "The Lumber-Room" from *The Short Stories of Saki* by H. H. Munro. Reprinted by permission of The Viking Press, Inc. and The Bodley Head, Ltd. All rights reserved. For "Araby" from *The Dubliners* by James Joyce. Reprinted by permission of The Viking Press, Inc., Jonathan Cape, Ltd., and The Society of Authors. All rights reserved. For "Across the Bridge" from *Nineteen Stories* by Graham Greene. Copyright, 1947, by Graham Greene. Reprinted by permission of The Viking Press, Inc. and Laurence Pollinger, Ltd.

CONTENTS

MODERN
ENGLISH
WRITERS

INTRODUCTION

One of the outstanding characteristics of modern literature is its emphasis on realism and the study of man as man, with all his contradictory desires, ambitions, and fears. In both verse and prose, writers have sought to interpret what people feel, not in the old, idealistic way of the romanticists, but by studying and analyzing human action in the light of its immediate surroundings.

Certain writers of this new realistic school, however, satisfied their romantic desire for adventure and the strange by setting their stories and poems in mysterious, far-off places, while, at the same time, describing these scenes with a realism and a fidelity to detail unsurpassed in literature. Among these writers were Rudyard Kipling, Joseph Conrad, and W. Somerset Maugham.

By the end of the nineteenth century, most readers were discontented with the stories and poems that were being written. They felt that the literature they read was too romantic and genteel and did not come to grips with the more energetic and realistic aspects of life. It is no wonder then, that readers welcomed Kipling's vigorous prose and poetry about India, Masefield's verse with the freshness of the sea blowing through it, Katherine Mansfield's keen psychological stories of everyday people, and Conrad's powerful tales of the sea and the exotic African jungle.

It was to the poets in particular that men turned for a redefining of their place in the cosmic scheme of things. What they found was a diversity of minds and spirits—all eager to defend the cause of beauty and truth against the ugliness of industrialism and commercialism so prevalent in England. They found, too, that while many of the poets dealt with romantic themes—the beauty of nature, the love of man for his homeland, the old fascination for the supernatural and the unknown—yet, the directness of expression and realistic imagery made a strong, new appeal to their minds and hearts. Readers welcomed the idealism in Rupert Brooke's "Great Lover," the call to dynamic living in A. E. Housman's "Reveille," the

1

pictures of enchanted childhood as described by Walter de la Mare and Dylan Thomas, the beauty of Irish myths so musically evoked by William Butler Yeats.

It was to the poets, too, that men turned for an understanding of their own confused reactions to the dreadful effects of war and to the whole age of political and social unrest which followed World War I. Although soldiers needed no convincing that there was neither glamor nor glory in war, it took poets such as Wilfred Owen and Siegfried Sassoon to arouse the public to its horrors. These poets wrote of the rat-ridden trenches, the tensions and despair, the lost limbs and shell-shock of thousands, the dying in vain, which they had witnessed at close range for themselves. Between World War I and World War II, poets like Stephen Spender wrote critically of the economic and political unrest in the world and the effects of the machine age on people.

Finally, to prove that men must not only broaden their concepts of the themes about which poetry may be written, but must enlarge their ideas about poetic language, too, the poets set about the startling task of including things so "unpoetic" as gasworks, trains, pistons and bolts, and machines in their verse. Thus, even the "materialistic progress" of the twentieth century became for the poets a source of power and beauty.

On the whole, the literature since the turn of the century has reflected the spirit of the "age of anxiety" with its wars and rumors of wars reaching down into our own time. At its best, it has redefined and asserted anew the dignity and importance of the individual as opposed to the impersonal forces about him, and stressed his need for love and a deeper understanding of himself.

RUDYARD KIPLING

(1865–1936)

Rudyard Kipling stands as the bridge between Victorian and modern literature. He was one of the earliest writers to break with the old traditions and to introduce new themes and new forms of expression. His success stems from his keen understanding and vigorous picture of the common man, especially of the private British soldier with his simple appreciation of life's meaning.

Educated in England, Kipling, nevertheless, spent a great part of his life in India, which became the setting for many of his short stories and poems. For his material he studied the natives of that country, with their miseries and superstitions. He followed the British soldier into the confusion of battle. He observed with humor and pathos the scandals of the Anglo-Indian society of his day. All of this he put down with energy and style. His use of the cockney dialect in verse and prose shocked and delighted the public, and did much to popularize Kipling's work as a whole. In 1907, he became England's first Nobel Prize winner in literature.

A staunch patriot and supporter of British imperialism, Kipling has been accused of "jingoism," that is, of advocating a warlike, aggressive foreign policy and attempting to glamorize English nationalism. You will see strong indications of this in the poem "Recessional," which, nevertheless, was written primarily as a warning to the self-satisfied and smug statesmen of Kipling's time.

In the poems that follow and in the short story on page 132, you will catch a glimpse of Kipling's variety of interests and subject matter—from the comical British soldier, who disguised himself as an Indian servant, through the admirable native, Fuzzy-Wuzzy, who "broke the British square," to the warning yet jubilant notes of his marching "Recessional," which has since been set to music.

RECESSIONAL

God of our fathers, known of old,
 Lord of our far-flung battle-line,
Beneath whose awful hand we hold
 Dominion over palm and pine—
Lord God of Hosts, be with us yet,
Lest we forget—lest we forget!

5

The tumult and the shouting dies;
   The captains and the kings depart:
Still stands Thine ancient sacrifice,
   An humble and a contrite heart.   10
Lord God of Hosts, be with us yet,
Lest we forget—lest we forget!

Far-called, our navies melt away;
   On dune and headland sinks the fire:
Lo, all our pomp of yesterday   15
   Is one with Nineveh and Tyre!
Judge of the Nations, spare us yet,
Lest we forget—lest we forget!

If, drunk with sight of power, we loose
   Wild tongues that have not Thee in awe,   20
Such boastings as the Gentiles use,
   Or lesser breeds without the Law—
Lord God of Hosts, be with us yet,
Lest we forget—lest we forget!

For heathen heart that puts her trust   25
   In reeking tube and iron shard,
All valiant dust that builds on dust,
   And, guarding, calls not Thee to guard,
For frantic boast and foolish word—
Thy Mercy on Thy People, Lord!   30

MANDALAY

By the old Moulmein Pagoda, lookin' lazy at the sea,
There's a Burma girl a-settin', and I know she thinks o' me;
For the wind is in the palm-trees, and the temple-bells they say:
"Come you back, you British soldier; come you back to Mandalay!"
   Come you back to Mandalay,   5
   Where the old Flotilla lay:
   Can't you 'ear their paddles chunkin' from Rangoon
      to Mandalay?
   On the road to Mandalay,
   Where the flyin'-fishes play,

An' the dawn comes up like thunder outer China 'crost
    the Bay!   10

'Er petticoat was yaller an' 'er little cap was green,
An' 'er name was Supi-yaw-lat—jes' the same as Theebaw's * Queen,
An' I seed her first a-smokin' of a whackin' white cheroot,
An' a-wastin' Christian kisses on an 'eathen idol's foot:
    Bloomin' idol made o' mud—   15
    Wot they called the Great Gawd Budd—
    Plucky lot she cared for idols when I kissed 'er where she stud!
    On the road to Mandalay . . .

When the mist was on the rice-fields an' the sun was droppin' slow,
She'd git 'er little banjo an' she'd sing *"Kulla-lo-lo!"*   20
With 'er arm upon my shoulder an' 'er cheek agin my cheek
We useter watch the steamers an' the *hathis* * pilin' teak.
    Elephints a'pilin' teak
    In the sludgy, squdgy creek,
    Where the silence 'ung that 'eavy you was 'arf afraid to speak! 25
    On the road to Mandalay . . .

But that's all shove be'ind me—long ago an' fur away,
An' there ain't no 'busses runnin' from the Bank to Mandalay;
An' I'm learnin' 'ere in London what the ten-year soldier tells:
"If you've 'eard the East a-callin', you won't never 'eed naught else." 30
    No! you won't 'eed nothin' else
    But them spicy garlic smells,
    An' the sunshine an' the palm-trees an' the tinkly-temple-bells;
    On the road to Mandalay . . .

I am sick o' wastin' leather on these gritty pavin'-stones,   35
An' the blasted English drizzle wakes the fever in my bones;
Tho' I walks with fifty 'ousemaids outer Chelsea to the Strand,
An' they talks a lot o' lovin', but wot do they understand?
    Beefy face an' grubby 'and—
    Law! wot do they understand?   40
    I've a neater, sweeter maiden in a cleaner, greener land!
    On the road to Mandalay . . .

Theebaw: the last King of Burma
hathis: elephants

Ship me somewheres east of Suez, where the best is like the worst
Where there aren't no Ten Commandments an' a man can raise a
 thirst;
For the temple-bells are callin', an' it's there that I would be— 45
By the old Moulmein Pagoda, lookin' lazy at the sea;
 On the road to Mandalay,
 Where the old Flotilla lay,
 With our sick beneath the awnings when we went to Mandalay!
 O the road to Mandalay,   50
 Where the flyin'-fishes play,
 An' the dawn comes up like thunder outer China 'crost the Bay!

FUZZY-WUZZY *

We've fought with many men acrost the seas,
 An' some of 'em was brave an' some was not;
The Paythan an' the Zulu an' Burmese;
 But the Fuzzy was the finest o' the lot.
We never got a ha'porth's change of 'im: 5
 'E squatted in the scrub an' 'ocked our 'orses,
'E cut our sentries up at Sua*kim*,*
 An' 'e played the cat an' banjo with our forces.
  So 'ere's *to* you, Fuzzy-Wuzzy, at your 'ome in the Sudan;
  You're a pore benighted 'eathen but a first-class fightin' man; 10
  We gives you your certificate, an' if you want it signed,
  We'll come an' 'ave a romp with you whenever you're inclined.

We took our chanst among the Kyber 'ills,
The Boers knocked us silly at a mile,
The Burman give us Irriwaddy chills,   15
 An' a Zulu *impi* * dished us up in style:
But all we ever got from such as they
 Was pop to what the Fuzzy made us swaller;
We 'eld our bloomin' own, the papers say,
 But man for man the Fuzzy knocked us 'oller.   20
  Then 'ere's *to* you, Fuzzy-Wuzzy, an' the missis and the kid;
  Our orders was to break you, an' of course we went an' did.

Fuzzy-Wuzzy: a native of the Anglo-Egyptian Sudan
Suakim: a seaport on the Red Sea
Zulu impi: a body of Zulu troops

We sloshed you with Martinis,* an' it wasn't 'ardly fair;
But for all the odds agin' you, Fuzzy-Wuz, you broke the square.

'E 'asn't got no papers of 'is own,   25
  'E 'asn't got no medals nor rewards,
So *we* must certify the skill 'e's shown
  In usin' of 'is long two-'anded swords:
When 'e's 'oppin' in an' out among the bush
  With 'is coffin-'eaded shield an' shovel-spear,   30
An 'appy day with Fuzzy on the rush
  Will last an 'ealthy Tommy for a year.
    So 'ere's *to* you, Fuzzy-Wuzzy, an' your friends which are no more,
    If we 'adn't lost some messmates, we would 'elp you to deplore.
    But give an' take's the gospel, an' we'll call the bargain fair,   35
    For if you 'ave lost more than us, you crumpled up the square!

'E rushes at the smoke when we let drive,
  An', before we know, 'e 's 'ackin' at our 'ead;
'E's all 'ot sand an' ginger when alive,
  An 'e 's generally shammin' when 'e 's dead.   40
'E's a daisy, 'e 's a ducky, 'e 's a lamb!
  'E's a injia-rubber idiot on the spree,
'E's the on'y thing that doesn't give a damn
  For a Regiment o' British Infantree!
    So 'ere's *to* you, Fuzzy-Wuzzy, at your 'ome in the Sudan;   45
    You're a poor benighted 'eathen but a first-class fightin' man;
    An' 'ere's *to* you, Fuzzy-Wuzzy, with your 'ayrick 'ead of 'air—
    You big black boundin' beggar—for you broke a British square!

Martinis: a type of rifle

For Discussion

"Recessional"

1. Explain the allusions and discuss the meaning of lines 9–10; 15–16;
   21–22. What does "we hold/Dominion over palm and pine" mean?
2. Choose five other figures of speech and explain their meaning. What
   are "reeking tube" and "iron shard" metaphors for? Do you consider
   them effective metaphors? Explain.
3. In line 22, the speaker implies that England is the chosen nation of
   God; all other people are the "lesser breeds." Does this idea contradict

the poet's attitude evidenced in many of his dialect poems? Discuss fully.

4. Is the theme of this poem restricted to England, or do you consider it a universal theme? How could it apply to America or Russia, for example? Have some of Kipling's warnings been realized in England since his death? Explain.

"Mandalay"

1. Part of Kipling's romantic nature is his fondness for exotic settings. Observe the numerous oriental names the speaker employs in this poem, illustrating his knowledge of life and manners in the great city of his beloved "Burma girl." Discuss the details of this strange land and clime. Describe the girl's appearance and occupation. Mention other sights and sounds alluring to the "ten-year soldier" back in England.

2. In stanza 5, what contrasting ugliness does the soldier, home from the East, find in England?

3. How does Kipling's philosophy come to light in the last stanza? When the speaker says "there aren't no Ten Commandments," does he mean it literally, or is he merely suggesting that the glamorous Orient has no need for rules? In what sense does he mean that the "best is like the worst"?

4. Considering both "Fuzzy-Wuzzy" and "Mandalay" together, what impression does Kipling's ex-soldier give you of the countries "east of Suez"? Of their people? Of their beliefs, virtues, manners, customs?

"Fuzzy-Wuzzy"

1. The speaker, probably a veteran of the English expeditionary forces in the Sudan, celebrates in retrospect "the first-class fightin' man" who broke the British military formation called "the square." Point out lines which show the variety of ways in which this native outwitted the respected forces of Her Majesty's men.

2. Point out lines which describe Fuzzy-Wuzzy's physical appearance; his manner of attack; his methods of weakening the enemy's supplies.

3. Explain the comparisons made in stanza 2. Why would you expect the newspapers to report that the British were victorious? What is the truth?

4. Which class of soldiers is the speaker satirizing in the first two lines of the third stanza? Will the *oral* certification of Fuzzy's courage carry weight? Why or why not? How does the poem in this instance, and in other ways, emphasize Victorian manners and ideals?

5. How does the poem as a whole reflect Kipling's ideas and style? Discuss fully.

A. E. HOUSMAN

(1859–1936)

Born in Worcestershire, England, Alfred Edward Housman spent much of his life in London and Cambridge as a classical scholar and professor of Latin. Most of his poems, however, notably in A *Shropshire Lad*, published in 1896, are about the rural scenes near Shropshire where he was born.

A classicist in form, Housman was nevertheless a romanticist in his subject matter. His frequently melancholy themes, such as the swift passage of time, the inevitability of death, and the blight of war, reveal a mind disillusioned and pessimistic. Despite the subject matter, however, his poems are always lyrical. They have a simplicity and directness, and present some of the most exquisite pictures of nature. His poetry, tinged with gentle irony, shows a man struggling to adapt himself to the rapidly changing environment of the Victorian era.

Although Housman wrote comparatively few poems, comprising only three small volumes, A *Shropshire Lad* has become one of the most popular books of poetry in English, and had an important influence on the poets of his time and later.

XXV

This time of year a twelvemonth past,
    When Fred and I would meet,
We needs must jangle, till at last
    We fought and I was beat.

So then the summer fields about,   5
    Till rainy days began,
Rose Harland on her Sundays out
    Walked with the better man.

The better man she walks with still,
    Though now 'tis not with Fred: 10
A lad that lives and has his will
    Is worth a dozen dead.

Fred keeps the house all kinds of weather,
    And clay's the house he keeps;

When Rose and I walk out together   15
Stock-still lies Fred and sleeps.

REVEILLE

Wake: the silver dusk returning
    Up the beach of darkness brims,
And the ship of sunrise burning
    Strands upon the eastern rims.

Wake: the vaulted shadow shatters,   5
    Trampled to the floor it spanned,
And the tent of night in tatters
    Straws the sky-pavilioned land.

Up, lad, up, 'tis late for lying:
    Hear the drums of morning play;   10
Hark, the empty highways crying
    "Who'll beyond the hills away?"

Towns and countries woo together,
    Forelands beacon, belfries call;
Never lad that trod on leather   15
    Lived to feast his heart with all.

Up, lad: thews that lie and cumber
    Sunlit pallets never thrive;
Morns abed and daylight slumber
    Were not meant for man alive.   20

Clay lies still, but blood's a rover;
    Breath's a ware that will not keep.
Up, lad: when the journey's over
    There'll be time enough to sleep.

TO AN ATHLETE DYING YOUNG

The time you won your town the race
We chaired you through the marketplace;
Man and boy stood cheering by,
And home we brought you shoulder-high.

Today, the road all runners come,   5
Shoulder-high we bring you home,
And set you at your threshold down,
Townsman of a stiller town.

Smart lad, to slip betimes away
From fields where glory does not stay,   10
And early though the laurel grows,
It withers quicker than the rose.

Eyes the shady night has shut
Cannot see the record cut,
And silence sounds no worse than cheers   15
After earth has stopped the ears.

Now you will not swell the rout
Of lads that wore their honors out,
Runners whom renown outran
And the name died before the man.   20

So set, before its echoes fade,
The fleet foot on the sill of shade,
And hold to the low lintel up
The still-defended challenge-cup.

And round that early-laureled head   25
Will flock to gaze the strengthless dead,
And find unwithered on its curls
The garland briefer than a girl's.

THE FIRST OF MAY

The orchards half the way
   From home to Ludlow fair
Flowered on the first of May
   In Mays when I was there;
And seen from stile or turning   5
   The plume of smoke would show
Where fires were burning
   That went out long ago.

The plum broke forth in green,
   The pear stood high and snowed,   10
My friends and I between
   Would take the Ludlow road;
Dressed to the nines and drinking
   And light in heart and limb,
And each chap thinking   15
   The fair was held for him.

Between the trees in flower
   New friends at fairtime tread
The way where Ludlow tower
   Stands planted on the dead.   20
Our thoughts, a long while after,
   They think, our words they say;
Theirs now's the laughter,
   The fair, the first of May.

Ay, yonder lads are yet   25
   The fools that we were then;
For oh, the sons we get
   Are still the sons of men.
The sumless tale of sorrow
   Is all unrolled in vain: 30
May comes to-morrow
   And Ludlow fair again.

WHEN I WAS ONE-AND-TWENTY

When I was one-and-twenty
   I heard a wise man say,
"Give crowns and pounds and guineas
   But not your heart away;
Give pearls away and rubies   5
   But keep your fancy free."
But I was one-and-twenty,
   No use to talk to me.

When I was one-and-twenty
   I heard him say again,   10

"The heart out of the bosom
   Was never given in vain;
'Tis paid with sighs a plenty
   And sold for endless rue."
And I am two-and-twenty,   15
   And oh, 'tis true, 'tis true.

BREDON HILL

In summertime on Bredon
   The bells they sound so clear;
Round both the shires they ring them
   In steeples far and near,
   A happy noise to hear.   5

Here of a Sunday morning
   My love and I would lie,
And see the coloured counties,
   And hear the larks so high
   About us in the sky.   10

The bells would ring to call her
   In valleys miles away:
"Come all to church, good people;
   Good people, come and pray."
   But here my love would stay.   15

And I would turn and answer
   Among the springing thyme,
"Oh, peal upon our wedding,
   And we will hear the chime,
   And come to church in time."   20

But when the snows at Christmas
   On Bredon top were strown,
My love rose up so early
   And stole out unbeknown
   And went to church alone.   25

They tolled the one bell only,
   Groom there was none to see,

The mourners followed after,
And so to church went she,
And would not wait for me.   30

The bells they sound on Bredon,
And still the steeples hum,
"Come all to church, good people,"—
Oh, noisy bells, be dumb;
I hear you, I will come.   35

1887

From Clee * to heaven the beacon burns,
    The shires have seen it plain,
From north and south the sign returns
    And beacons burn again.

Look left, look right, the hills are bright,   5
    The dales are light between,
Because 'tis fifty years to-night
    That God has saved the Queen.

Now, when the flame they watch not towers
    About the soil they trod,   10
Lads, we'll remember friends of ours
    Who shared the work with God.

To skies that knit their heartstrings right,
    To fields that bred them brave,
The saviours come not home to-night: 15
    Themselves they could not save.

It dawns in Asia, tombstones show
    And Shropshire names are read;
And the Nile * spills his overflow
    Beside the Severn's * dead.   20

Clee: a hill in the southern part of Shropshire
Nile: During the 1850's (when *1887* was composed), there was much fighting
    along the Nile.
Severn: a river in Shropshire

> We pledge in peace by farm and town
> The Queen they served in war,
> And fire the beacons up and down
> The land they perished for.
>
> "God save the Queen," we living sing,   25
> From height to height 'tis heard;
> And with the rest your voices ring,
> Lads of the Fifty-third.*
>
> Oh, God will save her, fear you not:
> Be you the men you've been,   30
> Get you the sons your fathers got,
> And God will save the Queen.

the Fifty-third: the Shropshire Regiment of Infantry

For Discussion

"XXV"

1. In what respects is this a typical ballad?
2. Point out indications of Housman's philosophy of life from this poem.
3. Comment on Housman's use of the word "better" in stanza 2 and of the same word in stanza 3.

"Reveille"

1. This poem is considered one of Housman's most beautiful because of its poetic imagery. Discuss the effectiveness of each of the following: (a) "beach of darkness brims," (b) "ship of sunrise," (c) "tent of night," (d) "straws the sky-pavilioned land," (e) "clay lies still, but blood's a rover."
2. How does Housman give the impression of haste? Why does he want to give this impression?
3. What do you think is the theme of the poem?
4. Discuss Housman's use of strong verbs and nouns instead of descriptive adjectives.
5. Do you agree with Housman's idea of eternity as a time for sleep? Why or why not?

"To an Athelete Dying Young"

1. Discuss the theme of this poem.
2. What image does the poet use to link stanzas 1 and 2?

3. Can you detect irony in the poet's contemplation of the fame of a young athlete? Explain. What is the mood of stanza 4?
4. Compare the first and last stanzas. Point out how Housman achieves dramatic contrast.
5. How is the expression "smart lad" connotative of Housman's pessimistic views of life?

"The First of May"

1. Study at least six descriptive words in the poem and tell why each seems to be exactly the right word for the thought it expresses.
2. How does the poet use contrast?
3. Analyze lines 3 and 4 in the last stanza.
4. Do you think that the theme, imagery, music, and emotion blend in this poem? Why or why not?

"When I Was One-and-Twenty"

1. What is the significance of Housman's use of "one-and-twenty" and "two-and-twenty"?
2. Discuss the effect of the repetition in the last line.
3. Do you think this poem is completely serious or is there a slight note of humor? Explain.

"Bredon Hill"

1. Do you think that Housman shows a pessimistic philosophy concerning love? Explain.
2. Housman couples classical restraint with the romantic spirit. Explain, using this poem as an example.
3. In his lecture, "The Name and Nature of Poetry," Housman considered the metaphor and the simile as "accessories" and as "inessential to poetry." Discuss the metaphors used in this poem in view of the poet's own definition.
4. How does Housman reveal his view of established religion? Do you detect a touch of irony in the last stanza?

"1887"

1. Discuss the occasion for the writing of this poem. Find a direct reference to the occasion in the poem itself.
2. What type of stanza is Housman using in this poem? Do you think it appropriate for the thought? Why?
3. Some critics have found the last line to be one of bitter sarcasm; others have found it one of obvious sincerity. What is your reaction? Discuss your reasons.

WILLIAM BUTLER YEATS

(1865–1939)

William Butler Yeats is not only the most important poet Ireland has produced, but he also ranks among the major lyric poets in modern literature. In 1923, he received the Nobel Prize for literature. He firmly believed that truth could be arrived at through beauty, and that the common man keeps watch "over the roots of all religion and romance."

Yeats' poetry has a strong mystical quality. His earlier poems, in particular, steeped in Irish myths and legends about fairies, ancient heroes, and enchantments, are romantic and exquisitely melodious. At the same time, Yeats used his mind vigorously. He was constantly involved in Irish politics and took a leading part in the founding of the famous Abbey Theater. It was largely through his efforts in the early part of the century that Ireland's spirit of independence and love of culture flourished.

According to Yeats, a poem should be for the reader "a vision of reality which satisfies the whole being." To achieve this purpose, he worked to perfect his craft and his use of imagery, metaphors, and symbols. The results have placed him in the foremost rank of our contemporary poets.

A PRAYER FOR MY DAUGHTER

Once more the storm is howling, and half hid
Under this cradle-hood and coverlid
My child sleeps on. There is no obstacle
But Gregory's wood and one bare hill
Whereby the haystack- and roof-levelling wind,   5
Bred on the Atlantic, can be stayed;
And for an hour I have walked and prayed
Because of the great gloom that is in my mind.

I have walked and prayed for this young child an hour
And heard the sea-wind scream upon the tower,   10
And under the arches of the bridge, and scream
In the elms above the flooded stream;
Imagining in excited reverie

17

That the future years had come,
Dancing to a frenzied drum,　　　　　　　　　　　15
Out of the murderous innocence of the sea.

May she be granted beauty and yet not
Beauty to make a stranger's eye distraught,
Or hers before a looking-glass, for such,
Being made beautiful overmuch,　　　　　　　20
Consider beauty a sufficient end,
Lose natural kindness and maybe
The heart-revealing intimacy
That chooses right, and never find a friend.

Helen being chosen found life flat and dull　　25
And later had much trouble from a fool,
While that great Queen, that rose out of the spray,
Being fatherless could have her way
Yet chose a bandy-leggèd smith for man.
It's certain that fine women eat　　　　　　30
A crazy salad with their meat
Whereby the Horn of Plenty is undone.

In courtesy I'd have her chiefly learned;
Hearts are not had as a gift but hearts are earned
By those that are not entirely beautiful;　　35
Yet many, that have played the fool
For beauty's very self, has charm made wise,
And many a poor man that has roved,
Loved and thought himself beloved,
From a glad kindness cannot take his eyes.　　40

May she become a flourishing hidden tree
That all her thoughts may like the linnet be,
And have no business but dispensing round
Their magnanimities of sound,
Nor but in merriment begin a chase,　　　　45
Nor but in merriment a quarrel.
O may she live like some green laurel
Rooted in one dear perpetual place.

My mind, because the minds that I have loved,
The sort of beauty that I have approved,   50
Prosper but little, has dried up of late,
Yet knows that to be choked with hate
May well be of all evil chances chief.
If there's no hatred in a mind
Assault and battery of the wind   55
Can never tear the linnet from the leaf.

An intellectual hatred is the worst,
So let her think opinions are accursed.
Have I not seen the loveliest woman born
Out of the mouth of Plenty's horn,   60
Because of her opinionated mind
Barter that horn and every good
By quiet natures understood
For an old bellows full of angry wind?

Considering that, all hatred driven hence,   65
The soul recovers radical innocence
And learns at last that it is self-delighting,
Self-appeasing, self-affrighting,
And that its own sweet will is Heaven's will;
She can, though every face should scowl   70
And every windy quarter howl
Or every bellows burst, be happy still.

And may her bridegroom bring her to a house
Where all's accustomed, ceremonious;
For arrogance and hatred are the wares   75
Peddled in the thoroughfares.
How but in custom and in ceremony
Are innocence and beauty born?
Ceremony's a name for the rich horn,
And custom for the spreading laurel tree.   80

THE WILD SWANS AT COOLE

The trees are in their autumn beauty,
The woodland paths are dry,
Under the October twilight the water
Mirrors a still sky;

Upon the brimming water among the stones   5
Are nine-and-fifty swans.

The nineteenth autumn has come upon me
Since I first made my count;
I saw, before I had well finished,
All suddenly mount   10
And scatter wheeling in great broken rings
Upon their clamorous wings.

I have looked upon those brilliant creatures,
And now my heart is sore.
All's changed since I, hearing at twilight,   15
The first time on this shore,
The bell-beat of their wings above my head,
Trod with a lighter tread.

Unwearied still, lover by lover,
They paddle in the cold   20
Companionable streams or climb the air;
Their hearts have not grown old;
Passion or conquest, wander where they will,
Attend upon them still.

But now they drift on the still water   25
Mysterious, beautiful;
Among what rushes will they build,
By what lake's edge or pool
Delight men's eyes when I awake some day
To find they have flown away?   30

THE LAMENTATION OF THE OLD PENSIONER

Although I shelter from the rain
Under a broken tree,
My chair was nearest to the fire
In every company
That talked of love or politics,   5
Ere Time transfigured me.

Though lads are making pikes again
For some conspiracy,
And crazy rascals rage their fill
At human tyranny,   10
My contemplations are of Time
That has transfigured me.

There's not a woman turns her face
Upon a broken tree,
And yet the beauties that I loved   15
Are in my memory;
I spit into the face of Time
That has transfigured me.

WHEN YOU ARE OLD

When you are old and grey and full of sleep,
And nodding by the fire, take down this book,
And slowly read, and dream of the soft look
Your eyes had once, and of their shadows deep;

How many loved your moments of glad grace,   5
And loved your beauty with love false or true,
But one man loved the pilgrim soul in you,
And loved the sorrows of your changing face;

And bending down beside the glowing bars,
Murmur, a little sadly, how Love fled   10
And paced upon the mountains overhead
And hid his face amid a crowd of stars.

THE CAP AND BELLS

The jester walked in the garden:
The garden had fallen still;
He bade his soul rise upward
And stand on her window-sill.

It rose in a straight blue garment,   5
When owls began to call:

It had grown wise-tongued by thinking
Of a quiet and light footfall;

But the young queen would not listen;
She rose in her pale night-gown;   10
She drew in the heavy casement
And pushed the latches down.

He bade his heart go to her,
When the owls called out no more;
In a red and quivering garment   15
It sang to her through the door.

It had grown sweet-tongued by dreaming
Of a flutter of flower-like hair;
But she took up her fan from the table
And waved it off on the air.   20

'I have cap and bells,' he pondered,
'I will send them to her and die';
And when the morning whitened
He left them where she went by.

She laid them upon her bosom,   25
Under a cloud of her hair,
And her red lips sang them a love-song
Till stars grew out of the air.

She opened her door and her window,
And the heart and the soul came through,   30
To her right hand came the red one,
To her left hand came the blue.

They set up a noise like crickets,
A chattering wise and sweet,
And her hair was a folded flower   35
And the quiet of love in her feet.

THE LAKE ISLE OF INNISFREE

I will arise and go now, and go to Innisfree,
And a small cabin build there, of clay and wattles made:
Nine bean-rows will I have there, a hive for the honeybee,
And live alone in the bee-loud glade.

And I shall have some peace there, for peace comes dropping slow,   5
Dropping from the veils of the morning to where the cricket sings;
There midnight's all a glimmer, and noon a purple glow,
And evening full of the linnet's wings.

I will arise and go now, for always night and day
I hear lake water lapping with low sounds by the shore;   10
While I stand on the roadway, or on the pavements grey,
I hear it in the deep heart's core.

FOR ANNE GREGORY

Never shall a young man,
Thrown into despair
By those great honey-coloured
Ramparts at your ear,
Love you for yourself alone   5
And not your yellow hair.'

'But I can get a hair-dye
And set such colour there,
Brown, or black, or carrot,
That young men in despair   10
May love me for myself alone
And not my yellow hair.'

'I heard an old religious man
But yesternight declare
That he had found a text to prove   15
That only God, my dear,
Could love you for yourself alone
And not your yellow hair.'

SAILING TO BYZANTIUM

1

That is no country for old men. The young
In one another's arms, birds in the trees
—(Those dying generations)—at their song,
The salmon-falls, the mackerel-crowded seas,
Fish, flesh, or fowl, commend all summer long   5
Whatever is begotten, born, and dies.
Caught in that sensual music, all neglect
Monuments of unaging intellect.

2

An aged man is but a paltry thing,
A tattered coat upon a stick, unless   10
Soul clap its hands and sing, and louder sing
For every tatter in its mortal dress,
Nor is there singing school but studying
Monuments of its own magnificence;
And therefore I have sailed the seas and come   15
To the holy city of Byzantium.

3

O sages, standing in God's holy fire
As in the gold mosaic of a wall,
Come from the holy fire, perne in a gyre,
And be the singing-masters of my soul.   20
Consume my heart away—sick with desire
And fastened to a dying animal
It knows not what it is—and gather me
Into the artifice of eternity.

4

Once out of nature I shall never take   25
My bodily form from any natural thing,
But such a form as Grecian goldsmiths make
Of hammered gold and gold enamelling
To keep a drowsy Emperor awake;

Or set upon a golden bough to sing   30
To lords and ladies of Byzantium
Of what is past, or passing, or to come.

For Discussion

"A Prayer for My Daughter"

1. Which five gifts does the speaker ask for his new-born daughter? What reason is given for each?
2. In stanza 6, he prays that his daughter may live "like some green laurel/Rooted in one dear perpetual place," and not become a prey to every wind. To what "winds" does he refer in stanzas 7 and 8? In stanza 9, how does he connect the idea of howling winds with his daughter's happiness?
3. Explain the meaning of each of the following images:
   (a) "her thoughts . . . like the linnet be,
       And have no business but dispensing round
       Their magnanimities of sound."
   (b) "Hearts are not had as a gift but hearts are earned
       By those that are not entirely beautiful."
   (c) "An intellectual hatred is the worst,
       So let her think opinions are accursed."
   (d) "For arrogance and hatred are the wares
       Peddled in the thoroughfares."

"The Wild Swans at Coole"

1. The speaker states that the same fifty-nine swans have lived at Coole for nineteen years. Is this statement to be taken literally? Why or why not? If not, what second meaning does he imply?
2. Does he mean the reader to take the "Passion or conquest . . . /Attend upon them still" as referring to these same swans? What reason does he give for feeling sadness at the sight of their unweariedness?
3. In the words, ". . . when I awake some day," the speaker hints at his own passing from the scene. He will then be immortal, while the swans will still, somewhere, "delight men's eyes." What emotion overcomes him at the thought? The thought, itself, like the appearance of the swans in lines 25–26, is "mysterious, beautiful." What effect does the thought of awakening some day to find all earth's beauties flown, have on *you*? Discuss.
4. Explain each of the following italicized words in their contexts.
   (a) "*wheeling* . . . Upon *clamorous* wings"
   (b) "*bell-beat* of their wings"
   (c) "*Companionable* streams or *climb* the air"
   (d) "*Passion or conquest* . . . /*Attend* . . . them"

"The Lamentation of the Old Pensioner"

1. What does the old man lament most? Do you think his position is like that of today's retired pensioner?
2. The word "transfigured" is used ironically. Explain its double meaning.
3. Why is the "broken tree" image a particularly fitting one? What causes a tree to break?

"When You Are Old"

1. Describe the woman addressed in this poem. How does the phrase, "pilgrim soul" add to your conception of her?
2. What is the speaker's way of life? Has he followed his calling wholeheartedly? Prove your answer. Do you think he still loves the woman? Refer to line 8.
3. Yeats said of himself that when he was young, he wrote as an old man; and when he was old, he wrote as a young man. Compare the style of this poem, written about 1893 with that of "For Anne Gregory" (page 23) written about forty years later.

"The Cap and the Bells"

1. Symbolically, the blue garment represents the intellect and the appeal to logic; the red garment symbolizes emotion or passion. When the jester finds his young "queen" rejecting both, he gives all he has left, his "cap and bells," which she lovingly accepts. What do the cap and bells symbolize? Discuss.
2. Why does the queen's acceptance of these two objects pave the way for the admittance of the jester's "heart and soul"? Is this true of people in general? Discuss.
3. Describe the rhythm and mood of the poem.

"The Lake Isle of Innisfree"

1. Why does the speaker wish to go to Innisfree? Is the emotional experience a universal one? Discuss.
2. This is one of the most musical poems of Yeats. Observe how the repetition of certain vowels links the *ideas* in the poem. In stanza 1, for example, "clay," "made," and "glade" link the *kind* of residence desired with the *place* where it will be. In the same way, show how the short *i*-sounds of "cricket," "sings," "midnights," "glimmer," and "linnet's wings" in stanza 2, bring out the *atmosphere* of the envisioned solitude. Do you agree that his "glade" would constantly have a twilight hue? Why?
3. In the closing stanza, the speaker repeats his resolution to "arise and go now." Is this the word of a man of action, to be taken literally?

If not, what does it reflect? Explain your answer. Where is the speaker at the time?

"For Anne Gregory"

1. In this simple direct dialogue, what do you learn about Anne Gregory? Why is the argument necessarily ended with stanza 3?
2. Is the mood of the poem a serious one? Does the rhythm fit the mood? Which lines act as a little refrain throughout?

"Sailing to Byzantium"

1. Byzantium, at one time the ancient Greek center of art and culture, stands for the achievement of the human spirit, especially in the world of art. Why has the speaker left the "country" of stanza 1 for "Byzantium"? Describe the contrast between the world of fertility described in the first stanza with that of the aged man in the second.
2. In stanza 3, the speaker asks the saints, consumed in the fire of God's love, to burn away his body that he may become the great artificer, the craftsman, skilled to perfection in his art. How does the figure of speech in the last stanza bear out his desire? Will it be easier for him, "Once out of eternity," to sing "Of what is past, or passing, or to come"? Why? Will he sing of the flesh or of the soul? Prove your answer.
3. Would you say that the entire poem is a plea? If so, for what?

Poets of World War I

When World War I broke out, three English poets, Rupert Brooke, Siegfried Sassoon, and Wilfred Owen, enlisted with all the fervor and enthusiasm of the English youth of that period. Their reactions, however, to the terrible conflict were quite different, as their poems show.

Rupert Brooke thought self-sacrifice the highest of spiritual values. It has been said that he "had weighed in full the value of the life that he was casting away. It was to him a 'red, sweet wine' precious for the 'work and joy' it promised, and the sacred seed of immortality. It is this, above all, that his poetry signifies: a rich and exuberant life, keenly conscious of itself and fully aware of the realities by which it is surrounded." [1]

Brooke's romantic idealism is sharply contrasted by the cynicism and bitterness which pervades the work of Siegfried Sassoon. Army life and the ravages of war are never more savagely and brutally exposed than in Sassoon's poetry. Unlike Brooke, who died of blood poisoning while in service, and Wilfred Owen, who was killed just before the Armistice, Sassoon lived to recount the horrors of life in the trenches and to expose the truth behind the "glory" of war.

It was to Wilfred Owen, however, perhaps the finest poet of the three, that later war poets turned for their inspiration. Many of his poems were written in a war hospital in 1917 while he was re-cuperating from wounds received in battle. It was there that he met Siegfried Sassoon, who collected and published Owen's poems two years after his death. While expressing bitterness, his poetry has a deep pity and compassion for suffering mankind and for each individual soldier. His poems are some of the most authentic and musical expressions of any wartime poet.

It is to these poets that we owe, in part, our present-day awareness of the need to seek not only peace among all nations, but a genuine reawakening and strengthening of the inner life of every man.

[1] Mary C. Sturgeon, *Studies of Contemporary Poets*, George C. Harrap & Co., Ltd., London, 1920, page 40.

RUPERT BROOKE

(1887–1915)

THE SOLDIER

If I should die, think only this of me:
  That there's some corner of a foreign field
That is forever England. There shall be
  In that rich earth a richer dust concealed;
A dust whom England bore, shaped, made aware,   5
  Gave, once, her flowers to love, her ways to roam,
A body of England's, breathing English air,
  Washed by the rivers, blest by suns of home.

And think, this heart, all evil shed away,
  A pulse in the eternal mind, no less   10
    Gives somewhere back the thought by England given;
Her sights and sounds; dreams happy as her day;
  And laughter, learnt of friends; and gentleness,
    In hearts at peace, under an English heaven.

THE GREAT LOVER

I have been so great a lover: filled my days
So proudly with the splendor of Love's praise,
The pain, the calm, the astonishment,
Desire illimitable, and still content,
And all dear names men use, to cheat despair,   5
For the perplexed and viewless streams that bear
Our hearts at random down the dark of life.
Now, ere the unthinking silence on that strife
Steals down, I would cheat drowsy Death so far,
My night shall be remembered for a star   10
That outshone all the suns of all men's days.
Shall I not crown them with immortal praise
Whom I have loved, who have given me, dared with me
High secrets, and in darkness knelt to see
The inenarrable godhead of delight?   15

29

Love is a flame—we have beaconed the world's night;
A city—and we have built it, these and I;
An emperor—we have taught the world to die.
So, for their sakes I loved, ere I go hence,
And the high cause of Love's magnificence,   20
And to keep loyalties young, I'll write those names
Golden forever, eagles, crying flames,
And set them as a banner, that men may know,
To dare the generations, burn, and blow
Out on the wind of Time, shining and streaming.   25

These I have loved:
                            White plates and cups, clean-gleaming,
Ringed with blue lines; and feathery, fairy dust;
Wet roofs, beneath the lamplight; the strong crust
Of friendly bread; and many-tasting food;
Rainbows; and the blue bitter smoke of wood;   30
And radiant raindrops couching in cool flowers;
And flowers themselves, that sway through sunny hours,
Dreaming of moths that drink them under the moon;
Then, the cool kindliness of sheets, that soon
Smooth away trouble; and the rough male kiss   35
Of blankets; grainy wood; live hair that is
Shining and free; blue-massing clouds; the keen
Unpassioned beauty of a great machine;
The benison of hot water; furs to touch;
The good smell of old clothes; and other such—   40
The comfortable smell of friendly fingers,
Hair's fragrance, and the musty reek that lingers
About dead leaves and last year's ferns—
                                        Dear names,
And thousand others throng to me! Royal flames;
Sweet water's dimpling laugh from tap or spring;   45
Holes in the ground; and voices that do sing—
Voices in laughter, too; and body's pain,
Soon turned to peace; and the deep-panting train;
Firm sands; the little dulling edge of foam
That browns and dwindles as the wave goes home;   50
And washen stones, gay for an hour; the cold
Graveness of iron; moist black earthen mold;

Sleep; and high places; footprints in the dew;
And oaks; and brown horse chestnuts, glossy-new;
And new-peeled sticks; and shining pools on grass—   55
All these have been my loves. And these shall pass.
Whatever passes not, in the great hour,
Nor all my passion, all my prayers, have power
To hold them with me through the gate of Death.
They'll play deserter, turn with the traitor breath,   60
Break the high bond we made, and sell Love's trust
And sacramental covenant to the dust.
—Oh, never a doubt but, somewhere, I shall wake,
And give what's left of love again, and make
New friends, new strangers—
                 But the best I've known,   65
Stays here, and changes, breaks, grows old, is blown
About the winds of the world, and fades from brains
Of living men, and dies.
                Nothing remains.

O dear my loves, O faithless, once again   70
This one last gift I give: that after men
Shall know, and later lovers, far-removed,
Praise you, "All these were lovely"; say, "He loved."

DINING-ROOM TEA

When you were there, and you, and you,
Happiness crowned the night; I too,
Laughing and looking, one of all,
I watched the quivering lamplight fall
On plate and flowers and pouring tea   5
And cup and cloth; and they and we
Flung all the dancing moments by
With jest and glitter. Lip and eye
Flashed on the glory, shone and cried,
Improvident, unmemoried;   10
And fitfully, and like a flame
The light of laughter went and came.
Proud in their careless transience moved
The changing faces that I loved.

Till suddenly, and otherwhence,   15
I looked upon your innocence.
For lifted clear and still and strange
From the dark woven flow of change
Under a vast and starless sky
I saw the immortal moment lie.   20
One instant I, an instant, knew
As God knows all. And it and you,
I, above Time, oh, blind! could see
In witless immortality.

I saw the marble cup; the tea,   25
Hung on the air, an amber stream;
I saw the fire's unglittering gleam,
The painted flame, the frozen smoke.
No more the flooding lamplight broke
On flying eyes and lips and hair;   30
But lay, but slept unbroken there,
On stiller flesh, and body breathless,
And lips and laughter stayed and deathless,
And words on which no silence grew.
Light was more alive than you.   35

For suddenly, and otherwhence,
I looked on your magnificence.
I saw the stillness and the light,
And you, august, immortal, white,
Holy and strange; and every glint   40
Posture and jest and thought and tint
Freed from the mask of transiency,
Triumphant in eternity,
Immote, immortal.

                        Dazed at length   45
Human eyes grew, mortal strength
Wearied; and Time began to creep.
Change closed about me like a sleep.
Light glinted on the eyes I loved.
The cup was filled. The bodies moved,   50
The drifting petal came to ground.

The laughter chimed its perfect round,
The broken syllable was ended.
And I, so certain and so friended,
How could I cloud, or how distress,   55
The heaven of your unconsciousness?
Or shake at Time's sufficient spell,
Stammering of lights unutterable?
The eternal holiness of you,
The timeless end, you never knew,   60
The peace that lay, the light that shone.
You never knew that I had gone
A million miles away, and stayed
A million years. The laughter played
Unbroken round me; and the jest   65
Flashed on. And we that knew the best
Down wonderful hours grew happier yet
I sang at heart, and talked, and ate,
And lived from laugh to laugh, I too,
When you were there, and you, and you.   70

For Discussion

"The Soldier"

1. What is the theme of this sonnet? Is it a universal theme? Explain.
2. What is the poet's view on immortality? Indicate lines to prove your answer.
3. How does the poet reflect the cultural and political status of the England of his day?
4. Is the general mood of the poem serious or light? Is it romantic or realistic? Explain.

"The Great Lover"

1. In the first seven lines of this poem, the speaker enumerates his intellectual loves, devoting the rest of the stanza to his life's objectives. Explain each part in detail.
2. List the things he has loved, labeling them sight, sound, taste, smell, or touch. Observe how unrelated the objects seem to be. Do you think this makes for a greater sense of life? Why or why not?
3. In "The Great Lover," as in many other of Brooke's poems, there is a shift in mood from somberness to gaiety and back again. Point out where these changes occur.

4. Do you think the language at the beginning and end of "The Great Lover" is in keeping with lines 26–60, where the "loves" are listed? What quality redeems it from becoming mere artificial eloquence?

"Dining-Room Tea"

1. Describe the changing moods the speaker experiences. What is the setting of the poem? How does it set off the strangeness of the speaker's vision? Describe the vision. Discuss the meaning of "I saw the immortal moment lie . . ."
2. Why do you think the speaker returns in the last seven lines to the opening scene, repeating the opening line at the close?
3. How does the speaker envision his beloved in the state of immortality? Describe in detail, pointing out lines to prove your point.
4. How would you express the main idea in the poem? How does the poet see the relation of the permanent and the impermanent?
5. Explain the meaning of each of the following figures of speech:
   (a) "Light was more alive than you."
   (b) "Change closed about me like a sleep."
   (c) "The drifting petal came to ground."
   (d) "How could I cloud or how distress
         The heaven of your unconsciousness?"

SIEGFRIED SASSOON

(1886–   )

AFTERMATH

Have you forgotten yet? . . .
For the world's events have rumbled on since those gagged days,
Like traffic checked a while at the crossing of city ways:
And the haunted gap in your mind has filled with thoughts that flow
Like clouds in the lit heavens of life; and you're a man reprieved
    to go,   5
Taking your peaceful share of Time, with joy to spare.
But the past is just the same,—and War's a bloody game. . . .
Have you forgotten yet? . . .
Look down, and swear by the slain of the War that you'll never
    forget.

Do you remember the dark months you held the sector at Ma-
    metz,—   10
The nights you watched and wired and dug and piled sand-bags on
    parapets?
Do you remember the rats; and the stench
Of corpses rotting in front of the front-line trench,—
And dawn coming, dirty-white, and chill with a hopeless rain?
Do you ever stop and ask, "Is it all going to happen again?"   15

Do you remember that hour of din before the attack,—
And the anger, the blind compassion that seized and shook you then
As you peered at the doomed and haggard faces of your men?
Do you remember the stretcher-cases lurching back
With dying eyes and lolling heads, those ashen-gray   20
Masks of the lads who once were keen and kind and gay?

Have you forgotten yet? . . .
Look up, and swear by the green of the Spring that you'll never forget!

DREAMERS

Soldiers are citizens of death's gray land,
  Drawing no dividend from time's tomorrows.
In the great hour of destiny they stand,
  Each with his feuds, and jealousies, and sorrows.
Soldiers are sworn to action; they must win   5
  Some flaming, fatal climax with their lives.
Soldiers are dreamers; when the guns begin
  They think of firelit homes, clean beds, and wives.

I see them in foul dug-outs, gnawed by rats,
  And in the ruined trenches, lashed with rain.   10
Dreaming of things they did with balls and bats,
  And mocked by hopeless longing to regain
Bank-holidays, and picture shows, and spats,
  And going to the office in the train.

EVERYONE SANG

Everyone suddenly burst out singing;
And I was filled with such delight
As prisoned birds must find in freedom
Winging wildly across the white
Orchards and dark green fields; on; on; and out of sight.   5

Everyone's voice was suddenly lifted,
And beauty came like the setting sun.
My heart was shaken with tears, and horror
Drifted away. . . . O, but everyone
Was a bird; and the song was wordless; the singing will never be
  done.   10

For Discussion

"Aftermath"

1. How do you know that the speaker is addressing an officer? Is the
   officer living? Explain, using the last lines of stanzas 1 and 4.
2. The speaker is listing dreadful things they both have seen. What
   poetic device does he use to make this forceful and vivid?

3. Why does he want the person addressed to "swear" that he will "never forget"? Is this command meant for that one man only? Has the command been heeded? Discuss.
4. What is the dominant mood of the poem? What symbol of hope can you find?
5. After reading other poems of Sassoon, explain why you think his poems were not overly welcome after World War I.

"Dreamers"

1. The first eight lines of this sonnet deal, for the most part, with general concepts about soldiers. What are these concepts? In the last six lines, however, the reader is told how soldiers appear in actuality. Which is easier to believe? Do the "things" they "dream of" make the men seem childish? Why or why not?
2. Point out how the poet mingles the strange and the everyday dramatically.
3. Compare this poem with Rupert Brooke's "The Soldier" (page 29). Which has the greater emotional appeal? Which is more realistic? Why?

"Everyone Sang"

1. Why does the single bird's song give the speaker the impression that "everyone" is singing? Where might the person be at the time of his musing on the illusion? How can you tell? Why does he say that the "singing . . . (will) never be done"?
2. In wht way does this poem illustrate the power of the aesthetic imagination?
3. Point out examples of irony, hyperbole, alliteration, assonance.

WILFRED OWEN

(1893–1918)

STRANGE MEETING

It seemed that out of the battle I escaped
Down some profound dull tunnel, long since scooped
Through granites which Titanic wars had groined.
Yet also there encumbered sleepers groaned,
Too fast in thought or death to be bestirred.   **5**
Then, as I probed them, one sprang up, and stared
With piteous recognition in fixed eyes,
Lifting distressful hands as if to bless.
And by his smile, I knew that sullen hall;
By his dead smile I knew we stood in Hell.   **10**
With a thousand pains that vision's face was grained;
Yet no blood reached there from the upper ground,
And no guns thumped, or down the flues made moan,
"Strange, friend," I said, "here is no cause to mourn."
"None," said the other, "save the undone years,   **15**
The hopelessness. Whatever hope is yours,
Was my life also; I went hunting wild
After the wildest beauty in the world,
Which lies not calm in eyes, or braided hair,
But mocks the steady running of the hour,   **20**
And if it grieves, grieves richlier than here.
For by my glee might many men have laughed,
And of my weeping something has been left,
Which must die now. I mean the truth untold,
The pity of war, the pity war distilled.   **25**
Now men will go content with what we spoiled,
Or, discontent, boil bloody, and be spilled.
They will be swift with swiftness of the tigress.
None will break ranks, though nations trek from progress.
Courage was mine, and I had mystery,   **30**
Wisdom was mine, and I had mastery;
To miss the march of this retreating world
Into vain citadels that are not walled.
Then when much blood had clogged their chariot-wheels

I would go up and wash them from sweet wells,   35
Even with truths that lie too deep for taint.
I would have poured my spirit without stint
But not through wounds; not on the cess of war.
Foreheads of men have bled where no wounds were.
I am the enemy you killed, my friend.   40
I knew you in this dark; for so you frowned
Yesterday through me as you jabbed and killed.
I parried; but my hands were loath and cold.
Let us sleep now. . . ."

THE SEND-OFF

Down the close, darkening lanes they sang their way
To the siding-shed,
And lined the train with faces grimly gay.
Their breasts were stuck all white with wreath and spray
As men's are, dead.   5

Dull porters watched them, and a casual tramp
Stood staring hard,
Sorry to miss them from the upland camp.
Then, unmoved, signals nodded, and a lamp
Winked to the guard.   10

So secretly, like wrongs hushed-up, they went.
They were not ours:
We never heard to which front these were sent.
Nor there if they yet mock what women meant
Who gave them flowers.   15

Shall they return to beatings of great bells
In wild trainloads?
A few, a few, too few for drums and yells,
May creep back, silent, to still village wells
Up half-known roads.   20

APOLOGIA PRO POEMATE MEO

I, too, saw God through mud.—
   The mud that cracked on cheeks when wretches smiled.
   War brought more glory to their eyes than blood,
   And gave their laughs more glee than shakes a child.

Merry it was to laugh there—   5
  Where death becomes absurd and life absurder.
  For power was on us as we slashed bones bare
  Not to feel sickness or remorse of murder.

I, too, have dropped off fear—
  Behind the barrage, dead as my platoon,   10
  And sailed my spirit surging, light and clear
  Past the entanglement where hopes lay strewn;

And witnessed exultation—
  Faces that used to curse me, scowl for scowl,
  Shine and lift up with passion of oblation,   15
  Seraphic for an hour; though they were foul.

I have made fellowships—
  Untold of happy lovers in old song.
  For love is not the binding of fair lips
  With the soft silk of eyes that look and long.   20

By Joy, whose ribbon slips,—
  But wound with war's hard wire whose stakes are strong;
  Bound with the bandage of the arm that drips;
  Knit in the webbing of the rifle-thong.

I have perceived much beauty   25
  In the hoarse oaths that kept our courage straight;
  Heard music in the silentness of duty;
  Found peace where shell-storms spouted reddest spate.

Nevertheless, except you share
  With them in hell the sorrowful dark of hell,   30
  Whose world is but the trembling of a flare,
  And heaven but as the highway for a shell,

You shall not hear their mirth:
  You shall not come to think them well content
  By any jest of mine. These men are worth   35
  Your tears. You are not worth their merriment.

For Discussion

"Strange Meeting"

1. The "setting" of this poem might have been imagined within the framework of a poet's dream. What is the setting? The time?
2. What is the reason for the stranger's "thousand fears" despite his apparent safety from the war's raging above ground? (Note lines 22–23.)
3. Who is the stranger? Might he be the speaker's other self—the poet within the soldier? In the light of this possible solution to his identity, explain the meaning of the poem. Had the stranger's life been spared, what might his purpose in life have been?
4. How did this "stranger" meet his end? Why didn't he defend himself?
5. What universal meaning do you see in this poem?

"The Send-off"

1. One of the most striking elements of this poem is the impersonal tone used throughout. Which details give you the impression that no one is really concerned about these men preparing to go to some unknown "front"? What added irony is contained in the "flower" image? Do the individuals seeing the train off heighten the sense of irony? Discuss.
2. How does this poem reveal the reality beneath the "drums and yells" of public "send-offs" in time of war and widespread disaster?
3. Who are the "few" who will "creep back/Up half-known roads"? Why does the speaker call the villages struck by war, "village wells"? Why will the roads be only "half-known" at the few's return?
4. How is the meaning of this poem applicable to life in general?

"Apologia Pro Poemate Meo"

1. Here is the strange paradox of experiencing mirth in the midst of battle. How does the poet succeed in seeing "God through mud"? In perceiving beauty in "hoarse oaths"? In throwing off fear, though "behind the barrage"? Discuss fully, indicating lines to back up your answers.
2. Explain each paradox in stanza 7. In stanza 8, to which "hell" is the speaker referring? What is the meaning of the poet's message to those he is addressing?
3. How do the comparisons, or contrasts, presented in stanzas 5–6 add to the sharpness of the beauty-in-ugliness effect of the whole? Choose several other vivid images for discussion.

JOHN MASEFIELD

(1878–   )

Here is a poet with whom you are probably familiar, for his poems of the sea are found in literature for both old and young, and for people in every walk of life.

In his youth, John Masefield was a sailor on the British ship *Convoy*. From his first-hand knowledge, he was able to paint in words the sea pictures so vividly described in "Cargoes," the longing of the retired pirate in "Spanish Waters," the delight of the "wheel's kick" in "Sea Fever." But there are other themes present in Masefield's work which you will learn to value, particularly his dedication to Truth and Beauty, and his great love for the common man.

John Masefield's formal education ceased when he was barely sixteen. When he gave up life at sea, he worked for three years as a common laborer in New York, and during this time, he spent his spare hours devouring the works of Chaucer, Keats, Milton, and Shakespeare. His efforts at self-education were richly rewarded when, in 1897, he returned to London to begin his own career as a playwright and poet. In 1930, he was appointed Poet Laureate of England, thus achieving one of the highest honors in the literary world.

CARGOES

Quinquireme * of Nineveh from distant Ophir,
Rowing home to haven in sunny Palestine,
With a cargo of ivory,
And apes and peacocks,
Sandalwood, cedarwood, and sweet white wine.   5

Stately Spanish galleon coming from the Isthmus,
Dipping through the Tropics by the palm-green shores,
With a cargo of diamonds,
Emeralds, amethysts,
Topazes, and cinnamon, and gold moidores.   10

Dirty British coaster with a salt-caked smoke-stack,
Butting through the Channel in the mad March days,

Quinquireme: an ancient ship which had five banks of oars

With a cargo of Tyne coal,
Road-rails, pig-lead,
Firewood, iron-ware, and cheap tin trays.   15

SPANISH WATERS

Spanish waters, Spanish waters, you are ringing in my ears,
Like a slow sweet piece of music from the grey forgotten years;
Telling tales, and beating tunes, and bringing weary thoughts to me
Of the sandy beach at Muertos,* where I would that I could be.

There's a surf breaks on Los Muertos, and it never stops to roar,   5
And it's there we came to anchor, and it's there we went ashore,
Where the blue lagoon is silent amid snags of rotting trees,
Dropping like the clothes of corpses cast up by the seas.

We anchored at Los Muertos when the dipping sun was red,
We left her half-a-mile to sea, to west of Nigger Head;   10
And before the mist was on the Cay, before the day was done,
We were all ashore on Muertos with the gold that we had won.

We bore it through the marshes in a half-score battered chests,
Sinking, in the sucking quagmires, to the sunburn on our breasts,
Heaving over tree-trunks, gasping, damning at the flies and heat, 15
Longing for a long drink, out of silver, in the ship's cool lazareet.

The moon came white and ghostly as we laid the treasure down,
There was gear there'd make a beggarman as rich as Lima Town,
Copper charms and silver trinkets from the chests of Spanish crews,
Gold doubloons and double moidores, louis d'ors and portagues,   20

Clumsy yellow-metal earrings from the Indians of Brazil,
Uncut emeralds out of Rio, bezoar stones from Guayaquil; *
Silver, in the crude and fashioned, pots of old Arica * bronze,
Jewels from the bones of Incas desecrated by the Dons.

We smoothed the place with mattocks, and we took and blazed the
    tree,   25

Los Muertos: an island off Puerto Rico
Guayaquil: a seaport on the Gueyas River in Ecuador
Arica: a region in Chile

Which marks yon where the gear is hid that none will ever see,
And we laid aboard the ship again, and south away we steers,
Through the loud surf of Los Muertos which is beating in my ears.

I'm the last alive that knows it. All the rest have gone their ways,
Killed, or died, or come to anchor in the old Mulatas Cays,*   30
And I go singing, fiddling, old and starved and in despair,
And I know where all that gold is hid, if I were only there.

It's not the way to end it all. I'm old, and nearly blind,
And an old man's past's a strange thing, for it never leaves his mind.
And I see in dreams, awhiles, the beach, the sun's disc dipping red, 35
And the tall ship, under topsails, swaying in past Nigger Head.

I'd be glad to step ashore there. Glad to take a pick and go
To the lone blazed coco-palm tree in the place no others know,
And lift the gold and silver that has moldered there for years
By the loud surf of Los Muertos which is beating in my ears.   40

TRUTH

Man with his burning soul
Has but an hour of breath
To build a ship of Truth
In which his soul may sail,
Sail on the sea of death.   5
For death takes toll
Of beauty, courage, youth,
Of all but Truth.

Life's city ways are dark,
Men mutter by; the wells   10
Of the great waters moan.
O death, O sea, O tide,
The waters moan like bells.
No light, no mark,
The soul goes out alone   15
On seas unknown.

Mulatas Cays: low islands off the eastern coast of Panama

Stripped of all purple robes,
Stripped of all golden lies,
I will not be afraid.
Truth will preserve through death;   20
Perhaps the stars will rise,
The stars like globes.
The ship my striving made
May see night fade.

ON GROWING OLD

Be with me, Beauty, for the fire is dying;
My dog and I are old, too old for roving;
Man, whose young passion sets the spindrift flying,
Is soon too lame to march, too cold for loving.
I take the book and gather to the fire,   5
Turning old yellow leaves; minute by minute
The clock ticks to my heart; a withered wire
Moves a thin ghost of music in the spinet.
I cannot sail your seas, I cannot wander
Your cornland nor your hill-land nor your valleys   10
Ever again, nor share the battle yonder
Where the young knight the broken squadron rallies.
      Only stay quiet, while my mind remembers
      The beauty of fire from the beauty of embers.

Beauty, have pity, for the strong have power,   15
The rich their wealth, the beautiful their grace,
Summer of man its sunlight and its flower,
Springtime of man all April in a face.
Only, as in the jostling in the Strand,
Where the mob thrusts or loiters or is loud,   20
The beggar with the saucer in his hand
Asks only a penny from the passing crowd,
So, from this glittering world with all its fashion,
Its fire and play of men, its stir, its march,
Let me have wisdom, Beauty, wisdom and passion,   25
Bread to the soul, rain where the summers parch.
      Give me but these, and though the darkness close
      Even the night will blossom as the rose.

THE WEST WIND

It's a warm wind, the west wind, full of birds' cries;
I never hear the west wind but tears are in my eyes.
For it comes from the west lands, the old brown hills,
And April's in the west wind, and daffodils.

It's a fine land, the west land, for hearts as tired as mine;   5
Apple orchards blossom there, and the air's like wine.
There is cool green grass there, where men may lie at rest,
And the thrushes are in song there, fluting from the nest.

"Will you not come home, brother? You have been long away,
It's April, and blossom time, and white is the spray;   10
And bright is the sun, brother, and warm is the rain,—
Will you not come home, brother, home to us again?

"The young corn is green, brother, where the rabbits run,
It's blue sky, and white clouds, and warm rain and sun.
It's song to a man's soul, brother, fire to a man's brain,   15
To hear the wild bees and see the merry spring again.

"Larks are singing in the west, brother, above the green wheat,
So will ye not come home, brother, and rest your tired feet?
I've a balm for bruised hearts, brother, sleep for aching eyes,"
Says the warm wind, the west wind, full of birds' cries.   20

It's the white road westwards is the road I must tread
To the green grass, the cool grass, and rest for heart and head,
To the violets and the brown brooks and the thrushes' song,
In the fine land, the west land, the land where I belong.

For Discussion

"Cargoes"

1. Which three periods and types of civilizations do the separate ships
   portray? Show how each one's freight is symbolic of the age and of
   the region it represents.

2. What is the relationship implied in each of the ship's motions? Show how the verbs "rowing," "dipping," and "butting" are significant of the ideas mentioned in question one.
3. Discuss the philosophy underlying the poem as a whole. What do you think the speaker, in stanza 3, is pointing out about present-day England? Do the "mad March days" imply more than mere weather conditions? Explain.
4. Does the strictly objective tone give greater weight to the poem as a whole? Why or why not? Compare the mood and tone here with others of Masefield's sea poems. How are they alike? How do they differ?
5. How does the rhythm add to the effect? What meter and rhyme scheme does the poet employ? Is there any direct imagery which you find unfamiliar? What do the names of unfamiliar places in the first stanza add to the poem?

"Spanish Waters"

1. Do you think the speaker's longing is only to recover the buried treasure? Why or why not? Give proof for your answer.
2. How does the old sailor make clear the exact type of treasure he has lost? Mention in detail concrete objects included in the treasure.
3. Observe how the poet has specified the time of night, the movements of the men, the type of tools they use. Would a story writer or movie producer have sufficient help from the descriptions to make a novel or picture from this poem? Point out lines where color is employed. How does its use add to the mood of mystery and suspense?
4. Describe the change of moods in the poem. Does the rhythm reflect the sea and its beating in the old sailor's ears? Compare the rhythm of the poem with that of "Sea Fever." Would the latter's rhythm have been a fitting one for "Spanish Waters"? Why or why not?

"Truth"

1. The thought of this poem, that "Truth will preserve through death," is arrived at only after serious meditation on the shortness of life and on the impermanence of "beauty, courage, youth." To what does the poet compare man's whole occupation in life? How is this figure of speech borne out in the second stanza?
2. Do you agree with the thought expressed in the two closing lines of the second stanza? Discuss.
3. What is the speaker referring to in his allusion to "purple robes" and "golden lies" in stanza 3?
4. What is the full meaning of the final two lines? In what sense shall "night fade"?

"On Growing Old"

1. What is the "penny" the poet-beggar asks from the world? To what does he compare the excellent gifts, wisdom and passion? Is the comparison a good one? Discuss.
2. Explain the figure of speech in each of the following:
   (a) ". . . a withered wire
      Moves a thin ghost of music in the spinet."
   (b) ". . . while the mind remembers
      The beauty of fire from the beauty of embers."
3. Could each sonnet serve as a poem in itself? Why or why not?
4. Do you think this poem has the strength and appeal of Yeats' "Sailing to Byzantium" (page 24)? Discuss fully.

"The West Wind"

1. Here is one of Masefield's most musical poems. It seems to catch the rhythm of the "west wind," in addition to picturing the sights and sounds the wind brings back to him. What gives the impression that it is a gentle wind? What time of year is it? Prove your answers by indicating specific lines.
2. What idea is brought out by the wind's addressing the speaker as "brother"? How is this idea typical of the home-loving "westerner"? Can you name some American folk songs which bring out a similar notion?
3. Which images bring out the kind of life to which the wind is calling the speaker? Make a list of the color images and the sound images.
4. The poem is more than a simple picture of a farm or ranch out west. What deeper meaning does it convey? What do the "white road" and the greenness of things symbolize? What do "heart and head" symbolize in man? What is the dominant mood of this poem?

EILEEN DUGGAN

(1900?–1952)

Although born and raised in New Zealand, Eileen Duggan gives evidence
in her poems of the strong Catholic influence of her Irish ancestry. Of
her poetry, Walter de la Mare has stated that "However much she may
have nourished her mind on what other poets have written, she tells
always of the direct experience of her own body, mind, and spirit."

In the poems which follow, you will observe this directness of experience as Miss Duggan transmits it. You will see her skill at work not
only through the wide variety of her verse forms, but also through her
economy of expression and her exceptional control of words in conveying
the central meaning of each poem.

AUTUMN

Ah royal, surely royal, I concede you.
What else this rush of homage on their part?
But all these hot salutes, these dusty honours,
I see them with a wary, brooding heart.
If multitudes of fruits come forth to greet you,   5
If flowers and clouds give you a king's estate,
What is it but a justice, a fulfilment?
Why should I sadden that they shout you great?
The trees have spread their garments down before you.
Larks lead you in, a living haze of cries,   10
Thrones and dominions in the hills avow you,
The winds and the mid-winds unto you arise.
It is not long, God knows, you do the monarch.
This ardent irony that is the land
Sends you upon an ass into your winter   15
That drives a nail of sleet through either hand.

PILGRIMAGE

Now are the bells unlimbered from their spires
In every steeple-loft from pole to pole:
The four winds wheel and blow into this gate,
And every wind is wet with carillons.

The two Americas at eagle-height,   5
The pure, abstracted Himalayan chimes,
Great ghosts of clappers from the Russian fries,
And sweet, wind-sextoned tremblers from Cathay;
The bells of Ireland, jesting all the way,
The English bells, slowbosomed as a swan,   10
The queenly, weary din of Notre Dame,
And the Low Countries ringing back the sea.
Then Spain, the Moor still moaning through the saint,
The frosty, fiery bells of Germany,
And on before them, baying, sweeping down,   15
The heavy, joyful pack of thunder-jowls
That tongue hosannas from the leash of Rome—
All float untethered over Jaffa Gate
To fling one peal when angels cheat the stone.
But if one little gaping country bell,   20
Blown from its weather-boarding in the south,
Should be too lost to keep its covenant,
Or lift its heart and reins up to the hour,
Know that its dumbness riots more than sound.

AFTER THE ANNUNCIATION

Mary, the maiden, walked out in the country,
Telling the wheat what the angel had told her;
The bees tumbled out of the flag-flowers to listen,
The birds stopped their fledglings and told them to heed her.

A woman in blue with wheat to her knees,   5
Mid a silence of birds and a stillness of bees,
Singing, "Golden, ah golden, with seedsprays unfurled,
Ripen within me, O wheat of the world!"

Mary, bluewimpled, walked out in the country,
Telling the vine what none other must know yet;   10
The butterflies yearned to her hems as to harebells;
The flowers of the bushes fawned softly upon her.

A woman, gold-wet, with rainbow eyes,
And a border of living butterflies,

Singing, "Purple, ah purple, with tendrils close curled,   15
Ripen within me, O vine of the world!"

ST. PETER

Each has his saint, and one may dream
Of Francis walking in a field,
Another turn where Michael dark
Springs slim and wild to lift his shield.

A third may let his loving light   5
Upon the whirling torch of Paul;
I dream of Peter's shaggy head
Bent blinking o'er his haul.

I smile for that warm, simple tongue,
So quick, so breathless to begin,   10
That snubbed and silenced o'er and o'er
Could never lock its wonder in.

I kneel to those old dogged feet
That padded on from shore to city;
I cry for that fierce, troubled heart   15
That tried to tempt God out of pity.

I mourn his body's cowardice
That crept out sobbing from the light,
Closing its ears against the bird
And beating blindly through the night!   20

How could he know except in tales
The majesty, the rune of law,
An old man, bred to nets and sails,
Betrayed by ignorance and awe?

Oh he who saw that flesh alight,   25
Yet fled when terror clubbed his feet,
But drew the vengeance of a trust,
And turned his banners on retreat.

Both earth and heaven are in these,
That fear, that fleeing from the rod,   30
That ancient infidelity
Rewarded by a risen God.

For Discussion

"Autumn"

1. Why is autumn pictured as "royal," as containing "a King's estate," and as a "monarch"? How do autumn's colors bear out the regal images? How do autumn's fruits and general productivity add to the idea of its "kingship"?
2. List and discuss the many creatures paying homage to this "season of fulfillment." Why does the speaker see them with a "wary, brooding heart"?
3. What is the underlying meaning of the whole poem? Show how each image symbolizes a deeper, spiritual significance.
4. Who are the "thrones and dominions" referred to in line 11? Analyze the meaning of line 7, and lines 11–13.

"Pilgrimage"

1. In a great hymn of praise, all the world's bells chime together Christ's glorious resurrection, the moment "when angels cheat the stone." How is each country characterized through the description of its chimes? Discuss. What is the impact of the "one peal" though the diversity of chimes is so marked?
2. What is the meaning of the figure of speech in lines 15–17?
3. To which branch of the church might the speaker be referring in lines 20–25? Explain the paradox in line 25.
4. Discuss the effectiveness of each of the following phrases:
   (a) "unlimbered from their spires"
   (b) "the four winds wheel"
   (c) "the leash of Rome"
   (d) "one little gaping country bell'
   (e) "too lost to keep its covenant"
   (f) "its dumbness riots more than sound"
5. Explain the title of the poem.

"After the Annunciation"

1. What is the meaning of the two figures of speech with which Mary addresses her divine Son? Refer to lines 7–8; 15–16.
2. Is it really out of the ordinary for the bees, birds, and flowers to attend on her words? Why? What is the rainbow a symbol of? Does

this explain why it is seen in her eyes? List several other images which appeal to the sight; to sound. Which are images of movement?

3. Compare this poem with any other on Our Lady's Annunciation. Which had greater appeal for you? Why?

"St. Peter"

1. Explain in a single sentence why the speaker loves St. Peter.
2. Explain each of the saint's failings mentioned here in the light of the story as recounted in the New Testament. When did St. Peter "turn his banners on retreat"?
3. What is the meaning of the final stanza? Do you agree that "Both earth and heaven are in these"? Explain.
4. Show how the author has succeeded in making the saint humanly appealing.
5. Give examples of alliteration and personification. What is the dominant meter of the poem? Scan a few lines for proof.

WALTER DE LA MARE

(1873–1956)

Like other poets of the Romantic school, Walter de la Mare went to the enchanted world of the imagination for his material, and showed how ordinary situations and experiences had wonder and mystery in them. One of his favorite subjects was childhood and the way the world is seen through a child's eyes. Like Lewis Carroll and A. A. Milne, De la Mare wrote books of poetry and prose for children, as well as for adults. He felt that every true poet's aim was to record "his experience of a strange, absorbing, and baffling world in the briefest and loveliest terms within his power."

In the poems that follow, you will see De la Mare's love for the eerie, the mysterious, and the fanciful, mingled with the everyday. You will also see his power to capture with cameo-like precision the fleetingness of beauty.

THE LISTENERS

"Is there anybody there?" said the Traveler,
   Knocking on the moonlit door;
And his horse in the silence champed the grasses
   Of the forest's ferny floor;
And a bird flew up out of the turret,   5
   Above the Traveler's head:
And he smote upon the door again a second time;
   "Is there anybody there?" he said.
But no one descended to the Traveler;
   No head from the leaf-fringed sill   10
Leaned over and looked into his gray eyes,
   Where he stood perplexed and still.
But only a host of phantom listeners
   That dwelt in the lone house then
Stood listening in the quiet of the moonlight   15
   To that voice from the world of men:
Stood thronging the faint moonbeams on the dark stair,
   That goes down to the empty hall,
Hearkening in an air stirred and shaken
   By the lonely Traveler's call.   20

54

And he felt in his heart their strangeness,
    Their stillness answering his cry,
While his horse moved, cropping the dark turf,
    'Neath the starred and leafy sky;
For he suddenly smote on the door, even   25
    Louder, and lifted his head:—
"Tell them I came, and no one answered,
    That I kept my word," he said.
Never the least stir made the listeners,
    Though every word he spake   30
Fell echoing through the shadowiness of the still house
    From the one man left awake:
Ay, they heard his foot upon the stirrup,
    And the sound of iron on stone,
And how the silence surged softly backward,   35
    When the plunging hoofs were gone.

SCHOLARS

    Logic does well at school;
And Reason answers every question right;
Poll-parrot Memory unwinds her spool;
And Copy-cat keeps Teacher well in sight:

The Heart's a truant; nothing does by rule;   5
Safe in its wisdom, is taken for a fool;
Nods through the morning on the dunce's stool;
    And wakes to dream all night.

A DULL BOY

"Work?" Well, not *work*—this stubborn desperate quest
To conjure life, love, wonder into words;
Far happier songs than any me have blest
Were sung, at ease, this daybreak by the birds.

I watch with breathless envy in her glass   5
The dreamlike beauty of the silent swan;
As mute a marvel is the bladed grass
Springing to life again, June's sickle gone.

What music could be mine compared with that
The idling wind woos from the sand-dune's bent?   10
What meaning deeper than the smile whereat
A burning heart conceives the loved intent?

"And what did'st *thou*" . . . I see the vaulted throng,
The listening heavens in that dread array
Fronting the Judge to whom all dooms belong:—   15
Will the lost child in me cry bravely, "Play"?

THE BURNING-GLASS

No map shows my Jerusalem,
　　No history my Christ;
Another language tells of them,
　　A hidden evangelist.

Words may create rare images   5
　　Within their narrow bound;
'Twas speechless childhood brought me these,
　　As music may, in sound.

Yet not the loveliest song that ever
　　Died on the evening air   10
Could from my inmost heart dissever
　　What life had hidden there.

It is the blest reminder of
　　What earth in shuddering bliss
Nailed on a cross—that deathless Love—   15
　　Through all the eternities.

I am the Judas whose perfidy
　　Sold what no eye hath seen,
The rabble in dark Gethsemane,*
　　And Mary Magdalene.   20

To very God who day and night
　　Tells me my sands out-run,
I cry in misery infinite,
　　"I am thy long-lost son."

Gethsemane: scene of the betrayal and arrest of Jesus

ONCE

Once would the early sun steal in through my eastern window,
    A sea of time ago;
Tracing a stealthy trellis of shadow across the pictures
    With his gilding trembling glow;
Brimming my mind with rapture, as though of some alien spirit,   5
    In those eternal hours
I spent with my self as a child; alone, in a world of wonder—
    Air, and light and flowers;
Tenderness, longing, grief, intermingling with bodiless beings
    Shared else with none: 10
How would desire flame up in my soul; with what passionate yearning
    As the rays stole soundlessly on!—
Rays such as Rembrandt adored, such as dwell on the faces of seraphs,
    Wings-folded, solemn head,
Piercing the mortal sorrow past all comprehension. . . .   15

    Little of that I read
In those shadowy runes in my bedroom. But one wild notion
    Made my heart with tears overflow—
The knowledge that love unsought, unspoken, unshared,
    unbetokened,
    Had mastered me through and through: 20
And yet—the children we are!—that nought of its ardour and beauty
    Even the loved should know.

THE RAPIDS

    Grieve must my heart. Age hastens by.
    No longing can stay Time's torrent now.
    Once would the sun in eastern sky
    Pause on the solemn mountain's brow.
    Rare flowers he still to bloom may bring,   5
    But day approaches evening;
    And ah, how swift their withering!

    The birds, that used to sing, sang then
    As if in an eternal day;
    Ev'n sweeter yet their grace notes, when   10

> *Farewell . . . farewell* is theirs to say.
> Yet, as a thorn its drop of dew
> Treasures in shadow, crystal clear,
> All that I loved I love anew,
> Now parting draweth near.　　**15**

For Discussion

"The Listeners"

1. Describe the scene dramatized in this poem. How does the poet achieve a "haunted" effect? Find ten expressions which emphasize the ghostlike quality of the scene. Point out several contrasting images from the real world of the "traveler."
2. Who are the "listeners"? In what way might they be connected with memories of the "traveler's" youth?
3. Is the form of the poem in keeping with the content? If the poet had chosen to write it in the old ballad form of nine quatrains, would the effect have been the same? Why or why not? How do the alternating long and short lines effect the mood? Discuss.
4. Find several examples of alliteration; of consonance; of assonance.

"Scholars"

1. Show how the entire poem is a study in personification.
2. Why does the speaker say "The Heart's a truant"? Do you agree with the poet's reasoning? What, in general, is the poet endeavoring to tell us about Love?

"A Dull Boy"

1. Explain the connection of the first and last words of the poem in relation to the theme. Does the speaker fear the judgment?
2. The speaker has, in a sense, summed up the sources of the poet's materials. Two of these are, the song of the birds, and the "dreamlike beauty of the silent swan." Mention the other objects and ideas upon which his craft is formed.
3. In which single line does De la Mare summarize the poet's calling?
4. Identify the figures of speech in the poem. Which appeal directly to the eye? To the ear? To the intellect?

"The Burning-Glass"

1. According to Webster, a burning-glass is a "convex lens for focusing the sun's rays so as to produce heat or set fire to something." Explain, in the light of this definition, the title of the poem. What, precisely, is the "burning-glass" for the speaker? If he were without this sense

of sin, of his own fallibility, would he have the depth of compassion evidenced in the fourth stanza?

2. In what sense is every man a "Judas" and "the rabble in dark Gethsemane"? When does he become a "Magdalene"? To what Gospel story does the "long-lost son" allude?

3. Do you thing the ballad stanza form is appropriate here, or is it a flaw in the work? Do the non-punctuated line-endings help alleviate the otherwise monotonous rhythm? Illustrate by rereading aloud.

"Once"

1. List the various ways in which the sunlight affected the poet as a child. Does his first "love" affect him with the same emotions?

2. Which has the greater impact on him, the actual experience of love which had "mastered (him) through and through" or the fact that "nought of its ardor and beauty/Even the loved should know"?

3. What is the relation of his love having gone "unspoken" and the child's sharing "with none" the experience of "tenderness" and "longing" evoked by the sunbeam's rays?

4. Explain the meaning of each of the following:
   (a) "A sea of time ago"   (d) "Rays such as Rembrandt adored"
   (b) "in a world of wonder" (e) "those shadowy runes in my bed-
   (c) "bodiless beings"   room"

"The Rapids"

1. Compare this poem on old age with Shakespeare's Sonnet 47 ("That time of year thou may'st in me behold"). In what sense are the two poems similar? In what sense do they differ? Do you agree that when "parting draweth near," you "love anew" the old, familiar things you have always loved? Consider the idea in terms of a journey you must make, or beginning a new way of life.

2. To what "rare flowers" does the speaker refer in the first stanza?

3. What is the dominant mood of the poem? Does the mood differ from the old man's in Yeats' "Sailing to Byzantium"? Discuss. Which is the more hopeful?

EDITH SITWELL

(1887–   )

Edith Sitwell, like Emily Brontë, comes of a family remarkable for literary genius. Her two brothers, Osbert and Sacheverell, are also famous writers.

In an effort to get away from "dead and expected patterns," Edith Sitwell experimented with words in the rhythm of dance measures such as polkas and foxtrots. However, her sometimes startling images have met with severe criticism. She speaks, for example, of the rain "squawking down," of fire "furry as a bear," of morning light "creaking down." But, like E. E. Cummings, she believes it the business of poetical comparison to startle the reader and so to refashion thought by bringing things together that have never met.

Among her many stirring themes are those which deal with the world's corruption through materialism and the sadness of the unimaginative mind. The following poems show her ability to create delightful images and haunting rhythms, as well as her desire to convey a vision of life.

AUBADE

Jane, Jane,
Tall as a crane,
The morning light creaks down again.

Comb your cockscomb-ragged hair;
Jane, Jane, come down the stair.   5

Each dull blunt wooden stalactite
Of rain creaks, hardened by the light,

Sounding like an overtone
From some lonely world unknown.

But the creaking empty light   10
Will never harden into sight,

Will never penetrate your brain
With overtones like the blunt rain.

60

The light would show (if it could harden)
Eternities of kitchen-garden,   15

Cockscomb flowers that none will pluck,
And wooden flowers that 'gin to cluck.

In the kitchen you must light
Flames as staring, red and white

As carrots or as turnips, shining   20
Where the cold dawn light lies whining.

Cockscomb hair on the cold wind
Hangs limp, turns the milk's weak mind. . . .

  Jane, Jane,
  Tall as a crane,   25
  The morning light creaks down again!

EN FAMILLE

In the early spring-time, after their tea,
Through the young fields of the springing Bohea,
Jemima, Jocasta, Dinah, and Deb
Walked with their father, Sir Joshua Jebb,—
An admiral red, whose only notion   5
(A butterfly poised on a pigtailed ocean)
Is of the peruked sea whose swell
Breaks on the flowerless rocks of Hell.
Under the thin trees, Deb and Dinah,
Jemima, Jocasta, walked, and finer   10
Their black hair seemed (flat-sleek to see)
Than the young leaves of the springing Bohea;
Their cheeks were like nutmeg-flowers when swells
The rain into foolish silver bells.
They said, "If the door you would only slam,   15
Or if, Papa, you would once say 'Damn'—
Instead of merely roaring 'Avast'
Or boldly invoking the nautical Blast—
We should now stand in the street of Hell
Watching siesta shutters that fell   20

With a noise like amber softly sliding;
Our moon-like glances through these gliding
Would see at her table preened and set
Myrrhina sitting at her toilette
With eyelids closed as soft as the breeze   25
That flows from gold flowers on the incense-trees."

    .   .   .   .   .

The Admiral said, "You could never call—
I assure you it would not do at all!
She gets down from table without saying 'Please,'
Forgets her prayers and to cross her T's,   30
In short, her scandalous reputation
Has shocked the whole of the Hellish nation;
And every turbaned Chinoiserie,
With whom we should sip our black Bohea,
Would stretch out her simian fingers thin   35
To scratch you, my dears, like a mandoline;
For Hell is just as properly proper
As Greenwich, or as Bath, or Joppa!"

MARINER MEN

"What are you staring at, mariner-man,
Wrinkled as sea-sand and old as the sea?"
"Those trains will run over their tails, if they can,
Snorting and sporting like porpoises. Flee
The burly, the whirligig wheels of the train,   5
As round as the world and as large again,
Running half the way over to Babylon, down
Through fields of clover to gay Troy town—
A-puffing their smoke as grey as the curl
On my forehead as wrinkled as sands of the sea!—   10
But what can that matter to you, my girl?
(And what can that matter to me?)"

THE LITTLE GHOST WHO DIED FOR LOVE

FOR ALLANAH HARPER

Deborah Churchill, born in 1678, was hanged in 1708 for shielding
her lover in a duel. His opponent was killed, her lover fled to Holland,
and she was hanged in his stead, according to the law of the time. The

chronicle said, "Though she died at peace with God, the malefactor
could never understand the justice of her sentence, to the last moment
of her life."

"Fear not, O maidens, shivering
As bunches of the dew-drenched leaves
In the calm moonlight . . . it is the cold sends quivering
My voice, a little nightingale that grieves.

Now Time beats not, and dead Love is forgotten . . .   5
The spirit too is dead and dank and rotten,

And I forget the moment when I ran
Between my lover and the sworded man—
Blinded with terror lest I lose his heart.
The sworded man dropped, and I saw depart   10

Love and my lover and my life . . . he fled
And I was strung and hung upon the tree.
It is so cold now that my heart is dead
And drops through time . . . night is too dark to see

Him still. . . . But it is spring; upon the fruit-boughs of your lips,   15
Young maids, the dew like India's splendour drips;
Pass by among the strawberry beds, and pluck the berries
Cooled by the silver moon; pluck boughs of cherries

That seem the lovely lucent coral bough
(From streams of starry milk those branches grow)   20
That Cassopeia feeds with her faint light,
Like Ethiopia ever jewelled bright.

Those lovely cherries do enclose
Deep in their sweet hearts the silver snows,

And the small budding flowers upon the trees   25
Are filled with sweetness like the bags of bees.

Forget my fate . . . but I, a moonlight ghost,
Creep down the strawberry paths and seek the lost

World, the apothecary at the Fair.
I, Deborah, in my long cloak of brown   30
Like the small nightingale that dances down
The cherried boughs, creep to the doctor's bare
Booth . . . cold as ivy in the air,

And, where I stand, the brown and ragged light
Holds something still beyond, hid from my sight.   35

Once, plumaged like the sea, his swanskin head
Had wintry white quills . . . 'Hearken to the Dead . . .
I was a nightingale, but now I croak
Like some dark harpy hidden in night's cloak,
Upon the walls; among the Dead, am quick;   40
Oh, give me medicine, for the world is sick;
Not medicines, planet-spotted like fritillaries *
For country sins and old stupidities,
Nor potions you may give a country maid
When she is lovesick . . . love in earth is laid,   45
Grown dead and rotten' . . . so I sank me down,
Poor Deborah in my long cloak of brown.
Though cockcrow marches, crying of false dawns,
Shall bury my dark voice, yet still it mourns
Among the ruins,—for it is not I   50
But this old world, is sick and soon must die!"

fritillaries: silver-spotted butterflies

For Discussion

"Aubade"

1. According to the poet, "Aubade" is a "poem about a country servant,
   a girl on a farm, plain and neglected and unhappy, and with a sad,
   bucolic stupidity, coming down in the dawn to light the fire." What
   picture does the reader get in the first two stanzas of Jane's personal
   appearance?
2. In keeping with Jane's stolid appearance is the condition of her
   unimaginative mind. Point out evidence of this in stanzas 5–7.
3. "Light" is symbolic of many things: warmth, illumination to the
   intellect, the absence of darkness both physical and spiritual, the
   eternal truth of Christ. What would light mean for Jane if it could

"harden," that is, if she could view her own little world in the morning light for a considerable period of time?

4. An "aubade" is a serenade at dawn. Do you see any irony in the title?

5. How does the rhythm suit the mood and tone of the poem? Does the sing-song quality fit Jane's monotonous life?

"En Famille"

1. Read the poem aloud to appreciate the delightful experiments with sound. How is the sound balance achieved? Note, for example, the constant interchanging of one, two, and three-syllabled words, the pleasant effect of the long vowel sounds, and the use of alliteration.

2. Into an oriental setting, the poet has skillfully projected a combination of English, Hebrew, and Chinese customs and names. Illustrate this statement with examples.

3. What kind of man is the admiral? What connotation has the word "red"?

4. What age are his daughters? Give proof for your answers.

5. Describe "Myrrhina" (a) as the girls picture her, (b) as their father understands her to be. In what three areas does Myrrhina offend?

6. What would you say is the reason for the father's censure of Myrrhina? What does his upbringing or his position as "admiral" have to do with it?

7. Do you agree with the thought in the last two lines? What irony is expressed here?

"Mariner Man"

1. Miss Sitwell states that the poems in *Facade*, from which "Mariner Man" is taken, are, "for the most part, abstract patterns, difficult technical experiments. Some deal with materialism, and the world crumbling into dust, some have as protagonists shadows . . . in a highly mechanical universe." Which technical devices has the poet used to give the sense of speed and confusion in "Mariner Man?" Who is the "protagonist"? What ordeal is he confronted with?

2. Every word in the mariner's reply contributes to the speed-image of the train. Point out examples of this. How are porpoises like trains?

3. Why is there a hint of hopelessness in the final two lines? Why does the speaker think neither he nor the girl will profit by his warning to "flee" the train?

4. Of the many possible famous cities the mariner might have mentioned, only Babylon and Troy are given. What is the significance of each?

5. "Wrinkled as sea-sand" is a highly original image. Explain this image as you see it.

"The Little Ghost Who Died for Love"

NOTE: Deborah in the Bible was a prophetess and one of the Judges of Israel who freed her people from the Canaanites.

1. What is the speaker's attitude toward her subject? Toward her listeners? The speaker in the poem tells her entire story in six lines. Which lines are they?
2. Does she still love the man whose punishment she suffered? Give proof for your answer by quoting lines from the poem.
3. Why does Deborah feel that the world is "lost"? How does the time of year when the little ghost returns heighten the poignancy of her fate? In which lines is the imagery indicating the season most vivid?
4. What is the speaker's motive in seeking the "apothecary"? Is the use of the nightingale image for the girl's voice effective? Why?
5. Explain the meaning of each of the following images, pointing out ambiguity where it occurs:
   (a) "Those lovely cherries do enclose
        Deep in their sweet hearts the silver snows"
   (b) "And the small budding flowers upon the trees
        Are filled with sweetness like the bags of bees."
   (c) ". . . the lost
        World, the apothecary at the Fair"
   (d) "I . . . among the Dead, am quick"
   (e) ". . . cockrow marches, crying of false dawns"

STEPHEN SPENDER

(1909–   )

Here is a poet sensitive in the extreme to the economic and political implications of his time. He has known the results of cruelly waged war, has watched the stream of refugees swelling year by year, has studied the growth of mechanical developments. All of these have a place in his poetry, which is grounded in the world of reality as he knows it. His passion for individual freedom and for justice among men has sometimes been interpreted as advocating Communism; yet, he stoutly inveighs against anything that reduces his fellow men to automations or cogs in a machine.

Spender's poetry expresses not only his abhorrence of war and materialism, but it captures the very sounds and diction of the machine age. It also reveals his love for nature and his keen perception of life's intricacies. The poems that follow will give you a glimpse into the poetic world of Spender with its variety and originality of presentation.

OH YOUNG MEN, OH YOUNG COMRADES

Oh young men, oh young comrades
it is too late now to stay in those houses
your fathers built where they build you to breed
money on money   it is too late
to make or even to count what has been made   5
Count rather those fabulous possessions
which begin with your body and your fiery soul:
the hairs on your head the muscles extending
in ranges with lakes across your limbs
Count your eyes as jewels and your valued sex   10
then count the sun and the innumerable coined light
sparkling on waves and spangling under trees
It is too late now to stay in great houses where the ghosts are prisoned
—those ladies like flies perfect in amber
those financiers like fossils of bones in coal.   15
Oh comrades, step beautifully from the solid wall
advance to rebuild and sleep with friend on hill
advance to rebel and remember what you have
no ghost ever had, immured in his hall.

ULTIMA RATIO REGUM

The guns spell money's ultimate reason
In letters of lead on the spring hillside.
But the boy lying dead under the olive trees
Was too young and too silly
To have been notable to their important eye.   5
He was a better target for a kiss.

When he lived, tall factory hooters never summoned him.
Nor did restaurant plate-glass doors revolve to wave him in.
His name never appeared in the papers.
The world maintained its traditional wall   10
Round the dead with their gold sunk deep as a well,
Whilst his life, intangible as a Stock Exchange rumour, drifted
        outside.

O too lightly he threw down his cap
One day when the breeze threw petals from the trees.
The unflowering wall sprouted with guns,   15
Machine-gun anger quickly scythed the grasses;
Flags and leaves fell from hands and branches;
The tweed cap rotted in the nettles.

Consider his life which was valueless
In terms of employment, hotel ledgers, news files.   20
Consider. One bullet in ten thousand kills a man.
Ask. Was so much expenditure justified
On the death of one so young and so silly
Lying under the olive trees, O world, O death?

THE EXPRESS

After the first powerful plain manifesto
The black statement of pistons, without more fuss
But gliding like a queen, she leaves the station.
Without bowing and with restrained unconcern
She passes the houses which humbly crowd outside,   5
The gasworks and at last the heavy page
Of death, printed by gravestones in the cemetery.
Beyond the town there lies the open country

Where, gathering speed, she acquires mystery,
The luminous self-possession of ships on ocean.   10
It is now she begins to sing—at first quite low
Then loud, and at last with a jazzy madness—
The song of her whistle screaming at curves,
Of deafening tunnels, brakes, innumerable bolts.
And always light, aerial, underneath   15
Goes the elate meter of her wheels.
Steaming through metal landscape on her lines
She plunges new eras of wild happiness
Where speed throws up strange shapes, broad curves
And parallels clean like the steel of guns.   20
At last, further than Edinburgh or Rome,
Beyond the crest of the world, she reaches night
Where only a low streamline brightness
Of phosphorus on the tossing hills is white.
Ah, like a comet through flame, she moves entranced   25
Wrapt in her music no bird song, no, nor bough
Breaking with honey buds, shall ever equal.

THE JOURNEY

Upon what confident iron rails
    We seemed to move to the clear view
At the end of the line, where, without fail,
    My visions would come true.

There, where the sun melts the curved hills   5
    In one transparent wave against the skies,
I'd see your tender smile, more than your will,
    Shine through the coldness of your eyes.

Our harsh tongues of to-day would run in tears
    Back to this buried Now become the past.   10
In the cool shadows we'd unclasp our fears
    Transformed to love at last.

Oh, but then suddenly the line
    Swung onto another view
Barren with myself, and the blank pain   15
    Of the crammed world without you.

THE BARN

Half hidden by trees, the sheer roof of the barn
Is a river of tiles, warped
By winding currents of weather
Suns and storms ago.

Through beech leaves, its vermilion seems   5
A Red Admiral's wing, with veins
Of lichen and rust, an underwing
Of winter-left leaves.

Now, in the Spring, a sapling's jet
Of new, pure flame, cuts across   10
The low long gutter. One leaf holds up
Red tiles reflected in its cup.

At the side of the road where cars crash past,
The barn lies under the sky like a throat
Full of dark gurgitation: 15

A ghost of a noise—a hint of a gust
Caught in the rafters centuries ago:
The creak of a winch, the wood turn of a wheel.

Entangled in murmurs, as in a girl's hair,
Is the enthusiastic scent   20
Of coarse, yellow straw—lit by that sunbeam,
Which, laden with motes, strikes across the floor.

For Discussion

"Oh Young Men, Oh Young Comrades"

1. What sort of life does the speaker urge his young comrades to abandon? What new way of life does he urge them to adopt?
2. Is "solid wall" a fitting epithet for the houses they have inherited from their fathers? Why?
3. From lines 6–12, draw up a list of the things which the speaker considers the real riches of life to be.
4. Why is "breed money on money" so applicable to the accumulation

of wealth? Explain the full significance of this expression in reference to the whole idea of the poem.

5. Explain the meaning of each of the images in lines 13–15.

6. The lack of punctuation in the poem gives the general feeling of haste and of strident progress. Which other factors in the *form* of the poem add to this effect?

"Ultima Ratio Regum"

1. In this poem, Spender presents one of his favorite themes: the stupidity of accumulating wealth for the sake of destroying. In which lines is this theme most aptly expressed? To whom is the poem addressed?

2. Point out lines where the speaker ironically notes the importance of "statistics." By what standards does the world measure the boy's value, or lack of it?

3. What is the precise connotation of the word "silly" here? Is there a special significance in the "olive trees" being the place of his death? What time of year is it? Would the impact have been the same had he been killed in autumn or winter? How does this add to the irony of the situation?

4. Certain stanzas sound like a news report. What effect does this prose-like quality achieve?

5. Discuss the effectiveness of each of the following:
   (a) "letters of lead"   (d) "intangible as a stock exchange
   (b) "target for a kiss"   rumor"
   (c) "tall factory hooters" (e) "Machine-gun anger scythed the
                                    grasses"

"The Express"

1. Robert Frost has said that a poem "should begin in delight and end in wonder." Is this true of "The Express"? Explain.

2. How is the entire poem an extended personification? Define the personality traits of the express. What is her song? Her accompaniment?

3. Describe each change of character in the express. Point out through specific lines how with each change there is a proportionate change in the meter, rhythm, and diction of the poem. Pick out five striking figures of speech, identify each, and discuss their aptness.

"The Journey"

1. Throughout the first three stanzas the speaker is strongly expressing a wish. In the last stanza, however, he abruptly announces the reality. What are his "visions"? What is the reality of his situation?

2. Is the use of the train journey effective in depicting the hoped-for fulfillment of his dream? Describe the "scenery," mile by mile.
3. Examine stanza 3 for a hint of the reasons for his regret. What do you think occurred to make for this "blank pain"?

"The Barn"

1. This poem reveals Spender's skill in producing vivid pictures with exact, concrete details of color and sound. Describe the barn in its precise setting as an artist about to paint it would see it.
2. What images are suggested by
   (a) "a river of tiles"
   (b) "an underwing of winter-left leaves"
   (c) "a sapling's jet of new, pure flame"
3. Explain the images in stanza 6. Point out how this stanza catches up and unites into a harmonious whole sound, scent, color, and light.
4. Give examples of alliteration, assonance, and consonance.

DYLAN THOMAS

(1914–1953)

Great vitality keynotes the poetry of this well-known poet of Wales, whose education terminated with his sixteenth birthday, and who never learned the Welsh language, despite his passionate love for the country and customs of his native land.

Dylan Thomas' poems, written, as he said, to be read aloud, are among the finest of the modern school, dealing always with the themes closest to man: birth, death, and love. This poet's outlook on life may appear dark at times, but it is never cynical; his pessimism never becomes despair.

The piling up of images, especially in his nature poems, is not for the images' sake alone. Reading the poems aloud and thoughtfully, one sees the beauty and feels the exuberance of Thomas' seacoast world, the wonderland that was the boy's world of growing up, and the delight and terror of the life-and-death force embracing every man.

The poem "Author's Prologue," is actually one of Thomas' last. It was written as an introduction to his collected works shortly before his death. In it, he states his purpose, which is to celebrate in song the beauties of the natural world surrounding him. How well he achieved this end will be seen in the poems that follow.

DO NOT GO GENTLE INTO THAT GOOD NIGHT

> Do not go gentle into that good night,
> Old age should burn and rave at close of day;
> Rage, rage against the dying of the light.
>
> Though wise men at their end know dark is right,
> Because their words had forked no lightning they   5
> Do not go gentle into that good night.
>
> Good men, the last wave by, crying how bright
> Their frail deeds might have danced in a green bay,
> Rage, rage against the dying of the light.
>
> Wild men who caught and sang the sun in flight,   10
> And learn, too late, they grieved it on its way,
> Do not go gentle into that good night.

Grave men, near death, who see with blinding sight
Blind eyes could blaze like meteors and be gay,
Rage, rage against the dying of the light.   15

And you, my father, there on the sad height,
Curse, bless, me now with your fierce tears, I pray.
Do not go gentle into that good night.
Rage, rage against the dying of the light.

FERN HILL

Now as I was young and easy under the apple boughs
About the lilting house and happy as the grass was green,
    The night above the dingle starry,
        Time let me hail and climb
    Golden in the heydays of his eyes,   5
And honored among wagons I was prince of the apple towns
And once below a time I lordly had the trees and leaves
        Trail with daisies and barley
    Down the rivers of the windfall light.

And as I was green and carefree, famous among the barns   10
About the happy yard and singing as the farm was home,
    In the sun that is young once only,
        Time let me play and be
    Golden in the mercy of his means,
And green and golden I was huntsman and herdsman, the calves   15
Sang to my horn, the foxes on the hills barked clear and cold,
        And the sabbath rang slowly
    In the pebbles of the holy streams.

All the sun long it was running, it was lovely, the hay
Fields high as the house, the tunes from the chimneys, it was air   20
        And playing, lovely and watery
            And fire green as grass.
        And nightly under the simple stars
As I rode to sleep the owls were bearing the farm away,
All the moon long I heard, blessed among stables, the night-
        jars *   25

night-jars: a type of bird

Flying with the ricks,* and the horses
  Flashing into the dark.

And then to awake, and the farm, like a wanderer white
With the dew, come back, the cock on his shoulder: it was all
  Shining, it was Adam and maiden,   30
    The sky gathered again
  And the sun grew round that very day.
So it must have been after the birth of the simple light
In the first, spinning place, the spellbound horses walking warm
  Out of the whinnying green stable   35
    On to the fields of praise.

And honored among foxes and pheasants by the gay house
Under the new made clouds and happy as the heart was long,
  In the sun born over and over,
    I ran my heedless ways,   40
  My wishes raced through the house high hay
And nothing I cared, at my sky blue trades, that time allows
In all his tuneful turning so few and such morning songs
  Before the children green and golden
    Follow him out of grace,   45

Nothing I cared, in the lamb white days, that time would take me
Up to the swallow thronged loft by the shadow of my hand,
  In the moon that is always rising,
    Nor that riding to sleep
  I should hear him fly with the high fields   50
And wake to the farm forever fled from the childless land.
Oh as I was young and easy in the mercy of his means,
    Time held me green and dying
  Though I sang in my chains like the sea.

POEM IN OCTOBER

    It was my thirtieth year to heaven
  Woke to my hearing from harbour and neighbour wood
    And the mussel pooled and the heron
        Priested shore
      The morning beckon   5

ricks: haystacks

9

With water praying and call of seagull and rook
And the knock of sailing boats on the net-webbed wall
                Myself to set foot
                That second
        In the still sleeping town and set forth.   10

        My birthday began with the water—
Birds and the birds of the winged trees flying my name
        Above the farms and the white horses
                And I rose
                In rainy autumn   15
And walked abroad in a shower of all my days.
High tide and the heron dived when I took the road
                Over the border
                And the gates
        Of the town closed as the town awoke.   20

        A springful of larks in a rolling
Cloud and the roadside bushes brimming with whistling
        Blackbirds and the sun of October
                Summery
                On the hill's shoulder,   25
Here were fond climates and sweet singers suddenly
Come in the morning where I wandered and listened
                To the rain wringing
                Wind blow cold
        In the wood faraway under me.   30

        Pale rain over the dwindling harbour
And over the sea-wet church the size of a snail
        With its horns through mist and the castle
                Brown as owls,
                But all the gardens   35
Of spring and summer were blooming in the tall tales
Beyond the border and under the lark-full cloud.
                There could I marvel
                My birthday
        Away but the weather turned around.   40

        It turned away from the blithe country,
And down the other air and the blue altered sky

Streamed again a wonder of summer
      With apples
      Pears and red currants,   45
And I saw in the turning so clearly a child's
Forgotten mornings when he walked with his mother
      Through the parables
      Of sunlight
And the legends of the green chapels   50

And the twice told fields of infancy
That his tears burned my cheeks and his heart moved in mine.
      These were the woods the river and sea
      Where a boy
      In the listening   55
Summertime of the dead whispered the truth of his joy
To the trees and the stones and the fish in the tide.
      And the mystery
      Sang alive
Still in the water and singing birds.   60

And there could I marvel my birthday
Away but the weather turned around. And the true
      Joy of the long-dead child sang burning
      In the sun.
      It was my thirtieth   65
Year to heaven stood there then in the summer noon
Though the town below lay leaved with October blood.
      O may my heart's truth
      Still be sung
On this high hill in a year's turning.   70

THE FORCE THAT THROUGH THE GREEN
FUSE DRIVES THE FLOWER

The force that through the green fuse drives the flower
Drives my green age; that blasts the roots of trees
Is my destroyer.
And I am dumb to tell the crooked rose
My youth is bent by the same wintry fever.   5

The force that drives the water through the rocks
Drives my red blood; that dries the mouthing streams
Turns mine to wax.
And I am dumb to mouth unto my veins
How at the mountain spring the same mouth sucks.   10

The hand that whirls the water in the pool
Stirs the quicksand; that ropes the blowing wind
Hauls my shroud sail.
And I am dumb to tell the hanging man
How of my clay is made the hangman's lime.   15

The lips of time leech to the fountain head;
Love drips and gathers, but the fallen blood
Shall calm her sores.
And I am dumb to tell a weather's wind
How time has ticked a heaven round the stars.   20

And I am dumb to tell the lover's tomb
How at my sheet goes the same crooked worm.

AUTHOR'S PROLOGUE

This day winding down now
At God speeded summer's end
In the torrent salmon sun,
In my seashaken house
On a breakneck of rocks   5
Tangled with chirrup and fruit,
Froth, flute, fin and quill
At a wood's dancing hoof,
By scummed, starfish sands
With their fishwife cross   10
Gulls, pipers, cockles, and sails,
Out there, crow black, men
Tackled with clouds, who kneel
To the sunset nets,
Geese nearly in heaven, boys   15
Stabbing, and herons, and shells

That speak seven seas,
Eternal waters away
From the cities of nine
Days' night whose towers will catch   20
In the religious wind
Like stalks of tall, dry straw,
At poor peace I sing
To you strangers (though song
Is a burning and crested act,   25
The fire of birds in
The world's turning wood,
For my sawn, splay sounds),
Out of these seathumbed leaves
That will fly and fall   30
Like leaves of trees and as soon
Crumble and undie
Into the dogdayed night.
Seaward the salmon sucked sun slips,
And the dumb swans drub blue   35
My dabbed bay's dusk, as I hack
This rumpus of shapes
For you to know
How I, a spinning man,
Glory also this star, bird   40
Roared, sea born, man torn, blood blest.
Hark: I trumpet the place,
From fish to jumping hill! Look:
I build my bellowing ark
To the best of my love   45
As the flood begins,
Out of the fountainhead
Of fear, rage red, manalive,
Molten and mountainous to stream
Over the wound asleep   50
Sheep white hollow farms
To Wales in my arms.
Hoo, there, in castle keep,
You king singsong owls, who moonbeam
The flickering runs and dive   55
The dingle furred deer dead!

Huloo, on plumbed bryns,
O my ruffled ring dove
In the hooting, nearly dark
With Welsh and reverent rook,   60
Coo rooing the woods' praise,
Who moons her blue notes from her nest
Down to the curlew herd!
Ho, hullaballoing clan
Agape, with woe   65
In your beaks, on the gabbing capes!
Heigh, on horseback hill, jack
Whisking hare! who
Hears, there, this fox light, my flood ship's
Clangour as I hew and smite   70
(A clash of anvils for my
Hubbub and fiddle, this tune
On a tongued puffball)
But animals thick as thieves
On God's rough tumbling grounds   75
(Hail to His beasthood!).
Beasts who sleep good and thin,
Hist, in hogsback woods! The haystacked
Hollow farms in a throng
Of waters cluck and cling,   80
And barnroofs cockcrow war!
O kingdom of neighbours, finned
Felled and quilled, flash to my patch
Work ark and the moonshine
Drinking Noah of the bay,   85
With pelt, and scale, and fleece:
Only the drowned deep bells
Of sheep and churches noise
Poor peace as the sun sets
And dark shoals every holy field.   90
We will ride out alone, and then,
Under the stars of Wales,
Cry, Multitudes of arks! Across
The water lidded lands,
Manned with their loves they'll move,   95
Like wooden islands, hill to hill.

Huloo, my prowed dove with a flute!
Ahoy, old, sea-legged fox,
Tom tit and Dai mouse!
My ark sings in the sun   100
At God speeded summer's end
And the flood flowers now.

THE HAND THAT SIGNED THE PAPER
FELLED A CITY

The hand that signed the paper felled a city;
Five sovereign fingers taxed the breath,
Doubled the globe of dead and halved a country;
These five kings did a king to death.

The mighty hand leads to a sloping shoulder,   5
The finger joints are cramped with chalk;
A goose's quill has put an end to murder
That put an end to talk.

The hand that signed the treaty bred a fever,
And famine grew, and locusts came;   10
Great is the hand that holds dominion over
Man by a scribbled name.

The five kings count the dead but do not soften
The crusted wound nor pat the brow;
A hand rules pity as a hand rules heaven;   15
Hands have no tears to flow.

For Discussion

"Do Not Go Gentle into That Goodnight"

1. In this concentrated study of man meeting with death ("that good
   night . . ./at close of day"), the poet urges his aging father to meet
   death with the spirit and courage and resistance characteristic of his
   whole life. Do you approve his advice? Who are the *wise* men, the
   good men, the *wild* men, the *grave* men to whom he refers? How did
   each meet death?
2. Can you tell what kind of man his father was? Prove your answer.

3. In what two ways may the words "good night" be taken?
4. The first and third lines of the first stanza run through the poem like a refrain. How does the repetition add to the urgency, the near-fury of the speaker's plea? Why would you say that the theme of this poem is universal? What is its theme?

"Fern Hill"

1. Read the poem aloud, enjoying the musical descriptions of the various sensations presented by the boy. Observe the almost imperceptible decline in joy as the poem progresses from exultation to passing regret. Where does this subtle change of mood actually begin?
2. It has been said that the soul of leisure is *celebration*. Show how genuine celebration is the very core of the speaker's carefree, innocent boyhood days. In the fourth stanza, this innocence takes on a second meaning. Explain and discuss.
3. In stanza 5, sin subtly enters the picture. The poet expresses it in a negative fashion. Discuss. Why are the children up to this point, both "green" and "golden"?
4. How are sunlight and dark used as symbols in the poem? Do they affect the structure of the poem? The tone and mood?
5. What is the effect achieved by the unrhymed lines in this poem?

"Poem in October"

1. What two ideas about time does the speaker convey in the first line?
2. Like "Fern Hill," this poem is made up of numerous sensations of sound, sight, and touch. List those in the first stanza.
3. What is the setting of the poem? What time of day is it? Describe the weather. How does it compare with the speaker's occupation at the moment?
4. At the end of the poem, where is the speaker standing? Starting with stanza 3, describe all that he sees from that viewpoint.
5. What inner meaning is contained in the last line of stanza 4 and continued through stanzas 5 and 6? What is the "other air" to which it turns him?
6. Who is the "long dead child" of stanza 7? Describe him within the setting of the speaker's boyhood. What idea is conveyed by the last three lines of the poem?
7. Discuss the full import of each of the following: (a) "lark-full cloud," (b) "parables of sunlight," (c) "legends of the green chapels," (d) "leaved with October blood."
8. What is the effect of the unrhymed lines? Does it add to the reminiscent tone of the poem? Does the poem have a definite pattern? Study it closely and discuss.

"The Force That Through the Green Fuse Drives the Flower"

1. What or who is the "force" the speaker refers to? Do you agree that this "force" is both the creator and destroyer, a life-and-death force working as one thing? Why is the speaker "dumb" (unable) to express himself about his "wintry fever"? Is this idea true of adolescents in general? Discuss.

2. What is the "force" pictured as doing in stanza 2?

3. In the third stanza, the force becomes personified. Can you explain the allusion to the moving of the waters? What thing of dread does this same "hand" also stir? On what occasion in the Gospel did Our Lord "rope/The blowing wind"? What further application of this power is contained in "Hauls my shroud sail"?

4. "The hangman's lime" was really a quick-lime in which the bodies of the executed were finally destroyed. What does the speaker mean by stating that of his "clay is made the hangman's lime"?

5. In the fourth stanza, time is compared to a leech sucking the life-blood at its very source. At the same time, the leech represents a process of healing. Can you explain this paradox? Note, too, that love's "sores" can be calmed only by sacrifice (". . . the fallen blood/Shall *calm* her sores.") How does time operate in the last verse of this stanza? Can you explain the irony here?

6. Show how the final couplet is a summing up of all the foregoing stanzas.

"Author's Prologue"

1. From the first 22 lines, list the images referring to the speaker's enchanted world of fish, fowl, sea, and sky. Describe the people inhabiting this world. Point out how all things are *in process*. Discuss.

2. In lines 22–24, the speaker declares his purpose: ". . . I sing/To you strangers," and in lines 44–52, he invites all this wonderful company "From fish to jumping hill" into his "ark," the "ark" of his poem, which is built "To the best of my love/As the flood begins." Trace the ark image throughout the rest of the poem. What is the flood which he anticipates? Would it mean only the incoming tide near his 'seashaken house" or does it have a deeper meaning? Explain.

3. Once the inhabitants are safely within, the "ark sings in the sun . . ./And the flood flowers" (lines 100–102). What idea is suggested here? How does the image in line 95 echo the Biblical account of the ark?

4. Explain the meaning of each of the following:
   (a) "on a breakneck of rocks'   (c) "Geese nearly in heaven"
   (b) "Tangled with chirrup and fruit" (d) "shells that speak seven
                                              seas"

"The Hand That Signed the Paper"

1. Unlike Thomas' other poems, this one is completely objective. It is concerned with the speaker's contemplation of the "system" under which most of the world is forced to live. State the thought of the poem.
2. Is the poem's comparison of the hand's "five fingers" to "five kings" a realistic one? Enumerate the deeds these "five fingers" perform.
3. What is the meaning of the last line in the poem? Explain each of the poem's metaphors.

Modern Short Stories

Modern short stories have deep roots in the past, and all ages have contributed to their development. For example, there is the myth of *Beowulf*, Chaucer's exempla or moral tales, Malory's legends of King Arthur, Swift's account of Gulliver's travels, and the sketches of Addison and Steele. Loosely constructed narratives though they are, they represent the beginnings of literature's most recent form—the short story.

It is generally conceded that the short story, as it is known today, began with Edgar Allan Poe in America. In 1842, Poe framed the first significant definition of this new literary type. According to him, (1) a story must not be so long that it cannot be read at one sitting; (2) that it must bring about a certain unique or single preconceived effect; (3) that it must contain no words which do not help the pre-established design of the story. Poe's definition became the accepted basis of the short-story technique.

From the middle of the nineteenth century, the short story flourished in America and England. Both countries became masters of this form. The stories of Rudyard Kipling in the late nineteenth century and W. Somerset Maugham in the twentieth century are typical of the "classic" short story.

Changing times, however, brought changing ideas, and the short story reflected these changes. The twentieth century saw the development of new short-story techniques and new subject matter. Writers rejected lengthy passages of exposition and description; they relied less on the romantic and sentimental for achieving their effects, and became more and more realistic in their approach. One of the outstanding new prose fiction writers of this period was Joseph Conrad, who was more interested in the struggle between good and evil *within* his characters than he was in what happened to them outwardly.

These new writers wanted to explore every aspect of man's existence and his environment, including his unconscious. To express this new approach, individual authors experimented with various techniques. James Joyce and Virginia Woolf used the *stream-of-consciousness* technique. Here, the author records the thoughts and reflections that flow through the mind of a character within a brief period of time. The reader penetrates the mind of a character and participates in his mental processes. Joyce also stressed what he called the *epiphany* or the *revelation*. By this he means the moment (indicated by a word, a movement, or a single object) when that which has been hidden is revealed and the meaning of things is realized.

Another distinguishing feature of the modern short story has been the increasing use of dramatization. This technique permits the characters in a story to act, and the reader to watch, much as he does in a play. Events, rather than the author's exposition, give rise to the emotion. Sean O'Faolain and Elizabeth Bowen are particularly skillful in using this approach.

Other writers, like Katherine Mansfield, have combined the stream-of-consciousness technique with the third-person point of view, while writers, like Graham Greene, use the third-person point of view exclusively.

With all the changes in style and content, however, writers have never wholly departed from the basic idea of the short story: to present in a dramatic fashion a single incident about a single character, usually against a single setting, to produce a single effect.

The Lumber-Room

SAKI (H. H. MUNRO)

H. H. Munro (1870–1916) is one of England's most eminent story-tellers. He chose as his pseudonym "Saki," from the Persian cupbearer in *The Rubaiyat of Omar Khayyam*. No name could be more appropriate. As the original Saki "poured millions of bubbles" to welcome guests, so England's "Saki" blows bubbles that explode in laughter to entertain his readers.

Saki's stories are slyly witty, satirical, and often macabre. But even when the reader is horrified, he finds himself laughing as Saki makes war on the complacency, hypocrisy, and snobbery of adults. His style is economical and impersonal; it leaves no room for sentiment or personal reflection. Consequently, it has no time for elaborate characterization. His characters are sharply defined in black or white: a few acutely significant details, even a name, and they come alive.

In "The Lumber-Room," Saki's satirical observations on the war between the adult's world and the child's world are delightfully presented. Under the humor, however, is a serious and critical comment on the way grownups see children and how children may retaliate.

———◆———

The children were to be driven, as a special treat, to the sands at Jagborough. Nicholas was not to be of the party; he was in disgrace. Only that morning he had refused to eat his wholesome bread-and-milk on the seemingly frivolous ground that there was a frog in it. Older and wiser and better people had told him that there could not possibly be a frog in his bread-and-milk and that he was not to talk nonsense; he continued, nevertheless, to talk what seemed the veriest nonsense, and described with much detail the colouration and markings of the alleged frog. The dramatic part of the incident was that there really was a frog in Nicholas' basin of bread-and-milk; he had put it there himself, so he felt entitled to know something about it. The sin of taking a frog from the garden and putting it into a bowl of wholesome bread-and-milk was enlarged on at great length, but the fact that stood out clearest in the whole affair, as it presented itself to the mind of Nicholas, was that the older, wiser, and better people had been proved to be profoundly in error in matters about which they had expressed the utmost assurance.

"You said there couldn't possibly be a frog in my bread-and-milk; there *was* a frog in my bread-and-milk," he repeated, with the insistence of a skilled tactician who does not intend to shift from favourable ground.

So his boy-cousin and girl-cousin and his quite uninteresting younger brother were to be taken to Jagborough sands that afternoon and he was to stay at home. His cousins' aunt, who insisted, by an unwarranted stretch of imagination, in styling herself his aunt also, had hastily invented the Jagborough expedition in order to impress on Nicholas the delights that he had justly forfeited by his disgraceful conduct at the breakfast-table. It was her habit, whenever one of the children fell from grace, to improvise something of a festival nature from which the offender would be rigorously debarred; if all the children sinned collectively they were suddenly informed of a circus in a neighbouring town, a circus of unrivalled merit and uncounted elephants, to which, but for their depravity, they would have been taken that very day.

A few decent tears were looked for on the part of Nicholas when the moment for the departure of the expedition arrived. As a matter of fact, however, all the crying was done by his girl-cousin, who scraped her knee rather painfully against the step of the carriage as she was scrambling in.

"How she did howl," said Nicholas cheerfully, as the party drove off without any of the elation of high spirits that should have characterized it.

"She'll soon get over that," said the *soi-disant* aunt; "it will be a glorious afternoon for racing about over those beautiful sands. How they will enjoy themselves!"

"Bobby won't enjoy himself much, and he won't race much either," said Nicholas with a grim chuckle; "his boots are hurting him. They're too tight."

"Why didn't he tell me they were hurting?" asked the aunt with some asperity.

"He told you twice, but you weren't listening. You often don't listen when we tell you important things."

"You are not to go into the gooseberry garden," said the aunt, changing the subject.

"Why not?" demanded Nicholas.

"Because you are in disgrace," said the aunt loftily.

Nicholas did not admit the flawlessness of the reasoning; he felt perfectly capable of being in disgrace and in a gooseberry garden at the same moment. His face took on an expression of considerable obstinacy. It was clear to his aunt that he was determined to get into the gooseberry garden, "only," as she remarked to herself, "because I have told him he is not to."

Now the gooseberry garden had two doors by which it might be entered, and once a small person like Nicholas could slip in there he could effectually disappear from view amid the masking growth of artichokes, raspberry canes, and fruit bushes. The aunt had many other things to do that afternoon, but she spent an hour or two in trivial gardening operations among flower beds and shrubberies, whence she could keep a watchful eye on the two doors that led to the forbidden paradise. She was a woman of few ideas, with immense powers of concentration.

Nicholas made one or two sorties into the front garden, wriggling his way with obvious stealth of purpose towards one or other of the doors, but never able for a moment to evade the aunt's watchful eye. As a matter of fact, he had no intention of trying to get into the gooseberry garden, but it was extremely convenient for him that his aunt should believe that he had; it was a belief that would keep her on self-imposed sentry-duty for the greater part of the afternoon. Having thoroughly confirmed and fortified her suspicions, Nicholas slipped back into the house and rapidly put into execution a plan of action that had long germinated in his brain. By standing on a chair in the library one could reach a shelf on which reposed a fat, important-looking key. The key was as important as it looked; it was the instrument which kept the mysteries of the lumber-room secure from unauthorized intrusion, which opened a way only for aunts and such-like privileged persons. Nicholas had not had much experience of the art of fitting keys into keyholes and turning locks, but for some days past he had practised with the key of the schoolroom door; he did not believe in trusting too much to luck and accident. The key turned stiffly in the lock, but it turned. The door opened, and Nicholas was in an unknown land, compared with which the gooseberry garden was a stale delight, a mere material pleasure.

Often and often Nicholas had pictured to himself what the lumber-room might be like, that region that was so carefully sealed from youthful eyes and concerning which no questions were ever answered. It came up to his expectations. In the first place it was large and dimly lit, one high window opening on to the forbidden garden being its only source of illumination. In the second place it was a storehouse of unimagined treasures. The aunt-by-assertion was one of those people who think that things spoil by use and consign them to dust and damp by way of preserving them. Such parts of the house as Nicholas knew best were rather bare and cheerless, but here there were wonderful things for the eye to feast on. First and foremost there was a piece of framed tapestry that was evidently meant to be a fire-screen. To Nicholas it was a living, breathing story; he sat down on a roll of Indian hangings, glowing in wonderful colours beneath a layer of dust, and took in all the details of the tapestry picture. A man, dressed in the hunting costume of some remote period, had just transfixed a stag with an arrow; it could not have been a difficult shot because the stag was only one or two paces away from him; in the thickly growing vegetation that the picture suggested it would not have been difficult to creep up to a feeding stag, and the two spotted dogs that were springing forward to join in the chase had evidently been trained to keep to heel till the arrow was discharged. That part of the picture was simple, if interesting, but did the huntsman see, what Nicholas saw, that four galloping wolves were coming in his direction through the wood? There might be more than four of them hidden behind the trees, and in any case would the man and his dogs be able to cope with the four wolves if they made an attack? The man had only two arrows left in his quiver, and he might miss with one or both of them; all one knew about his skill in shooting was that he could hit a large stag at a ridiculously short range. Nicholas sat for many golden minutes revolving the possibilities of the scene; he was inclined to think that there were more than four wolves and that the man and his dogs were in a tight corner.

But there were other objects of delight and interest claiming his instant attention: there were quaint twisted candlesticks in the shape of snakes, and a teapot fashioned like a china duck, out of whose open beak the tea was supposed to come. How dull and shapeless the nursery teapot seemed in comparison! And there was a carved sandal-wood box packed tight with aromatic cotton-wool, and between the layers of cotton-wool were little brass figures, hump-necked bulls, and peacocks and goblins, delightful to see and to handle. Less promising in appearance was a large square book with plain black covers; Nicholas peeped into it, and, behold, it was full of coloured pictures of birds. And such birds! In the garden, and in the lanes when he went for a walk, Nicholas came across a few birds, of which the largest were an occasional magpie or wood-pigeon; here were herons and bustards, kites, toucans, tiger-bitterns, brush turkeys, ibises, golden pheasants, a whole portrait gallery of undreamed-of creatures. And as he was admiring the colouring of the mandarin duck and assigning a life-history to it, the voice of his aunt in shrill vociferation of his name came from the gooseberry garden without. She had grown suspicious at his long disappearance, and had leapt to the conclusion that he had climbed over the wall behind the sheltering screen of the lilac bushes; she was now engaged in energetic and rather hopeless search for him among the artichokes and raspberry canes.

"Nicholas, Nicholas!" she screamed, "you are to come out of this at once. It's no use trying to hide there; I can see you all the time."

It was probably the first time for twenty years that any one had smiled in that lumber-room.

Presently the angry repetitions of Nicholas' name gave way to a shriek, and a cry for somebody to come quickly. Nicholas shut the book, restored it carefully to its place in a corner, and shook some dust from a neighbouring pile of newspapers over it. Then he crept from the room, locked the door, and replaced the key exactly where he had found it. His aunt was still calling his name when he sauntered into the front garden.

"Who's calling?" he asked.

"Me," came the answer from the other side of the wall; "didn't you hear me? I've been looking for you in the gooseberry garden, and I've slipped into the rain-water tank. Luckily there's no water in it, but the sides are slippery and I can't get out. Fetch the little ladder from under the cherry tree—"

"I was told I wasn't to go into the gooseberry garden," said Nicholas promptly.

"I told you not to, and now I tell you that you may," came the voice from the rain-water tank, rather impatiently.

"Your voice doesn't sound like aunt's," objected Nicholas; "you may be the Evil One tempting me to be disobedient. Aunt often tells me that the Evil One tempts me and that I always yield. This time I'm not going to yield."

"Don't talk nonsense," said the prisoner in the tank; "go and fetch the ladder."

"Will there be strawberry jam for tea?" asked Nicholas innocently.

"Certainly there will be," said the aunt, privately resolving that Nicholas should have none of it.

"Now I know that you are the Evil One and not aunt," shouted Nicholas gleefully; "when we asked aunt for strawberry jam yesterday she said there wasn't any. I know there are four jars of it in the store cupboard, because I looked, and of course you know it's there, but *she* doesn't, because she said there wasn't any. Oh, Devil, you *have* sold yourself!"

There was an unusual sense of luxury in being able to talk to an aunt as though one was talking to the Evil One, but Nicholas knew, with childish discernment, that such luxuries were not to be over-indulged in. He walked noisily away, and it was a kitchenmaid, in search of parsley, who eventually rescued the aunt from the rain-water tank.

Tea that evening was partaken of in a fearsome silence. The tide had been at its highest when the children had arrived at Jagborough Cove, so there had been no sands to play on—a circumstance that the aunt had overlooked in the haste of organizing her punitive expedition. The tightness of Bobby's boots had had disastrous effect on his temper the whole of the afternoon, and altogether the children could not have been said to have enjoyed themselves. The aunt maintained the frozen muteness of one who has suffered undignified and un-merited detention in a rain-water tank for thirty-five minutes. As for Nicholas, he, too, was silent, in the absorption of one who has much to think about; it was just possible, he considered, that the huntsman would escape with his hounds while the wolves feasted on the stricken stag.

For Discussion:

1. Saki's sly humor can be found in almost every sentence. Which paragraph do you consider the funniest? Why?
2. What is the purpose of the opening incident about the frog?
3. What common adult attitudes toward children does Saki satirize? Does the child in this case come off completely victorious? Explain.
4. Speaking of Nicholas' entry into the lumber-room, Saki says that the child ". . . was in an unknown land, compared with which the goose-berry garden was a stale delight, a mere material pleasure." What possible symbolic meaning might this have? How do the objects stored in the room compare with those in Nicholas' everyday life? Does this throw any new light on the child?
5. Why is it appropriate that Nicholas should ponder so long over the tapestry? What does his interest in the birds indicate?
6. Interpret the last sentence of the story. Is it a fitting close? Explain.

The Secret Sharer

JOSEPH CONRAD

Joseph Conrad (1857–1924) did not speak English until he was twenty, and did not begin seriously to write it until ten years later. By that time he had lived a life packed with excitement, hardship, and adventure from which he could fashion his tales.

At sixteen, Polish-born Jozef Konrad Korzeniowski left his uncle's home in Cracow, Poland to answer the call of the sea. During the next twenty-one years, he rose from apprentice to master on French and British merchant vessels. He visited the East Indies, South America, South Africa, and Australia, gathering along the way the ideas and impressions that would later become the materials for his stories.

When Conrad came ashore for good in 1894, he became a British citizen and settled down to the serious business of writing novels under his English name. Describing his chief aim as a writer, Conrad wrote "My task is to make you hear, to make you feel—it is before all to make you see." He succeeded. His novels *Lord Jim, Typhoon, Victory,* and his long short stories "Youth," "Heart of Darkness," and "The Secret Sharer" established him as a master of prose fiction.

The action of Conrad's stories takes place under merciless suns or in fearful nights, on winding rivers or in steaming jungles. His characters are men struggling with the problem of good and evil and the problem of accepting or rejecting the world. His plots bristle with action, but they are not ordinary tales of adventure. Conrad, as an artist, was primarily concerned with the nature of man as it is revealed in the choices he makes within his own mind and heart. This is to be seen in one of his most powerful stories, "The Secret Sharer."

On my right hand there were lines of fishing stakes resembling a mysterious system of half-submerged bamboo fences, incomprehensible in its division of the domain of tropical fishes, and crazy of aspect as if abandoned forever by some nomad tribe of fishermen now gone to the other end of the ocean; for there was no sign of human habitation as far as the eye could reach. To the left a group of barren islets, suggesting ruins of stone walls, towers, and blockhouses, had its foundations set in a blue sea that itself looked solid, so still and stable did it lie below my feet; even the track of light from the westering sun shone smoothly, without that animated glitter which tells of an im-

perceptible ripple. And when I turned my head to take a parting
glance at the tug which had just left us anchored outside the bar, I
saw the straight line of the flat shore joined to the stable sea, edge
to edge, with a perfect and unmarked closeness, in one leveled floor
half brown, half blue under the enormous dome of the sky. Corresponding in their insignificance to the islets of the sea, two small
clumps of trees, one on each side of the only fault in the impeccable
joint, marked the mouth of the river Meinam we had just left on the
first preparatory stage of our homeward journey; and, far back on the
inland level, a larger and loftier mass, the grove surrounding the great
Paknam pagoda, was the only thing on which the eye could rest from
the vain task of exploring the monotonous sweep of the horizon.
Here and there gleams as of a few scattered pieces of silver marked
the windings of the great river; and on the nearest of them, just
within the bar, the tug steaming right into the land became lost to
my sight, hull and funnel and masts, as though the impassive earth
had swallowed her up without an effort, without a tremor. My eye
followed the light cloud of her smoke, now here, now there, above
the plain, according to the devious curves of the stream, but always
fainter and farther away, till I lost it at last behind the miter-shaped
hill of the great pagoda. And then I was left alone with my ship,
anchored at the head of the Gulf of Siam.

She floated at the starting point of a long journey, very still in an
immense stillness, the shadows of her spars flung far to the eastward
by the setting sun. At that moment I was alone on her decks. There
was not a sound in her—and around us nothing moved, nothing
lived, not a canoe on the water, not a bird in the air, not a cloud in
the sky. In this breathless pause at the threshold of a long passage
we seemed to be measuring our fitness for a long and arduous enterprise, the appointed task of both our existences to be carried out, far
from all human eyes, with only sky and sea for spectators and for
judges.

There must have been some glare in the air to interfere with one's
sight, because it was only just before the sun left us that my roaming
eyes made out beyond the highest ridge of the principal islet of the
group something which did away with the solemnity of perfect solitude. The tide of darkness flowed on swiftly; and with tropical sud-
denness a swarm of stars came out above the shadowy earth, while
I lingered yet, my hand resting lightly on my ship's rail as if on the
shoulder of a trusted friend. But, with all that multitude of celestial

bodies staring down at one, the comfort of quiet communion with her was gone for good. And there were also disturbing sounds by this time—voices, footsteps forward; the steward flitted along the main deck, a busily ministering spirit; a hand bell tinkled urgently under the poop deck. . . .

I found my two officers waiting for me near the supper table, in the lighted cuddy. We sat down at once, and as I helped the chief mate, I said:

"Are you aware that there is a ship anchored inside the islands? I saw her mastheads above the ridge as the sun went down."

He raised sharply his simple face, overcharged by a terrible growth of whisker, and emitted his usual ejaculations: "Bless my soul, sir! You don't say so!"

My second mate was a round-cheeked, silent young man, grave beyond his years, I thought; but as our eyes happend to meet I detected a slight quiver on his lips. I looked down at once. It was not my part to encourage sneering on board my ship. It must be said, too, that I knew very little of my officers. In consequence of certain events of no particular significance, except to myself, I had been appointed to the command only a fortnight before. Neither did I know much of the hands forward. All these people had been together for eighteen months or so, and my position was that of the only stranger on board. I mention this because it has some bearing on what is to follow. But what I felt most was my being a stranger to the ship; and if all the truth must be told, I was somewhat of a stranger to myself. The youngest man on board (barring the second mate), and untried as yet by a position of the fullest responsibility, I was willing to take the adequacy of the others for granted. They had simply to be equal to their tasks; but I wondered how far I should turn out faithful to that ideal conception of one's own personality every man sets up for himself secretly.

Meantime the chief mate, with an almost visible effect of collaboration on the part of his round eyes and frightful whiskers, was trying to evolve a theory of the anchored ship. His dominant trait was to take all things into earnest consideration. He was of a painstaking turn of mind. As he used to say, he "liked to account to himself" for practically everything that came in his way, down to a miserable scorpion he had found in his cabin a week before. The why and the wherefore of that scorpion—how it got on board and came to select his room rather than the pantry (which was a dark place and more what a scorpion would be partial to), and how on earth it managed to drown itself in the inkwell of his writing desk—had exercised him infinitely. The ship within the islands was much more easily accounted for; and just as we were about to rise from the table he made his pronouncement. She was, he doubted not, a ship from home lately arrived. Probably she drew too much water to cross the bar except at the top of spring tides. Therefore she went into that natural harbor to wait for a few days in preference to remaining in an open roadstead.

"That's so," confirmed the second mate, suddenly, in his slightly hoarse voice. "She draws over twenty feet. She's the Liverpool ship *Sephora* with a cargo of coal. Hundred and twenty-three days from Cardiff."

We looked at him in surprise.

"The tugboat skipper told me when he came on board for your letters, sir," explained the young man. "He expects to take her up the river the day after tomorrow."

After thus overwhelming us with the extent of his information he slipped out of the cabin. The mate observed regretfully that he "could not account for that young fellow's whims." What prevented him telling us all about it at once, he wanted to know.

I detained him as he was making a move. For the last two days the crew had had plenty of hard work, and the night before they had very little sleep. I felt painfully that I—a stranger—was doing something unusual when I directed him to let all hands turn in without setting an anchor watch. I proposed to keep on deck myself till one o'clock or thereabouts. I would get the second mate to relieve me at that hour.

"He will turn out the cook and the steward at four," I concluded, "and then give you a call. Of course at the slightest sign of any sort of wind we'll have the hands up and make a start at once."

He concealed his astonishment. "Very well, sir." Outside the cuddy he put his head in the second mate's door to inform him of my unheard-of caprice to take a five hours' anchor watch on myself. I heard the other raise his voice incredulously: "What? The captain himself?" Then a few more murmurs, a door closed, then another. A few moments later I went on deck.

My strangeness, which had made me sleepless, had prompted that unconventional arrangement, as if I had expected in those solitary hours of the night to get on terms with the ship of which I knew nothing, manned by men of whom I knew very little more. Fast alongside a wharf, littered like any ship in port with a tangle of unrelated things, invaded by unrelated shore people, I had hardly seen her yet properly. Now, as she lay cleared for sea, the stretch of her main deck seemed to me very fine under the stars. Very fine, very roomy for her size, and very inviting. I descended the poop and paced the waist, my mind picturing to myself the coming passage through the Malay Archipelago, down the Indian Ocean, and up the Atlantic. All its phases were familiar enough to me, every characteristic, all the alternatives which were likely to face me on the high seas —everything! . . . except the novel responsibility of command. But I took heart from the reasonable thought that the ship was like other ships, the men like other men, and that the sea was not likely to keep any special surprises expressly for my discomfiture.

Arrived at that comforting conclusion, I bethought myself of a cigar and went below to get it. All was still down there. Everybody at the after end of the ship was sleeping profoundly. I came out again on the quarterdeck, agreeably at ease in my sleeping suit on that warm breathless night, barefooted, a glowing cigar in my teeth, and, going forward, I was met by the profound silence of the fore end of the ship. Only as I passed the door of the forecastle I heard a deep, quiet, trustful sigh of some sleeper inside. And suddenly I rejoiced in the great security of the sea as compared with the unrest of the land, in my choice of that untempted life presenting no disquieting problems, invested with an elementary moral beauty by the absolute straightforwardness of its appeal and by the singleness of its purpose.

The riding light in the fore-rigging burned with a clear, untroubled, as if symbolic, flame, confident and bright in the mysterious shades of the night. Passing on my way aft along the other side of the ship, I observed that the rope side ladder, put over, no doubt, for the master of the tug when he came to fetch away our letters, had not been hauled in as it should have been. I became annoyed at this, for exactitude in small matters is the very soul of discipline. Then I reflected that I had myself peremptorily dismissed my officers from duty, and by my own act had prevented the anchor watch being formally set and things properly attended to. I asked myself whether it was wise ever to interfere with the established routine of duties even from the kindest of motives. My action might have made me appear eccentric. Goodness only knew how that absurdly whiskered mate would "account" for my conduct, and what the whole ship thought of that informality of their new captain. I was vexed with myself.

Not from compunction certainly, but, as it were mechanically, I proceeded to get the ladder in myself. Now a side ladder of that sort is a light affair and comes in easily, yet my vigorous tug, which should have brought it flying on board, merely recoiled upon my body in a totally unexpected jerk. What the devil! . . . I was so astounded by the immovableness of that ladder that I remained stock-still, trying to account for it to myself like that imbecile mate of mine. In the end, of course, I put my head over the rail.

The side of the ship made an opaque belt of shadow on the darkling glassy shimmer of the sea. But I saw at once something elongated and pale floating very close to the ladder. Before I could form a guess a faint flash of phosphorescent light, which seemed to issue suddenly from the naked body of a man, flickered in the sleeping water with the elusive, silent play of summer lightning in a night sky. With a gasp I saw revealed to my stare a pair of feet, the long legs, a broad livid back immersed right up to the neck in a greenish cadaverous glow. One hand, awash, clutched the bottom rung of the ladder. He was complete but for the head. A headless corpse! The cigar dropped out of my gaping mouth with a tiny plop and a short hiss quite audible in the absolute stillness of all things under heaven. At that I suppose he raised up his face, a dimly pale oval in the shadow of the ship's side. But even then I could only barely make out down there the shape of his blackhaired head. However, it was enough for the horrid, frost-bound sensation which had gripped me about the chest to pass off. The moment of vain exclamations was past, too. I only climbed on the spare spar and leaned over the rail as far as I could, to bring my eyes nearer to that mystery floating alongside.

As he hung by the ladder, like a resting swimmer, the sea lightning played about his limbs at every stir; and he appeared in it ghastly, silvery, fishlike. He remained as mute as a fish, too. He made no motion to get out of the water, either. It was inconceivable that he should not attempt to come on board, and strangely troubling to suspect that perhaps he did not want to. And my first words were prompted by just that troubled incertitude.

"What's the matter?" I asked in my ordinary tone, speaking down to the face upturned exactly under mine.

"Cramp," it answered, no louder. Then slightly anxious, "I say, no need to call anyone."

"I was not going to," I said.

"Are you alone on deck?"

"Yes."

I had somehow the impression that he was on the point of letting go the ladder to swim away beyond my ken—mysterious as he came. But, for the moment, this being appearing as if he had risen from the bottom of the sea (it was certainly the nearest land to the ship) wanted only to know the time. I told him. And he, down there, tentatively:

"I suppose your captain's turned in?"

"I am sure he isn't," I said.

He seemed to struggle with himself, for I heard something like the low, bitter murmur of doubt. "What's the good?" His next words came out with a hesitating effort.

"Look here, my man. Could you call him out quietly?"

I thought the time had come to declare myself.

"I am the captain."

I heard a "By Jove!" whispered at the level of the water. The phosphorescence flashed in the swirl of the water all about his limbs, his other hand seized the ladder.

"My name's Leggatt."

The voice was calm and resolute. A good voice. The self-possession of that man had somehow induced a corresponding state in myself. It was very quietly that I remarked:

"You must be a good swimmer."

"Yes. I've been in the water practically since nine o'clock. The question for me now is whether I am to let go this ladder and go on swimming till I sink from exhaustion, or—to come on board here."

I felt this was no formula of desperate speech, but a real alternative in the view of a strong soul. I should have gathered from this that he was young; indeed, it is only the young who are ever confronted by such clear issues. But at the time it was pure intuition on my part. A mysterious communication was established already between us two—in the face of that silent, darkened tropical sea. I was young, too; young enough to make no comment. The man in the water began suddenly to climb up the ladder, and I hastened away from the rail to fetch some clothes.

Before entering the cabin I stood still, listening in the lobby at the foot of the stairs. A faint snore came through the closed door of the chief mate's room. The second mate's door was on the hook, but the darkness in there was absolutely soundless. He, too, was young and could sleep like a stone. Remained the steward, but he was not likely to wake up before he was called. I got a sleeping suit out of my room and, coming back on deck, saw the naked man from the sea sitting on the main hatch, glimmering white in the darkness, his elbows on his knees and his head in his hands. In a moment he had concealed his damp body in a sleeping suit of the same gray-stripe pattern as the one I was wearing and followed me like my double on the poop. Together we moved right aft, barefooted, silent.

"What is it?" I asked in a deadened voice, taking the lighted lamp out of the binnacle, and raising it to his face.

"An ugly business."

He had rather regular features; a good mouth; light eyes under somewhat heavy, dark eyebrows; a smooth, square forehead; no growth on his cheeks; a small, brown mustache, and a well-shaped, round chin. His expression was concentrated, meditative, under the inspecting light of the lamp I held up to his face; such as a man thinking hard in solitude might wear. My sleeping suit was just right for his size. A well-knit young fellow of twenty-five at most. He caught his lower lip with the edge of white, even teeth.

"Yes," I said, replacing the lamp in the binnacle. The warm, heavy tropical night closed upon his head again.

"There's a ship over there," he murmured.

"Yes, I know. The *Sephora*. Did you know of us?"

"Hadn't the slightest idea. I am the mate of her—" He paused and corrected himself. "I should say I *was*."

"Aha! Something wrong?"

"Yes. Very wrong indeed. I've killed a man."

"What do you mean? Just now?"

"No, on the passage. Weeks ago. Thirty-nine south. When I say a man—"

"Fit of temper," I suggested, confidently.

The shadowy, dark head, like mine, seemed to nod imperceptibly above the ghostly gray of my sleeping suit. It was, in the night, as though I had been faced by my own reflection in the depths of a somber and immense mirror.

"A pretty thing to have to own up to for a Conway boy," murmured my double, distinctly.

"You're a Conway boy?"

"I am," he said, as if startled. Then, slowly . . . "Perhaps you too—"

It was so; but being a couple of years older I had left before he joined. After a quick interchange of dates a silence fell; and I thought suddenly of my absurd mate with his terrific whiskers and the "Bless my soul—you don't say so" type of intellect. My double gave me an inkling of his thoughts by saying:

"My father's a parson in Norfolk. Do you see me before a judge and jury on that charge? For myself I can't see the necessity. There are fellows that an angel from heaven——And I am not that. He was one of those creatures that are just simmering all the time with a silly sort of wickedness. Miserable devils that have no business to live at all. He wouldn't do his duty and wouldn't let anybody else do theirs. But what's the good of talking! You know well enough the sort of ill-conditioned snarling cur—"

He appealed to me as if our experiences had been as identical as our clothes. And I knew well enough the pestiferous danger of such a character where there are no means of legal repression. And I knew well enough also that my double there was no homicidal ruffian. I did not think of asking him for details, and he told me the story roughly in brusque, disconnected sentences. I needed no more. I saw it all going on as though I were myself inside that other sleeping suit.

"It happened while we were setting a reefed foresail, at dusk. Reefed foresail! You understand the sort of weather. The only sail we had left to keep the ship running; so you may guess what it had been like for days. Anxious sort of job, that. He gave me some of his cursed insolence at the sheet. I tell you I was overdone with this terrific weather that seemed to have no end to it. Terrific, I tell you—and a deep ship. I believe the fellow himself was half crazed with funk. It was no time for gentlemanly reproof, so I turned round and felled him like an ox. He up and at me. We closed just as an awful sea made for the ship. All hands saw it coming and took to the rigging, but I had him by the throat, and went on shaking him like a rat, the men above us yelling, 'Look out! look out!' Then a crash as if the sky had fallen on my head. They say that for over ten minutes hardly anything was to be seen of the ship—just the three masts and a bit of the forecastle head and of the poop all awash driving along in a smother of foam. It was a miracle that they found us, jammed together behind the forebits. It's clear that I meant business, because I was holding him by the throat still when they picked us up. He was black in the face. It was too much for them. It seems they rushed us aft together, gripped as we were, screaming 'Murder!' like a lot of lunatics, and broke into the cuddy. And the ship running for her life, touch and go all the time, any minute her last in a sea fit to turn your hair gray only a-looking at it. I understand that the skipper, too, started raving like the rest of them. The man had been deprived of sleep for more than a week, and to have this sprung on him at the height of a furious gale nearly drove him out of his mind. I wonder they didn't fling me overboard after getting the carcass of their precious shipmate out of my fingers. They had rather a job to separate us, I've been told. A sufficiently fierce story to make an old judge and a respectable jury sit up a bit. The first thing I heard when I came to myself was the maddening howling of that endless gale, and on that the voice of the old man. He was hanging on to my bunk, staring into my face out of his sou'wester.

" 'Mr. Leggatt, you have killed a man. You can act no longer as chief mate of this ship.' "

His care to subdue his voice made it sound monotonous. He rested a hand on the end of the skylight to steady himself with, and all that time did not stir a limb, so far as I could see. "Nice little tale for a quiet tea party," he concluded in the same tone.

One of my hands, too, rested on the end of the skylight; neither did I stir a limb, so far as I knew. We stood less than a foot from each other. It occurred to me that if old "Bless my soul—you don't say so" were to put his head up the companion and catch sight of us, he would think he was seeing double, or imagine himself come upon a scene of weird witchcraft; the strange captain having a quiet confabulation by the wheel with his own gray ghost. I became very much concerned to prevent anything of the sort. I heard the other's soothing undertone.

"My father's a parson in Norfolk," it said. Evidently he had forgotten he had told me this important fact before. Truly a nice little tale.

"You had better slip down into my stateroom now," I said, moving off stealthily. My double followed my movements; our bare feet made no sound; I let him in, closed the door with care, and, after giving a call to the second mate, returned on deck for my relief.

"Not much sign of any wind yet," I remarked when he approached.

"No, sir. Not much," he assented, sleepily, in his hoarse voice, with just enough deference, no more, and barely suppressing a yawn.

"Well, that's all you have to look out for. You have got your orders."

"Yes, sir."

I paced a turn or two on the poop and saw him take up his position face foward with his elbow in the ratlines of the mizzen-rigging before I went below. The mate's faint snoring was still going on peacefully. The cuddy lamp was burning over the table on which stood a vase with flowers, a polite attention from the ships' provision merchant—the last flowers we should see for the next three months at the very least. Two bunches of bananas hung from the beam symmetrically, one on each side of the rudder casing. Everything was as before in the ship—except that two of her captain's sleeping suits were simultaneously in use, one motionless in the cuddy, the other keeping very still in the captain's stateroom.

It must be explained here that my cabin had the form of the capital letter L, the door being within the angle and opening into the short part of the letter. A couch was to the left, the bed-place to the right; my writing desk and the chronometers' table faced the door. But anyone opening it, unless he stepped right inside, had no view of what I call the long (or vertical) part of the letter. It contained some lockers surmounted by a book case; and a few clothes, a thick jacket or two, caps, oilskin coat, and such like, hung on hooks. There was at the bottom of that part a door opening into my bathroom, which could be entered also directly from the saloon. But that way was never used.

The mysterious arrival had discovered the advantage of this particular shape. Entering my room, lighted strongly by a big bulkhead lamp swung on gimbals above my writing desk, I did not see him anywhere till he stepped out quietly from behind the coats hung in the recessed part.

"I heard somebody moving about, and went in there at once," he whispered.

I, too, spoke under my breath.

"Nobody is likely to come in here without knocking and getting permission."

He nodded. His face was thin and the sunburn faded, as though he had been ill. And no wonder. He had been, I heard presently, kept under arrest in his cabin for nearly seven weeks. But there was nothing sickly in his eyes or in his expression. He was not a bit like me, really; yet, as we stood leaning over my bed-place, whispering side by side, with our dark heads together and our backs to the door, any-body bold enough to open it stealthily would have been treated to the uncanny sight of a double captain busy talking in whispers with his other self.

"But all this doesn't tell me how you came to hang on to our side ladder," I inquired, in the hardly audible murmurs we used, after he had told me something more of the proceedings on board the *Sephora* once the bad weather was over.

"When we sighted Java Head I had had time to think all those matters out several times over. I had six weeks of doing nothing else, and with only an hour or so every evening for a tramp on the quarter-deck."

He whispered, his arms folded on the side of my bed-place, star-ing through the open port. And I could imagine perfectly the man-ner of this thinking out—a stubborn if not a steadfast operation; something of which I should have been perfectly incapable.

"I reckoned it would be dark before we closed with the land," he continued, so low that I had to strain my hearing, near as we were to each other, shoulder touching shoulder almost. "So I asked to speak to the old man. He always seemed very sick when he came to see me—as if he could not look me in the face. You know, that foresail saved the ship. She was too deep to have run long under bare poles. And it was I that managed to set it for him. Anyway, he came. When I had him in my cabin—he stood by the door looking at me as if I had the halter around my neck already—I asked him right away to leave my cabin door unlocked at night while the ship was going through Sunda Straits. There would be the Java coast within two or three miles, off Angier Point. I wanted nothing more. I've had a prize for swimming my second year in the Conway."

"I can believe it," I breathed out.

"God only knows why they locked me in every night. To see some of their faces you'd have thought they were afraid I'd go about at night strangling people. Am I a murdering brute? Do I look it? By Jove! if I had been he wouldn't have trusted himself like that into my room. You'll say I might have chucked him aside and bolted out, there and then—it was dark already. Well, no. And for the same reason I wouldn't think of trying to smash the door. There would have been a rush to stop me at the noise, and I did not mean to get into a confounded scrimmage. Somebody else might have got killed—for I would not have broken out only to get chucked back, and I did not want any more of that work. He refused, looking more sick than ever. He was afraid of the men, and also of that old second mate of his who had been sailing with him for years—a gray-headed old humbug; and his steward, too, had been with him devil knows how long—seventeen years or more—a dogmatic sort of loafer who hated me like poison, just because I was the chief mate. No chief mate ever made more than one voyage in the *Sephora*, you know. Those two old chaps ran the ship. Devil only knows what the skipper wasn't afraid of (all his nerve went to pieces altogether in that hellish spell of bad weather we had)—of what the law would do to him—of his wife, perhaps. Oh, yes! she's on board. Though I don't think she would have meddled. She would have been only too glad to have me out of the ship in any way. The 'brand of Cain' business, don't you see. That's all right. I was ready enough to go off wandering on the face of the earth—and that was price enough to pay for an Abel of that sort. Anyhow, he wouldn't listen to me. 'This thing must take its course. I represent the law here.' He was shaking like a leaf. 'So you won't?' 'No!' 'Then I hope you will be able to sleep on that,' I said, and turned my back on him. 'I wonder that *you* can,' cries he, and locks the door.

"Well, after that, I couldn't. Not very well. That was three weeks ago. We have had a slow passage through the Java Sea; drifted about Carimata for ten days. When we anchored here they thought, I suppose, it was all right. The nearest land (and that's five miles) is the ship's destination; the consul would soon set about catching me; and there would have been no object in bolting to these islets there. I don't suppose there's a drop of water on them. I don't know how it was, but tonight that steward, after bringing me my supper, went out to let me eat it, and left the door unlocked. And I ate it—all there was, too. After I had finished I strolled out on the quarter-deck. I don't know that I meant to do anything. A breath of fresh air was all I wanted, I believe. Then a sudden temptation came over me. I kicked off my slippers and was in the water before I had made up my mind fairly. Somebody heard the splash and they raised an awful hullabaloo. 'He's gone! Lower the boats! He's committed suicide! No, he's swimming.' Certainly I was swimming. It's not so easy for a swimmer like me to commit suicide by drowning. I landed on the nearest islet before the boat left the ship's side. I heard them pulling about in the dark, hailing, and so on, but after a bit they gave up. Everything quieted down and the anchorage became as still as death.

I sat down on a stone and began to think. I felt certain they would start searching for me at daylight. There was no place to hide on those stony things—and if there had been, what would have been the good? But now I was clear of that ship, I was not going back. So after a while I took off all my clothes, tied them up in a bundle with a stone inside, and dropped them in the deep water on the outer side of that islet. That was suicide enough for me. Let them think what they liked, but I didn't mean to drown myself. I meant to swim till I sank—but that's not the same thing. I struck out for another of these little islands, and it was from that one that I first saw your riding light. Something to swim for. I went on easily, and on the way I came upon a flat rock a foot or two above water. In the daytime, I dare say, you might make it out with a glass from your poop. I scrambled up on it and rested myself for a bit. Then I made another start. That last spell must have been over a mile."

His whisper was getting fainter and fainter, and all the time he stared straight out through the porthole, in which there was not even a star to be seen. I had not interrupted him. There was something that made comment impossible in his narrative, or perhaps in himself; a sort of feeling, a quality, which I can't find a name for. And when he ceased, all I found was a futile whisper: "So you swam for our light?"

"Yes—straight for it. It was something to swim for. I couldn't see any stars low down because the coast was in the way, and I couldn't see the land, either. The water was like glass. One might have been swimming in a confounded thousand-feet deep cistern with no place for scrambling out anywhere; but what I didn't like was the notion of swimming round and round like a crazed bullock before I gave out; and as I didn't mean to go back . . . No. Do you see me being hauled back, stark naked, off one of these little islands by the scruff of the neck and fighting like a wild beast? Somebody would have got killed for certain, and I did not want any of that. So I went on. Then your ladder—"

"Why didn't you hail the ship?" I asked, a little louder.

He touched my shoulder lightly. Lazy footsteps came right over our heads and stopped. The second mate had crossed from the other side of the poop and might have been hanging over the rail, for all we knew.

"He couldn't hear us talking—could he?" My double breathed into my very ear, anxiously.

His anxiety was an answer, a sufficient answer, to the question I had put to him. An answer containing all the difficulty of that situation. I closed the porthole quietly, to make sure. A louder word might have been overheard.

"Who's that?" he whispered then.

"My second mate. But I don't know much more of the fellow than you do."

And I told him a little about myself. I had been appointed to take charge while I least expected anything of the sort, not quite a fortnight ago. I didn't know either the ship or the people. Hadn't had the time in port to look about me or size anybody up. And as to the crew, all they knew was that I was appointed to take the ship home. For the rest, I was almost as much of a stranger on board as himself, I said. And at the moment I felt it most acutely. I felt that it would take very little to make me a suspect person in the eyes of the ship's company.

He had turned about meantime; and we, the two strangers in the ship, faced each other in identical attitudes.

"Your ladder—" he murmured, after a silence. "Who'd have thought of finding a ladder hanging over at night in a ship anchored out here! I felt just then a very unpleasant faintness. After the life I've been leading for nine weeks, anybody would have got out of condition. I wasn't capable of swimming round as far as your rudder chains. And, lo and behold! there was a ladder to get hold of. After I gripped it I said to myself, 'What's the good?' When I saw a man's head looking over I thought I would swim away presently and leave him shouting—in whatever language it was. I didn't mind being looked at. I—I liked it. And then you speaking to me so quietly—as if you had expected me—made me hold on a little longer. It had been a confounded lonely time—I don't mean while swimming. I was glad to talk a little to somebody that didn't belong to the *Sephora*. As to asking for the captain, that was a mere impulse. It could have been no use, with all the ship knowing about me and the other people pretty certain to be round here in the morning. I don't know—I wanted to be seen, to talk with somebody, before I went on. I don't know what I would have said. . . . 'Fine night, isn't it?' or something of the sort."

"Do you think they will be round here presently?" I asked with some incredulity.

"Quite likely," he said, faintly.

He looked extremely haggard all of a sudden. His head rolled on his shoulders.

"H'm. We shall see then. Meantime get into that bed," I whispered. "Want help? There."

It was a rather high bed-place with a set of drawers underneath. This amazing swimmer really needed the lift I gave him by seizing his leg. He tumbled in, rolled over on his back, and flung one arm across his eyes. And then, with his face nearly hidden, he must have looked exactly as I used to look in that bed. I gazed upon my other self for a while before drawing across carefully the two green serge curtains which ran on a brass rod. I thought for a moment of pinning them together for greater safety, but I sat down on the couch, and once there I felt unwilling to rise and hunt for a pin. I would do it in a moment. I was extremely tired, in a peculiarly intimate way, by the strain of stealthiness, by the effort of whispering and the general secrecy of this excitement. It was three o'clock by now and I had been on my feet since nine, but I was not sleepy; I could not have gone to sleep. I sat there, fagged out, looking at the curtains, trying to clear my mind of the confused sensation of being in two places at once, and greatly bothered by an exasperating knocking in my head. It was a relief to discover suddenly that it was not in my head at all, but on the outside of the door. Before I could collect myself the words "Come in" were out of my mouth, and the steward entered with a tray, bringing in my morning coffee. I had slept, after all, and I was so frightened that I shouted, "This way! I am here, steward," as though he had been miles away. He put down the tray on the table next the couch and only then said, very quietly, "I can see you are here, sir." I felt him give me a keen look, but I dared not meet his eyes just then. He must have wondered why I had drawn the curtains of my bed before going to sleep on the couch. He went out, hooking the door open as usual.

I heard the crew washing decks above me. I knew I would have been told at once if there had been any wind. Calm, I thought, and I was doubly vexed. Indeed, I felt dual more than ever. The steward reappeared suddenly in the doorway. I jumped up from the couch so quickly that he gave a start.

"What do you want here?"

"Close your port, sir—they are washing decks."

"It is closed," I said, reddening.

"Very well, sir." But he did not move from the doorway and returned my stare in an extraordinary, equivocal manner for a time. Then his eyes wavered, all his expression changed, and in a voice unusually gentle, almost coaxingly:

"May I come in to take the empty cup away, sir?"

"Of course!" I turned my back on him while he popped in and out. Then I unhooked and closed the door and even pushed the bolt. This sort of thing could not go on very long. The cabin was as hot as an oven, too. I took a peep at my double, and discovered that he had not moved, his arm was still over his eyes; but his chest heaved; his hair was wet; his chin glistened with perspiration. I reached over him and opened the port.

"I must show myself on deck," I reflected.

Of course, theoretically, I could do what I liked, with no one to say nay to me within the whole circle of the horizon; but to lock my cabin door and take the key away I did not dare. Directly I put my head out of the companion I saw the group of my two officers, the second mate barefooted, the chief mate in long india-rubber boots, near the break of the poop, and the steward halfway down the poop ladder talking to them eagerly. He happened to catch sight of me and dived, the second ran down on the main deck shouting some order or other, and the chief mate came to meet me, touching his cap.

There was a sort of curiosity in his eye that I did not like. I don't know whether the steward had told them that I was "queer" only, or downright drunk, but I know the man meant to have a good look at me. I watched him coming with a smile which, as he got into point-blank range, took effect and froze his very whiskers. I did not give him time to open his lips.

"Square the yards by lifts and braces before the hands go to breakfast."

It was the first particular order I had given on board that ship; and I stayed on deck to see it executed, too. I had felt the need of asserting myself without loss of time. That sneering young cub got taken down a peg or two on that occasion, and I also seized the opportunity of having a good look at the face of every foremast man as they filed past me to go to the after braces. At breakfast time, eating nothing myself, I presided with such frigid dignity that the two mates were only too glad to escape from the cabin as soon as decency permitted and all the time the dual working of my mind distracted me almost to the point of insanity. I was constantly watching myself, my secret self, as dependent on my actions as my own personality, sleeping in that bed, behind that door which faced me as I sat at the head of the table. It was very much like being mad, only it was worse because one was aware of it.

I had to shake him for a solid minute, but when at last he opened his eyes it was in the full possession of his senses, with an inquiring look.

"All's well so far," I whispered. "Now you must vanish into the bathroom."

He did so, as noiseless as a ghost, and I then rang for the steward, and facing him boldly, directed him to tidy up my stateroom while I was having my bath—"and be quick about it." As my tone admitted of no excuses, he said, "Yes, sir," and ran off to fetch his dustpan and brushes. I took a bath and did most of my dressing, splashing, and whistling softly for the steward's edification, while the secret sharer of my life stood drawn up bolt upright in that little space, his face looking very sunken in daylight, his eyelids lowered under the stern, dark line of his eyebrows drawn together by a slight frown.

When I left him there to go back to my room the steward was finishing dusting. I sent for the mate and engaged him in some insignificant conversation. It was, as it were, trifling with the terrific character of his whiskers; but my object was to give him an opportunity for a good look at my cabin. And then I could at last shut, with a clear conscience, the door of my stateroom and get my double back into the recessed part. There was nothing else for it. He had to sit still on a small folding stool, half smothered by the heavy coats hanging there. We listened to the steward going into the bathroom out of the saloon, filling the water bottles there, scrubbing the bath, setting things to rights, whisk, bang, clatter—out again into the saloon—turn the key—click. Such was my scheme for keeping my second self invisible. Nothing better could be contrived under the circumstances. And there we sat; I at my writing desk ready to appear busy with some papers, he behind me, out of sight of the door. It would not have been prudent to talk in daytime; and I could not have stood the excitement of that queer sense of whispering to myself. Now and then, glancing over my shoulder, I saw him far back there, sitting rigidly on the low stool, his bare feet close together, his arms folded, his head hanging on his breast—and perfectly still. Anybody would have taken him for me.

I was fascinated by it myself. Every moment I had to glance

over my shoulder. I was looking at him when a voice outside the
door said:

"Beg pardon, sir."

"Well!" . . . I kept my eyes on him, and so, when the voice outside the door announced, "There's a ship's boat coming our way,
sir," I saw him give a start—the first movement he had made for
hours. But he did not raise his bowed head.

"All right. Get the ladder over."

I hesitated. Should I whisper something to him? But what? His
immobility seemed to have been never disturbed. What could I tell
him he did not know already? . . . Finally I went on deck.

II

The skipper of the *Sephora* had a thin red whisker all round his
face, and the sort of complexion that goes with hair of that color;
also the particular, rather smeary shade of blue in the eyes. He was
not exactly a showy figure; his shoulders were high, his stature but
middling—one leg slightly more bandy than the other. He shook
hands, looking vaguely around. A spiritless tenacity was his main
characteristic, I judged. I behaved with a politeness which seemed
to disconcert him. Perhaps he was shy. He mumbled to me as if he
were ashamed of what he was saying; gave his name (it was something like Archbold—but at this distance of years I hardly am sure),
his ship's name, and a few other particulars of that sort, in the manner of a criminal making a reluctant and doleful confession. He had
had terrible weather on the passage out—terrible—terrible—wife
aboard, too.

By this time we were seated in the cabin and the steward brought
in a tray with a bottle and glasses. "Thanks! No." Never took liquor.
Would have some water, though. He drank two tumblerfuls. Terrible thirsty work. Ever since daylight had been exploring the islands
round his ship.

"What was that for—fun?" I asked, with an appearance of polite interest.

"No!" He sighed. "Painful duty."

As he persisted in his mumbling and I wanted my double to hear
every word, I hit upon the notion of informing him that I regretted
to say I was hard of hearing.

"Such a young man, too!" he nodded, keeping his smeary blue, unintelligent eyes fastened upon me. "What was the cause of it—some disease?" he inquired, without the least sympathy and as if he thought that, if so, I'd got no more than I deserved.

"Yes; disease," I admitted in a cheerful tone which seemed to shock him. But my point was gained, because he had to raise his voice to give me his tale. It is not worth while to record that version. It was just over two months since all this had happened, and he had thought so much about it that he seemed completely muddled as to its bearings, but still immensely impressed.

"What would you think of such a thing happening on board your own ship? I've had the *Sephora* for these fifteen years. I am a well-known shipmaster."

He was densely distressed—and perhaps I should have sympathized with him if I had been able to detach my mental vision from the unsuspected sharer of my cabin as though he were my second self. There he was on the other side of the bulkhead, four or five feet from us, no more, as we sat in the saloon. I looked politely at Captain Archbold (if that was his name), but it was the other I saw, in a gray sleeping suit, seated on a low stool, his bare feet close together, his arms folded, and every word said between us falling into the ears of his dark head bowed on his chest.

"I have been at sea now, man and boy, for seven-and-thirty years, and I've never heard of such a thing happening in an English ship. And that it should be my ship. Wife on board, too."

I was hardly listening to him.

"Don't you think," I said, "that the heavy sea which, you told me, came aboard just then might have killed the man? I have seen the sheer weight of a sea kill a man very neatly, by simply breaking his neck."

"Good God!" he uttered, impressively, fixing his smeary blue eyes on me. "The sea! No man killed by the sea ever looked like that." He seemed positively scandalized at my suggestion. And as I gazed at him, certainly not prepared for anything original on his part, he advanced his head close to me and thrust his tongue out at me so suddenly that I couldn't help starting back.

After scoring over my calmness in this graphic way he nodded wisely. If I had seen the sight, he assured me, I would never forget it as long as I lived. The weather was too bad to give the corpse a proper sea burial. So next day at dawn they took it up on the poop, covering its face with a bit of bunting; he read a short prayer, and then, just as it was, in its oilskins and long boots, they launched it amongst those mountainous seas that seemed ready every moment to swallow up the ship herself and the terrified lives on board of her.

"That reefed foresail saved you," I threw in.

"Under God—it did," he exclaimed fervently. "It was by a special mercy, I firmly believe, that it stood some of those hurricane squalls."

"It was the setting of that sail which—" I began.

"God's own hand in it," he interrupted me. "Nothing less could have done it. I don't mind telling you that I hardly dared give the order. It seemed impossible that we could touch anything without losing it, and then our last hope would have been gone."

The terror of that gale was on him yet. I let him go on for a bit, then said, casually—as if returning to a minor subject:

"You were very anxious to give up your mate to the shore people, I believe?"

He was. To the law. His obscure tenacity on that point had in it something incomprehensible and a little awful; something, as it were, mystical, quite apart from his anxiety that he should not be suspected of "countenancing any doings of that sort." Seven-and-thirty virtuous years at sea, of which over twenty of immaculate command, and the last fifteen in the *Sephora*, seemed to have laid him under some pitiless obligation.

"And you know," he went on, groping shamefacedly amongst his feelings, "I did not engage that young fellow. His people had some interest with my owners. I was in a way forced to take him on. He looked very smart, very gentlemanly, and all that. But do you know—I never liked him, somehow. I am a plain man. You see, he wasn't exactly the sort for the chief mate of a ship like the *Sephora*."

I had become so connected in thoughts and impressions with the secret sharer of my cabin that I felt as if I, personally, were being given to understand that I, too, was not the sort that would have done for the chief mate of a ship like the *Sephora*. I had no doubt of it in my mind.

"Not at all the style of man. You understand," he insisted, superfluously, looking hard at me.

I smiled urbanely. He seemed at a loss for a while.

"I suppose I must report a suicide."

"Beg pardon?"

"Sui-cide! That's what I'll have to write to my owners directly I get in."

"Unless you manage to recover him before tomorrow," I assented, dispassionately. . . . "I mean, alive."

He mumbled something which I really did not catch, and I turned my ear to him in a puzzled manner. He fairly bawled:

"The land—I say, the mainland is at least seven miles off my anchorage."

"About that."

My lack of excitement, of curiosity, of surprise, of any sort of pronounced interest, began to arouse his distrust. But except for the felicitous pretense of deafness I had not tried to pretend anything. I had felt utterly incapable of playing the part of ignorance properly, and therefore was afraid to try. It is also certain that he had brought some ready-made suspicions with him, and that he viewed my politeness as a strange and unnatural phenomenon. And yet how else could I have received him? Not heartily! That was impossible for psychological reasons, which I need not state here. My only object was to keep off his inquiries. Surlily? Yes, but surliness might have provoked a point-blank question. From its novelty to him and from its nature, punctilious courtesy was the manner best calculated to restrain the man. But there was the danger of his breaking through my defense bluntly. I could not, I think, have met him by a direct lie, also for psychological (not moral) reasons. If he had only known how afraid I was of his putting my feeling of identity with the other to the test! But, strangely enough—(I thought of it only afterward)—I believe that he was not a little disconcerted by the reverse side of that weird situation, by something in me that reminded him of the man he was seeking—suggested a mysterious similitude to the young fellow he had distrusted and disliked from the first.

However that might have been, the silence was not very prolonged. He took another oblique step.

"I reckon I had no more than a two-mile pull to your ship. Not a bit more."

"And quite enough, too, in this awful heat," I said.

Another pause full of mistrust followed. Necessity, they say, is mother of invention, but fear, too, is not barren of ingenious suggestions. And I was afraid he would ask me point-blank for news of my other self.

"Nice little saloon, isn't it?" I remarked, as if noticing for the first time the way his eyes roamed from one closed door to the other. "And very well fitted out, too. Here, for instance," I continued, reaching over the back of my seat negligently and flinging the door open, "is my bathroom."

He made an eager movement, but hardly gave it a glance. I got up, shut the door of the bathroom, and invited him to have a look round, as if I were very proud of my accommodation. He had to rise and be shown round, but he went through the business without any raptures whatever.

"And now we'll have a look at my stateroom," I declared, in a voice as loud as I dared to make it, crossing the cabin to the starboard side with purposely heavy steps.

He followed me in and gazed around. My intelligent double had vanished. I played my part.

"Very convenient—isn't it?"

"Very nice. Very comf . . ." He didn't finish, and went out brusquely as if to escape from some unrighteous wiles of mine. But it was not to be. I had been too frightened not to feel vengeful; I felt I had him on the run, and I meant to keep him on the run. My polite insistence must have had something menacing in it, because he gave in suddenly. And I did not let him off a single item; mate's room, pantry, storerooms, the very sail locker which was also under the poop—he had to look into them all. When at last I showed him out on the quarter-deck he drew a long, spiritless sigh and mumbled dismally that he must really be going back to his ship now. I desired my mate, who had joined us, to see to the captain's boat.

The man of whiskers gave a blast on the whistle which he used to wear hanging round his neck, and yelled, "*Sephoras* away!" My double down there in my cabin must have heard, and certainly could not feel more relieved than I. Four fellows came running out from somewhere forward and went over the side, while my own men, appearing on deck too, lined the rail. I escorted my visitor to the gangway ceremoniously, and nearly overdid it. He was a tenacious beast. On the very ladder he lingered, and in that unique, guiltily conscientious manner of sticking to the point:

"I say . . . you . . . you don't think that—"

I covered his voice loudly:

"Certainly not. . . . I am delighted. Good-by."

I had an idea of what he meant to say, and just saved myself by the privilege of defective hearing. He was too shaken generally to insist, but my mate, close witness of that parting, looked mystified and his face took on a thoughtful cast. As I did not want to appear as if I wished to avoid all communication with my officers, he had the opportunity to address me.

"Seems a very nice man. His boat's crew told our chaps a very extraordinary story, if what I am told by the steward is true. I suppose you had it from the captain, sir?"

"Yes. I had a story from the captain."

"A very horrible affair—isn't it, sir?"

"It is."

"Beats all these tales we hear about murders in Yankee ships."

"I don't think it beats them. I don't think it resembles them in the least."

"Bless my soul—you don't say so! But of course I've no acquaintance whatever with American ships, not I, so I couldn't go against your knowledge. It's horrible enough for me. . . . But the queerest part is that those fellows seemed to have some idea the man was hidden aboard here. They had really. Did you ever hear of such a thing?"

"Preposterous—isn't it?"

We were walking to and fro athwart the quarterdeck. No one of the crew forward could be seen (the day was Sunday), and the mate pursued:

"There was some little dispute about it. Our chaps took offense. 'As if we would harbor a thing like that,' they said. 'Wouldn't you like to look for him in our coal hole?' Quite a tiff. But they made it up in the end. I suppose he did drown himself. Don't you, sir?"

"I don't suppose anything."

"You have no doubt in the matter, sir?"

"None whatever."

I left him suddenly. I felt I was producing a bad impression, but with my double down there it was most trying to be on deck. And it was almost as trying to be below. Altogether a nerve-trying situation. But on the whole I felt less torn in two when I was with him. There was no one in the whole ship whom I dared take into my confidence. Since the hands had got to know his story, it would have been impossible to pass him off for anyone else, and an accidental discovery was to be dreaded now more than ever. . . .

The steward being engaged in laying the table for dinner, we could talk only with our eyes when I first went down. Later in the afternoon we had a cautious try at whispering. The Sunday quietness of the ship was against us; the stillness of air and water around her was against us; the elements, the men were against us—everything was against us in our secret partnership; time itself—for this could not go on forever. The very trust in Providence was, I suppose, denied to his guilt. Shall I confess that this thought cast me down very much? And as to the chapter of accidents which counts for so much in the book of success, I could only hope that it was closed. For what favorable accident could be expected?

"Did you hear everything?" were my first words as soon as we took up our position side by side, leaning over my bed-place.

He had. And the proof of it was his earnest whisper, "The man told you he hardly dared to give the order."

I understood the reference to be to that saving foresail.

"Yes. He was afraid of it being lost in the setting."

"I assure you he never gave the order. He may think he did, but he never gave it. He stood there with me on the break of the poop after the maintopsail blew away, and whimpered about our last hope—positively whimpered about it and nothing else—and the night coming on! To hear one's skipper go on like that in such weather was enough to drive any fellow out of his mind. It worked me up into a sort of desperation. I just took it into my own hands and went away from him, boiling, and—. But what's the use telling you? *You* know! . . . Do you think that if I had not been pretty fierce with them I should have got the men to do anything? Not I! The bosun perhaps? Perhaps! It wasn't a heavy sea—it was a sea gone mad! I suppose the end of the world will be something like that; and a man may have the heart to see it coming once and be done with it—but to have to face it day after day—I don't blame anybody. I was precious little better than the rest. Only—I was an officer of that old coalwagon, anyhow—"

"I quite understand," I conveyed that sincere assurance into his ear. He was out of breath with whispering; I could hear him pant slightly. It was all very simple. The same strung-up force which had given twenty-four men a chance, at least, for their lives, had, in a sort of recoil, crushed an unworthy mutinous existence.

But I had no leisure to weigh the merits of the matter—footsteps in the saloon, a heavy knock. "There's enough wind to get under way with, sir." Here was the call of a new claim upon my thoughts and even upon my feelings.

"Turn the hands up," I cried through the door. "I'll be on deck directly."

I was going out to make the acquaintance of my ship. Before I left the cabin our eyes met—the eyes of the only two strangers on board. I pointed to the recessed part where the little campstool awaited him and laid my finger on my lips. He made a gesture—somewhat vague—a little mysterious, accompanied by a faint smile, as if of regret.

This is not the place to enlarge upon the sensations of a man who feels for the first time a ship move under his feet to his own independent word. In my case they were not unalloyed. I was not wholly alone with my command; for there was that stranger in my cabin. Or rather, I was not completely and wholly with her. Part of me was absent. That mental feeling of being in two places at once affected me physically as if the mood of secrecy had penetrated my very soul. Before an hour had elapsed since the ship had begun to move, having occasion to ask the mate (he stood by my side) to take a compass bearing of the Pagoda, I caught myself reaching up to his ear in whispers. I say I caught myself, but enough had escaped to startle the man. I can't describe it otherwise than by saying that he shied. A grave, preoccupied manner, as though he were in possession of some perplexing intelligence, did not leave him henceforth. A little later I moved away from the rail to look at the compass with such a stealthy gait that the helmsman noticed it—and I could not help noticing the unusual roundness of his eyes. These are trifling instances, though it's to no commander's advantage to be suspected of ludicrous eccentricities. But I was also more seriously affected. There are to a seaman certain words, gestures, that should in given conditions come as naturally, as instinctively as the winking of a menaced eye. A certain order should spring on to his lips without thinking; a certain sign should get itself made, so to speak, without reflection. But all unconscious alertness had abandoned me. I had to make an effort of will to recall myself back (from the cabin) to the conditions of the moment. I felt that I was appearing an irresolute commander to those people who were watching me more or less critically.

And, besides, there were the scares. On the second day out, for instance, coming off the deck in the afternoon (I had straw slippers on my bare feet) I stopped at the open pantry door and spoke to the steward. He was doing something there with his back to me. At the sound of my voice he nearly jumped out of his skin, as the saying is, and incidentally broke a cup:

"What on earth's the matter with you?" I asked, astonished.

He was extremely confused. "Beg pardon, sir. I made sure you were in your cabin."

"You see I wasn't."

"No, sir. I could have sworn I had heard you moving in there not a moment ago. It's most extraordinary . . . very sorry, sir."

I passed on with an inward shudder. I was so identified with my secret double that I did not even mention the fact in those scanty, fearful whispers we exchanged. I suppose he had made some slight noise of some kind or other. It would have been miraculous if he hadn't at one time or another. And yet, haggard as he appeared, he looked always perfectly self-controlled, more than calm—almost invulnerable. On my suggestion he remained almost entirely in the bathroom, which, upon the whole, was the safest place. There could be really no shadow of an excuse for anyone ever wanting to go in there, once the steward had done with it. It was a very tiny place. Sometimes he reclined on the floor, his legs bent, his head sustained on one elbow. At others I would find him on the campstool, sitting in his gray sleeping suit and with his cropped dark hair like a patient, unmoved convict. At night I would smuggle him into my bed-place, and we would whisper together, with the regular footfalls of the officer of the watch passing and repassing over our heads. It was an infinitely miserable time. It was lucky that some tins of fine preserves were stowed in a locker in my stateroom; hard bread I could always get hold of; and so he lived on stewed chicken, pâté de foie gras, asparagus, cooked oysters, sardines—on all sorts of abominable sham delicacies out of tins. My early morning coffee he always drank; and it was all I dared do for him in that respect.

Every day there was the horrible maneuvering to go through so that my room and then the bathroom should be done in the usual way. I came to hate the sight of the steward, to abhor the voice of that harmless man. I felt that it was he who would bring on the disaster of discovery. It hung like a sword over our heads.

The fourth day out, I think (we were then working down the east side of the Gulf of Siam, tack for tack, in light winds and smooth water)—the fourth day, I say, of this miserable juggling with the unavoidable, as we sat at our evening meal, that man, whose slightest movement I dreaded, after putting down the dishes ran up on deck busily. This could not be dangerous. Presently he came down again; and then it appeared that he had remembered a coat of mine which I had thrown over a rail to dry after having been wetted in a shower which had passed over the ship in the afternoon. Sitting stolidly at the head of the table I became terrified at the sight of the garment on his arm. Of course he made for my door. There was no time to lose.

"Steward," I thundered. My nerves were so shaken that I could not govern my voice and conceal my agitation. This was the sort of thing that made my terrifically whiskered mate tap his forehead with his forefinger. I had detected him using that gesture while talking on deck with a confidential air to the carpenter. It was too far to hear a word, but I had no doubt that this pantomime could only refer to the strange new captain.

"Yes, sir," the pale-faced steward turned resignedly to me. It was this maddening course of being shouted at, checked without rhyme or reason, arbitrarily chased out of my cabin, suddenly called into it, sent flying out of his pantry on incomprehensible errands, that accounted for the growing wretchedness of his expression.

"Where are you going with that coat?"

"To your room, sir."

"Is there another shower coming?"

"I'm sure I don't know, sir. Shall I go up again and see, sir?"

"No! never mind."

My object was attained, as of course my other self in there would have heard everything that passed. During this interlude my two officers never raised their eyes off their respective plates; but the lip of that confounded cub, the second mate, quivered visibly.

I expected the steward to hook my coat on and come out at once. He was very slow about it; but I dominated my nervousness sufficiently not to shout after him. Suddenly I became aware (it could be heard plainly enough) that the fellow for some reason or other was opening the door of the bathroom. It was the end. The place was literally not big enough to swing a cat in. My voice died in my throat and I went stony all over. I expected to hear a yell of surprise and terror, and made a movement, but had not the strength to get on my legs. Everything remained still. Had my second self taken the poor wretch by the throat? I don't know what I would have done next moment if I had not seen the steward come out of my room, close the door, and then stand quietly by the sideboard.

Saved, I thought. But, no! Lost! Gone! He was gone!

I laid my knife and fork down and leaned back in my chair. My head swam. After a while, when sufficiently recovered to speak in a steady voice, I instructed my mate to put the ship round at eight o'clock himself.

"I won't come on deck," I went on. "I think I'll turn in, and unless the wind shifts I don't want to be disturbed before midnight. I feel a bit seedy."

"You did look middling bad a little while ago," the chief mate remarked without showing any great concern.

They both went out, and I stared at the steward clearing the table. There was nothing to be read on that wretched man's face. But why did he avoid my eyes I asked myself. Then I thought I should like to hear the sound of his voice.

"Steward!"

"Sir!" Startled as usual.

"Where did you hang up that coat?"

"In the bathroom, sir." The usual anxious tone. "It's not quite dry yet, sir."

For some time longer I sat in the cuddy. Had my double vanished as he had come? But of his coming there was an explanation, whereas his disappearance would be inexplicable. . . . I went slowly into my dark room, shut the door, lighted the lamp, and for a time dared not turn round. When at last I did I saw him standing bolt upright in the narrow recessed part. It would not be true to say I had a shock, but an irresistible doubt of his bodily existence flitted through my mind. Can it be, I asked myself, that he is not visible to other eyes than mine? It was like being haunted. Motionless, with a grave face, he raised his hands slightly at me in a gesture which meant clearly, "Heavens! what a narrow escape!" Narrow indeed. I think I had come creeping quietly as near insanity as any man who has not actually gone over the border. That gesture restrained me, so to speak.

The mate with the terrific whiskers was now putting the ship on the other tack. In the moment of profound silence which follows upon the hands going to their stations I heard on the poop his raised voice: "Hard alee!" and the distant shout of the order repeated on the maindeck. The sails, in that light breeze, made but a faint fluttering noise. It ceased. The ship was coming round slowly; I held my breath in the renewed stillness of expectation; one wouldn't have thought that there was a single living soul on her decks. A sudden brisk shout, "Mainsail haul!" broke the spell, and in the noisy cries and rush overhead of the men running away with the main brace we two, down in my cabin, came together in our usual position by the bed-place.

He did not wait for my question. "I heard him fumbling here and just managed to squat myself down in the bath," he whispered to me. "The fellow only opened the door and put his arm in to hang the coat up. All the same—"

"I never thought of that," I whispered back, even more appalled than before at the closeness of the shave, and marveling at that something unyielding in his character which was carrying him through so finely. There was no agitation in his whisper. Whoever was being driven distracted, it was not he. He was sane. And the proof of his sanity was continued when he took up the whispering again.

"It would never do for me to come to life again."

It was something that a ghost might have said. But what he was alluding to was his old captain's reluctant admission of the theory of suicide. It would obviously serve his turn—if I had understood at all the view which seemed to govern the unalterable purpose of his action.

"You must maroon me as soon as ever you can get amongst these islands off the Cambodge shore," he went on.

"Maroon you! We are not living in a boy's adventure tale," I protested. His scornful whispering took me up.

"We aren't indeed! There's nothing of a boy's tale in this. But there's nothing else for it. I want no more. You don't suppose I am afraid of what can be done to me? Prison or gallows or whatever they may please. But you don't see me coming back to explain such things to an old fellow in a wig and twelve respectable tradesmen, do you? What can they know whether I am guilty or not—or of *what* I am guilty, either? That's my affair. What does the Bible say? 'Driven off the face of the earth.' Very well. I am off the face of the earth now. As I came at night so I shall go."

"Impossible!" I murmured. "You can't."

"Can't?. . . Not naked like a soul on the Day of Judgment. I shall freeze on to this sleeping suit. The Last Day is not yet—and . . . you have understood thoroughly. Didn't you?"

I felt suddenly ashamed of myself. I may say truly that I understood—and my hesitation in letting that man swim away from my ship's side had been a mere sham sentiment, a sort of cowardice.

"It can't be done now till next night," I breathed out. "The ship is on the offshore tack and the wind may fail us."

"As long as I know that you understand," he whispered. "But of course you do. It's a great satisfaction to have got somebody to understand. You seem to have been there on purpose." And in the same whisper, as if we two whenever we talked had to say things to each other which were not fit for the world to hear, he added, "It's very wonderful."

We remained side by side talking in our secret way—but sometimes silent or just exchanging a whispered word or two at long intervals. And as usual he stared through the port. A breath of wind came now and again into our faces. The ship might have been moored in dock, so gently and on an even keel she slipped through the water, that did not murmur even at our passage, shadowy and silent like a phantom sea.

At midnight I went on deck, and to my mate's great surprise put the ship round on the other tack. His terrible whiskers flitted round me in silent criticism. I certainly should not have done it if it had been only a question of getting out of that sleepy gulf as quickly as possible. I believe he told the second mate, who relieved him, that it was a great want of judgment. The other only yawned. That intolerable cub shuffled about so sleepily and lolled against the rails in such a slack, improper fashion that I came down on him sharply.

"Aren't you properly awake yet?"

"Yes, sir! I am awake."

"Well, then, be good enough to hold yourself as if you were. And keep a lookout. If there's any current we'll be closing with some islands before daylight."

The east side of the gulf is fringed with islands, some solitary, others in groups. On the blue background of the high coast they seem to float on silvery patches of calm water, arid and gray, or dark green and rounded like clumps of evergreen bushes, with the larger ones, a mile or two long, showing the outlines of ridges, ribs of gray rock under the dark mantle of matted leafage. Unknown to trade, to travel, almost to geography, the manner of life they harbor is an unsolved secret. There must be villages—settlements of fishermen at least—on the largest of them, and some communication with the world is probably kept up by native craft. But all that forenoon, as we headed for them, fanned along by the faintest of breezes, I saw no sign of man or canoe in the field of the telescope I kept on pointing at the scattered group.

At noon I gave no orders for a change of course, and the mate's whiskers became much concerned and seemed to be offering themselves unduly to my notice. At last I said:

"I am going to stand right in. Quite in—as far as I can take her."

The stare of extreme surprise imparted an air of ferocity also to his eyes, and he looked truly terrific for a moment.

"We're not doing well in the middle of the gulf," I continued, casually. "I am going to look for the land breezes tonight."

"Bless my soul! Do you mean, sir, in the dark amongst the lot of all them islands and reefs and shoals?"

"Well—if there are any regular land breezes at all on this coast one must get close inshore to find them, mustn't one?"

"Bless my soul!" he exclaimed again under his breath. All that afternoon he wore a dreamy, contemplative appearance which in him was a mark of perplexity. After dinner I went into my stateroom as if I meant to take some rest. There we two bent our dark heads over a half-unrolled chart lying on my bed.

"There," I said. "It's got to be Koh-ring. I've been looking at it ever since sunrise. It has got two hills and a low point. It must be inhabited. And on the coast opposite there is what looks like the mouth of a biggish river—with some town, no doubt, not far up. It's the best chance for you that I can see."

"Anything. Koh-ring let it be."

He looked thoughtfully at the chart as if surveying chances and distances from a lofty height—and following with his eyes his own figure wandering on the blank land of Cochin-China, and then passing off that piece of paper clean out of sight into uncharted regions. And it was as if the ship had two captains to plan her course for her. I had been so worried and restless running up and down that I had not had the patience to dress that day. I had remained in my sleeping suit, with straw slippers and a soft floppy hat. The closeness of the heat in the gulf had been most oppressive, and the crew were used to see me wandering in that airy attire.

"She will clear the south point as she heads now," I whispered into his ear. "Goodness only knows when, though, but certainly after dark. I'll edge her in to half a mile, as far as I may be able to judge in the dark—"

"Be careful," he murmured, warningly—and I realized suddenly that all my future, the only future for which I was fit, would perhaps go irretrievably to pieces in any mishap to my first command.

I could not stop a moment longer in the room. I motioned him to get out of sight and made my way on the poop. That unplayful cub had the watch. I walked up and down for a while thinking things out, then beckoned him over.

"Send a couple of hands to open the two quarter-deck ports," I said, mildly.

He actually had the impudence, or else so forgot himself in his wonder at such an incomprehensible order, as to repeat:

"Open the quarter-deck ports! What for, sir?"

"The only reason you need concern yourself about is because I tell you to do so. Have them open wide and fastened properly."

He reddened and went off, but I believe made some jeering remark to the carpenter as to the sensible practice of ventilating a ship's quarter-deck. I know he popped into the mate's cabin to impart the fact to him because the whiskers came on deck, as it were by chance, and stole glances at me from below—for signs of lunacy or drunkenness, I suppose.

A little before supper, feeling more restless than ever, I rejoined, for a moment, my second self. And to find him sitting so quietly was surprising, like something against nature, inhuman.

I developed my plan in a hurried whisper.

"I shall stand in as close as I dare and then put her round. I shall presently find means to smuggle you out of here into the sail locker, which communicates with the lobby. But there is an opening, a sort of square for hauling the sails out, which gives straight on the quarter-deck and which is never closed in fine weather, so as to give air to the sails. When the ship's way is deadened in stays and all the hands are aft at the main braces you will have a clear road to slip out and get overboard through the open quarter-deck port. I've had them both fastened up. Use a rope's end to lower yourself into the water so as to avoid a splash—you know. It could be heard and cause some beastly complication."

He kept silent for a while, then whispered, "I understand."

"I won't be there to see you go," I began with an effort. "The rest . . . I only hope I have understood, too."

"You have. From first to last," and for the first time there seemed to be a faltering, something strained in his whisper. He caught hold of my arm, but the ringing of the supper bell made me start. He didn't, though; he only released his grip.

After supper I didn't come below again till well past eight o'clock. The faint, steady breeze was loaded with dew; and the wet, darkened sails held all there was of propelling power in it. The night, clear and starry, sparkled darkly, and the opaque, lightless patches shifting slowly against the low stars were the drifting islets. On the port bow there was a big one more distant and shadowily imposing by the great space of sky it eclipsed.

On opening the door I had a back view of my very own self looking at a chart. He had come out of the recess and was standing near the table.

"Quite dark enough," I whispered.

He stepped back and leaned against my bed with a level, quiet glance. I sat on the couch. We had nothing to say to each other. Over our heads the officer of the watch moved here and there. Then I heard him move quickly. I knew what that meant. He was making for the companion; and presently his voice was outside my door.

"We are drawing in pretty fast, sir. Land looks rather close."

"Very well," I answered. "I am coming on deck directly."

I waited till he was gone out of the cuddy, then rose. My double moved too. The time had come to exchange our last whispers, for neither of us was ever to hear each other's natural voice.

"Look here!" I opened a drawer and took out three sovereigns. "Take this, anyhow. I've got six and I'd give you the lot, only I must keep a little money to buy some fruit and vegetables for the crew from native boats as we go through Sunda Straits."

He shook his head.

"Take it," I urged him, whispering desperately. "No one can tell what—"

He smiled and slapped meaningly the only pocket of the sleeping jacket. It was not safe, certainly. But I produced a large old silk handkerchief of mine, and tying the three pieces of gold in a corner, pressed it on him. He was touched, I suppose, because he took it at last and tied it quickly round his waist under the jacket, on his bare skin.

Our eyes met; several seconds elapsed, till, our glances still mingled, I extended my hand and turned the lamp out. Then I passed through the cuddy, leaving the door of my room wide open. . . . "Steward!"

He was still lingering in the pantry in the greatness of his zeal, giving a rub-up to a plated cruet stand the last thing before going to bed. Being careful not to wake up the mate, whose room was opposite, I spoke in an undertone.

He looked round anxiously. "Sir!"

"Can you get me a little hot water from the galley?"

"I am afraid, sir, the galley fire's been out for some time now."

"Go and see."

He fled up the stairs.

"Now," I whispered, loudly, into the saloon—too loudly, perhaps, but I was afraid I couldn't make a sound. He was by my side in an instant—the double captain slipped past the stairs—through the tiny dark passage . . . a sliding door. We were in the sail locker, scrambling on our knees over the sails. A sudden thought struck me. I saw myself wandering barefooted, bareheaded, the sun beating on my dark poll. I snatched off my floppy hat and tried hurriedly in the dark to ram it on my other self. He dodged and fended off silently. I wonder what he thought had come to me before he understood and suddenly desisted. Our hands met gropingly, lingered united in a steady, motionless clasp for a second. . . . No word was breathed by either of us when they separated.

I was standing quietly by the pantry door when the steward returned.

"Sorry, sir. Kettle barely warm. Shall I light the spirit lamp?"

"Never mind."

I came out on deck slowly. It was now a matter of conscience to shave the land as close as possible—for now he must go overboard whenever the ship was put in stays. Must! There could be no going back for him. After a moment I walked over to leeward and my heart flew into my mouth at the nearness of the land on the bow. Under any other circumstances I would not have held on a minute longer. The second mate had followed me anxiously.

I looked on till I felt I could command my voice.

"She will weather," I said then in a quiet tone.

"Are you going to try that, sir?" he stammered out incredulously.

I took no notice of him and raised my tone just enough to be heard by the helmsman.

"Keep her good full."

"Good full, sir."

The wind fanned my cheek, the sails slept, the world was silent.

The strain of watching the dark loom of the land grow bigger and denser was too much for me. I had shut my eyes—because the ship must go closer. She must! The stillness was intolerable. Were we standing still?

When I opened my eyes the second view started my heart with a thump. The black southern hill of Koh-ring seemed to hang right over the ship like a towering fragment of the everlasting night. On that enormous mass of blackness there was not a gleam to be seen, not a sound to be heard. It was gliding irresistibly toward us and yet seemed already within reach of the hand. I saw the vague figures of the watch grouped in the waist, gazing in awed silence.

"Are you going on, sir?" inquired an unsteady voice at my elbow. I ignored it. I had to go on.

"Keep her full. Don't check her way. That won't do now," I said warningly.

"I can't see the sails very well," the helmsman answered me, in strange, quavering tones.

Was she close enough? Already she was, I won't say in the shadow of the land, but in the very blackness of it, already swallowed up as it were, gone too close to be recalled, gone from me altogether.

"Give the mate a call," I said to the young man who stood at my elbow as still as death. "And turn all hands up."

My tone had a borrowed loudness reverberated from the height of the land. Several voices cried out together: "We are all on deck, sir."

Then stillness again, with the great shadow gliding closer, towering higher, without a light, without a sound. Such a hush had fallen on the ship that she might have been a bark of the dead floating in slowly under the very gate of Erebus.

"My God! Where are we?"

It was the mate moaning at my elbow. He was thunderstruck, and as it were deprived of the moral support of his whiskers. He clapped his hands and absolutely cried out, "Lost!"

"Be quiet," I said sternly.

He lowered his tone, but I saw the shadowy gesture of his despair. "What are we doing here?"

"Looking for the land wind."

He made as if to tear his hair, and addressed me recklessly.

"She will never get out. You have done it, sir. I knew it'd end in something like this. She will never weather, and you are too close now to stay. She'll drift ashore before she's round. O my God!"

I caught his arm as he was raising it to batter his poor devoted head, and shook it violently.

"She's ashore already," he wailed, trying to tear himself away.

"Is she? . . . Keep good full there!"

"Good full, sir," cried the helmsman in a frightened, thin, child-like voice.

I hadn't let go the mate's arm and went on shaking it. "Ready about, do you hear? You go forward"—shake—"and stop there"—shake—"and hold your noise"—shake—"and see these head-sheets properly overhauled"—shake, shake—shake.

And all the time I dared not look toward the land lest my heart should fail me. I released my grip at last and he ran forward as if fleeing for dear life.

I wondered what my double there in the sail locker thought of this commotion. He was able to hear everything—and perhaps he was able to understand why, on my conscience, it had to be thus close—no less. My first order, "Hard alee!" re-echoed ominously under the towering shadow of Koh-ring as if I had shouted in a mountain gorge. And then I watched the land intently. In that smooth water and light wind it was impossible to feel the ship coming-to. No! I could not feel her. And my second self was making now ready to slip out and lower himself overboard. Perhaps he was gone already . . . ?

The great black mass brooding over our very mastheads began to pivot away from the ship's side silently. And now I forgot the secret stranger ready to depart, and remembered only that I was a total stranger to the ship. I did not know her. Would she do it? How was she to be handled?

I swung the mainyard and waited helplessly. She was perhaps stopped, and her very fate hung in the balance, with the black mass of Koh-ring like the gate of the everlasting night towering over her taffrail. What would she do now? Had she way on her yet? I stepped to the side swiftly, and on the shadowy water I could see nothing except a faint phosphorescent flash revealing the glassy smoothness of the sleeping surface. It was impossible to tell—and I had not learned yet the feel of my ship. Was she moving? What I needed was something easily seen, a piece of paper, which I could throw overboard and watch. I had nothing on me. To run down for it I didn't dare. There was no time. All at once my strained, yearning stare distinguished a white object floating within a yard of the ship's side. White on the black water. A phosphorescent flash passed under it. What was that thing? . . . I recognized my own floppy hat. It must have fallen off his head . . . and he didn't bother. Now I had what I wanted—the saving mark for my eyes. But I hardly thought of my other self, now gone from the ship, to be hidden forever from all friendly faces, to be a fugitive and a vagabond on the earth, with no brand of the curse on his sane forehead to stay a slaying hand . . . too proud to explain.

And I watched the hat—the expression of my sudden pity for his mere flesh. It had been meant to save his homeless head from the dangers of the sun. And now—behold—it was saving the ship, by serving me for a mark to help out the ignorance of my strangeness. Ha! It was drifting forward, warning me just in time that the ship had gathered sternway.

"Shift the helm," I said in a low voice to the seaman standing still like a statue.

The man's eyes glistened wildly in the binnacle light as he jumped round to the other side and spun round the wheel.

I walked to the break of the poop. On the overshadowed deck all hands stood by the forebraces waiting for my order. The stars ahead seemed to be gliding from right to left. And all was so still in the world that I heard the quiet remark, "She's round," passed in a tone of intense relief between two seamen.

"Let go and haul."

The foreyards ran round with a great noise, amidst cheery cries. And now the frightful whiskers made themselves heard giving various orders. Already the ship was drawing ahead. And I was alone with her. Nothing! no one in the world should stand now between us, throwing a shadow on the way of silent knowledge and mute affection, the perfect communion of a seaman with his first command.

Walking to the taffrail, I was in time to make out, on the very edge of a darkness thrown by a towering black mass like the very gateway of Erebus—yes, I was in time to catch an evanescent glimpse of my white hat left behind to mark the spot where the secret sharer of my cabin and of my thoughts, as though he were my second self, had lowered himself into the water to take his punishment: a free man, a proud swimmer striking out for a new destiny.

For Discussion:

1. What significance has the title "The Secret Sharer"? Is it intended to mean: One who shares the secrets of another? One who shares but is himself secret? Or is there another interpretation?

2. Would you classify this story as one of plot, character, or setting? Explain.
3. How do the first two paragraphs contribute to the setting and mood? After reading the entire story, how does the second paragraph take on new meaning? What is the role of the sea in the unfolding of the story? Compare the first two paragraphs with the last two. What change has occurred in the Captain's "aloneness"?
4. What is the Captain's relationship with the individual members of his crew? How do these relationships affect the plot?
5. What physical characteristics or similarities of background do the Captain and the "secret sharer" have in common? Are there any real differences between them? If so do these play any part in the development of the plot? In the conveying of the theme?
6. What significance is there in the Captain's initial discovery of a man "complete but for the head"? Why does this incident occur on the night of the Captain's first watch? How is this related to the means by which the Captain saves his ship at the end of the story?
7. How does Conrad build tension and suspense in the story?
8. Conrad's attitude toward the men in his story will help you to discover what he finds worthwhile in a man. Describe Conrad's ideal man.
9. What change takes place in the Captain as a result of his encounter with the "secret sharer"?
10. Discuss the idea that the fugitive is really the Captain's "other self."

For Composition: Write a brief narrative that vividly presents an experience in which you tried "to be mature."

Miss Youghal's Sais*

RUDYARD KIPLING

Rudyard Kipling (1865–1936), the most eagerly read British writer of the nineteenth century, made his reputation with his stories of India. He caught the romance of this far-off country while interpreting its life and its people with a new and startling realism. Kipling's stories faithfully capture the dash and the color, the frustration and the boredom of colonial official life, with its civil servants, flunkies, soldiers, and sahibs.

In "Miss Youghal's Sais," you will see Kipling's talent for recreating the exotic life of India, and his ability to portray humorously and in realistic language the people living in what was then one of the most distant parts of the British Empire.

----◆----

When Man and Woman are agreed, what can the Kazi do?
　　　　　　　　　　　　　　　—*Mohammedan Proverb*

Some people saw that there is no romance in India. Those people are wrong. Our lives hold quite as much romance as is good for us. Sometimes more.

Strickland was in the police, and people did not understand him; so they said he was a doubtful sort of man and passed by on the other side. Strickland had himself to thank for this. He held the extraordinary theory that a policeman in India should try to know as much about the natives as the natives themselves. Now, in the whole of upper India, there is only *one* man who can pass for Hindu or Mohammedan, *chamar* * or *faquir,* * as he pleases. He is feared and respected by the natives from the Ghor Kathri to the Jamma Musjid; and he is supposed to have the gift of invisibility and executive control over many devils. But what good has this done him with the government? None in the world. He has never got Simla for his charge; and his name is almost unknown to Englishmen.

Strickland was foolish enough to take that man for his model; and, following out his absurd theory, dabbled in unsavory places no respectable man would think of exploring—all among the native riff-

sais: a servant in charge of horses
chamar: a skin dresser
faquir: priest

132

raff. He educated himself in this peculiar way for seven years, and people could not appreciate it. He was perpetually "going Fantee" among natives, which, of course, no man with any sense believes in. He was initiated into the *Sat Bhai* at Allahabad once, when he was on leave; he knew the Lizard Song of the Sansis, and the *Hálli-Hukk* dance, which is a religious cancan of a startling kind. When a man knows who dances the *Hálli-Hukk*, and how, and when, and where, he knows something to be proud of. He has gone deeper than the skin. But Strickland was not proud, though he had helped once, at Jagadhri, at the Painting of the Death Bull, which no Englishman must even look upon; had mastered the thieves' patter of the *chángars*; had taken a Eusufzai horse thief alone near Attock; and had stood under the *mimbar* board * of a Border mosque and conducted service in the manner of a Sunni Mollah.

His crowning achievement was spending eleven days as a *faquir* in the gardens of Baba Atal at Amritsar, and there picking up the threads of the great Nasiban murder case. But people said, justly enough, "Why on earth can't Strickland sit in his office and write up his diary, and recruit, and keep quiet, instead of showing up the incapacity of his seniors?" So the Nasiban murder case did him no good departmentally; but, after his first feeling of wrath, he returned to his outlandish custom of prying into native life. By the way, when a man once acquires a taste for this particular amusement, it abides with him all his days. It is the most fascinating thing in the world, Love not excepted. Where other men took ten days to the Hills, Strickland took leave for what he called *shikar*,* put on the disguise that appealed to him at the time, stepped down into the brown crowd, and was swallowed up for a while. He was a quiet, dark young fellow—spare; black eyes—and, when he was not thinking of something else, a very interesting companion. Strickland on Native Progress as he had seen it was worth hearing. Natives hated Strickland; but they were afraid of him. He knew too much.

When the Youghals came into the station, Strickland—very gravely, as he did everything—fell in love with Miss Youghal; and she, after a while, fell in love with him because she could not understand him. Then Strickland told the parents; but Mrs. Youghal said she was not going to throw her daughter into the worst-paid department in the Empire, and old Youghal said, in so many words, that

mimbar board: a structure over a pulpit
shikar: hunting

he mistrusted Strickland's ways and works, and would thank him not to speak or write to his daughter any more. "Very well," said Strickland, for he did not wish to make his ladylove's life a burden. After one long talk with Miss Youghal he dropped the business entirely.

The Youghals went up to Simla in April.

In July Strickland secured three months' leave on "urgent private affairs." He locked up his house—though not a native in the province would wittingly have touched "Estreekin Sahib's" gear for the world —and went down to see a friend of his, an old dyer, at Tarn Taran.

Here all trace of him was lost, until a *sais* met me on the Simla Mall with this extraordinary note:

DEAR OLD MAN,

Please give bearer a box of cheroots—Supers, No. 1, for preference. They are freshest at the Club. I'll repay when I reappear; but at present I'm out of society.

Yours,
E. STRICKLAND.

I ordered two boxes, and handed them over to the *sais* with my love. That *sais* was Strickland, and he was in old Youghal's employ, attached to Miss Youghal's Arab. The poor fellow was suffering for an English smoke, and knew that, whatever happened, I should hold my tongue till the business was over.

Later on, Mrs. Youghal, who was wrapped up in her servants, began talking at houses where she called of her paragon among *saises* —the man who was never too busy to get up in the morning and pick flowers for the breakfast table, and who blacked—actually *blacked*—the hoofs of his horse like a London coachman! The turn-out of Miss Youghal's Arab was a wonder and a delight. Strickland —Dulloo, I mean—found his reward in the pretty things that Miss Youghal said to him when she went out riding. Her parents were pleased to find she had forgotten all her foolishness for young Strickland and said she was a good girl.

Strickland vows that the two months of his service were the most rigid mental discipline he has ever gone through. Quite apart from the little fact that the wife of one of his fellow *saises* fell in love with him and then tried to poison him with arsenic because he would have nothing to do with her, he had to school himself into keeping quiet when Miss Youghal went out riding with some man who tried to flirt with her, and he was forced to trot behind, carrying the blanket and hearing every word! Also, he had to keep his temper when he was slanged in Benmore porch by a policeman—especially once when he was abused by a Naik he had himself recruited from Isser Jang village—or, worse still, when a young subaltern called him a pig for not making way quickly enough.

But the life had its compensations. He obtained great insight into the ways and thefts of *saises*—enough, he says, to have summarily convicted half the *chamar* population of the Punjab if he had been on business. He became one of the leading players at knuckle-bones, which all *jampanis* * and many *saises* play while they are waiting outside the Government House or the Gaiety Theater of nights; he learned to smoke tobacco that was three-fourths cow-dung; and he heard the wisdom of the grizzled *Jemadar* * of the Government House *saises*, whose words are valuable. He saw many things which amused him; and he states, on honor, that no man can appreciate Simla properly till he has seen it from the *sais's* point of view. He also says that if he chose to write all he saw, his head would be broken in several places.

Strickland's account of the agony he endured on wet nights, hearing the music and seeing the lights in "Benmore," with his toes tingling for a waltz and his head in a horse blanket, is rather amusing. One of these days, Strickland is going to write a little book on his experiences. That book will be worth buying; and even more worth suppressing.

Thus, he served faithfully as Jacob served for Rachel; and his leave was nearly at an end when the explosion came. He had really done his best to keep his temper in the hearing of the flirtations I have mentioned; but he broke down at last. An old and very distinguished general took Miss Youghal for a ride, and began that specially offensive "you're-only-a-little-girl" sort of flirtation—most difficult for a woman to turn aside deftly, and most maddening to listen to. Miss Youghal was shaking with fear at the things he said in the hearing of her *sais*. Dulloo—Strickland—stood it as long as he could. Then he caught hold of the general's bridle, and, in most fluent English, invited him to step off and be heaved over the cliff. Next minute Miss Youghal began crying; and Strickland saw that he had hopelessly given himself away, and everything was over.

jampanis: bearers of jampans or sedan chairs
Jemadar: a native sergeant

The general nearly had a fit, while Miss Youghal was sobbing out the story of the disguise and the engagement that was not recognized by the parents. Strickland was furiously angry with himself, and more angry with the general for forcing his hand; so he said nothing, but held the horse's head and prepared to thrash the general as some sort of satisfaction. But when the general had thoroughly grasped the story, and knew who Strickland was, he began to puff and blow in the saddle, and nearly rolled off with laughing. He said Strickland deserved a V.C.,* if it were only for putting on a *sais's* blanket. Then he called himself names, and vowed that he deserved a thrashing, but he was too old to take it from Strickland. Then he complimented Miss Youghal on her lover. The scandal of the business never struck him; for he was a nice old man, with a weakness for flirtations. Then he laughed again, and said that old Youghal was a fool. Strickland let go of the cob's head, and suggested that the general had better help them, if that was his opinion. Strickland knew Youghal's weakness for men with titles and letters after their names and high official position. "It's rather like a forty-minute farce," said the general, "but, begad, I *will* help, if it's only to escape that tremendous thrashing I deserve. Go along to your home, my *sais*-policeman, and change into decent kit, and I'll attack Mr. Youghal. Miss Youghal, may I ask you to canter home and wait?"

About seven minutes later, there was a wild hurroosh at the club. A *sais*, with blanket and headrobe, was asking all the men he knew: "For Heaven's sake lend me decent clothes!" As the men did not recognize him, there were some peculiar scenes before Strickland could get a hot bath, with soda in it, in one room, a shirt here, a collar there, a pair of trousers elsewhere, and so on. He galloped off, with half the club wardrobe on his back, and an utter stranger's pony under him, to the house of old Youghal. The general, arrayed in purple and fine linen, was before him. What the general had said Strickland never knew, but Youghal received Strickland with moderate civility; and Mrs. Youghal, touched by the devotion of the transformed Dulloo, was almost kind. The general beamed and chuckled, and Miss Youghal came in, and almost before old Youghal knew where he was, the parental consent had been wrenched out, and Strickland had departed with Miss Youghal to the telegraph office to wire for his kit. The final embarrassment was when a stranger attacked him on the Mall and asked for the stolen pony.

V.C.: the Victoria Cross, England's highest military decoration

So, in the end, Strickland and Miss Youghal were married, on the strict understanding that Strickland should drop his old ways, and stick to departmental routine, which pays best and leads to Simla. Strickland was far too fond of his wife, just then, to break his word, but it was a sore trial to him; for the streets and the bazaars, and the sounds in them, were full of meaning to Strickland, and these called to him to come back and take up his wanderings and his discoveries. Someday I will tell you how he broke his promise to help a friend. That was long since, and he has, by this time, been nearly spoiled for what he would call *shikar*. He is forgetting the slang, and the beggar's cant, and the marks, and the signs, and the drift of the undercurrents, which, if a man would master, he must always continue to learn.

But he fills in his departmental returns beautifully.

For Discussion:

1. Which short-story element is the center of interest in this story? Character? Plot? Theme? Explain.
2. Explain whether the setting and atmosphere provided by the author have any real function in relation to the action of the story.
3. How does Kipling develop his characters? Are they real? Why or why not?
4. What external or internal forces motivate the actions and personalities of the characters in the story? What is the essential conflict in the story?
5. In what way does this story affect your thinking? Has it given you new insight into people or life? Explain.

For Composition

1. Kipling suggests that Strickland's ideas on native progress, as he had seen it, were worth hearing. Write the speech Strickland might have delivered after his experience as *sais*.
2. "Strickland vows that the two months of his service were the most rigid mental discipline he has ever gone through." Imagine you are Strickland. In a letter to a friend in England, describe this mental discipline and what it consisted of.

Quality

JOHN GALSWORTHY

John Galsworthy's life (1867–1933) reached the halfway mark at the opening of the twentieth century. He belongs both to the Victorian and to the modern age. Though an aristocrat by birth and temperament, Galsworthy appreciated the social problems confronting England at the close of the nineteenth century. These became the themes of his plays *Justice* and *Strife*, his short stories and essays, and his novel *The Forsyte Saga*. In all of these he acknowledged what industrialization and mechanization were doing *for* man, but regretted what they were doing *to* him.

The Forsyte Saga, Galsworthy's masterpiece, won him the Nobel Prize for literature in 1932. The work is a social record which spans the Victorian and modern age and presents a panoramic view of the manners, morals, and values of successive generations of the Forsyte family. The author's primary purpose is to demonstrate the preoccupation of the middle class with private property, and its psychological and moral effect on people.

As a master craftsman, Galsworthy skillfully fuses the traditions of the short story and the new realistic approach. His style, though more tightly knit than that of earlier Victorian writers, still retains their leisurely pace and their scope. But few authors of his time were able to view their characters with so much objectivity as he. He himself said, "Take care of character; action and dialogue will take care of themselves." He did precisely that. Galsworthy wanted his readers to know his characters, their situations, and above all, their motives, so that in seeing them, readers might better understand and judge themselves.

———◆———

I knew him from the days of my extreme youth, because he made my father's boots; inhabiting with his elder brother two little shops let into one, in a small by-street—now no more, but then most fashionably placed in the West End.

That tenement had a certain quiet distinction; there was no sign upon its face that he made for any of the Royal Family—merely his own German name of Gessler Brothers; and in the window a few pairs of boots. I remember that it always troubled me to account for those unvarying boots in the window, for he made only what was ordered, reaching nothing down, and it seemed so inconceivable that what he made could ever have failed to fit. Had he bought them to put there? That, too, seemed inconceivable. He would never have tolerated in his house leather on which he had not worked himself. Besides, they were too beautiful—the pair of pumps, so inexpressibly slim, the patent leathers with cloth tops, making water come into one's mouth, the tall brown riding boots with marvellous sooty glow, as if, though new, they had been worn a hundred years. Those pairs could only have been made by one who saw before him the Soul of Boot—so truly were they prototypes incarnating the very spirit of all foot-gear. These thoughts, of course, came to me later, though even when I was promoted to him, at the age of perhaps fourteen, some inkling haunted me of the dignity of himself and brother. For to make boots—such boots as he made—seemed to me then, and still seems to me, mysterious and wonderful.

I remember well my shy remark, one day, while stretching out to him my youthful foot:

"Isn't it awfully hard to do, Mr. Gessler?"

And his answer, given with a sudden smile from out of the sardonic redness of his beard: "Id is an Ardt!"

Himself, he was a little as if made from leather, with his yellow crinkly face, and crinkly reddish hair and beard, and neat folds slanting down his cheeks to the corners of his mouth, and his guttural and one-toned voice; for leather is a sardonic substance, and stiff and slow of purpose. And that was the character of his face, save that his eyes, which were gray-blue, had in them the simple gravity of one secretly possessed by the Ideal. His elder brother was so very like him—though watery, paler in every way, with a great industry—that sometimes in early days I was not quite sure of him until the interview was over. Then I knew that it was he, if the words, "I will ask my brudder," had not been spoken; and, that, if they had, it was his elder brother.

When one grew old and wild and ran up bills, one somehow never ran them up with Gessler Brothers. It would not have seemed becoming to go in there and stretch out one's foot to that blue iron-spectacled glance, owing him for more than—say—two pairs, just the comfortable reassurance that one was still his client.

For it was not possible to go to him very often—his boots lasted terribly, having something beyond the temporary—some, as it were, essence of boot stitched into them.

One went in, not as into most shops, in the mood of: "Please serve me, and let me go!" but restfully, as one enters a church; and, sitting on the single wooden chair, waited—for there was never anybody there. Soon, over the top edge of that sort of well—rather dark, and smelling soothingly of leather—which formed the shop, there would be seen his face, or that of his elder brother, peering down. A guttural sound, and the tip-tap of bast slippers beating the narrow wooden stairs, and he would stand before one without coat, a little bent, in leather apron, with sleeves turned back, blinking—as if awakened from some dream of boots, or like an owl surprised in daylight and annoyed at this interruption.

And I would say: "How do you do, Mr. Gessler? Could you make me a pair of Russia leather boots?"

Without a word he would leave me, retiring whence he came, or into the other portion of the shop, and I would continue to rest in the wooden chair, inhaling the incense of his trade. Soon he would come back, holding in his thin, veined hand a piece of gold-brown leather. With eyes fixed on it, he would remark: "What a beaudiful biece!" When I, too, had admired it, he would speak again. "When do you wand dem?" And I would answer: "Oh! As soon as you conveniently can." And he would say. "To-morrow fordnighd?" Or if he were his elder brother: "I will ask my brudder!"

Then I would murmur: "Thank you! Good-morning, Mr. Gessler." "Goot-morning!" he would reply, still looking at the leather in his hand. And as I moved to the door, I would hear the tip-tap of his bast slippers restoring him, up the stairs, to his dream of boots. But if it were some new kind of foot-gear that he had not yet made me, then indeed he would observe ceremony—divesting me of my boot and holding it long in his hand, looking at it with eyes at once critical and loving, as if recalling the glow with which he had created it, and rebuking the way in which one had disorganized this masterpiece. Then, placing my foot on a piece of paper, he would two or three times tickle the outer edges with a pencil and pass his nervous fingers over my toes, feeling himself into the heart of my requirements.

I cannot forget that day on which I had occasion to say to him: "Mr. Gessler, that last pair of town walking-boots creaked, you know."

He looked at me for a time without replying, as if expecting me to withdraw or qualify the statement, then said:

"Id shouldn'd 'ave greaked."

"It did, I'm afraid."

"You god dem wed before dey found demselves?"

"I don't think so."

At that he lowered his eyes, as if hunting for memory of those boots, and I felt sorry I had mentioned this grave thing.

"Zend dem back!" he said; "I will look at dem."

A feeling of compassion for my creaking boots surged up in me, so well could I imagine the sorrowful long curiosity of regard which he would bend on them.

"Zome boods," he said slowly, "are bad from birdt. If I can do noding wid dem, I dake dem off your bill."

Once (once only) I went absent-mindedly into his shop in a pair of boots bought in an emergency at some large firm's. He took my order without showing me any leather, and I could feel his eyes penetrating the inferior integument of my foot. At last he said:

"Dose are nod my boods."

The tone was not one of anger, nor of sorrow, not even of contempt, but there was in it something quiet that froze the blood. He put his hand down and pressed a finger on the place where the left boot, endeavoring to be fashionable, was not quite comfortable.

"Id 'urds you dere," he said. "Dose big virms 'ave no self-respect. Drash!" And then, as if something had given way within him, he spoke long and bitterly. It was the only time I ever heard him discuss the conditions and hardships of his trade.

"Dey get id all," he said, "dey get id by adverdisement, nod by work. Dey dake it away from us, who lofe our boods. Id gomes to this—bresently I haf no work. Every year id gets less—you will see." And looking at his lined face I saw things I had never noticed before, bitter things and bitter struggle—and what a lot of gray hairs there seemed suddenly in his red beard!

As best I could, I explained the circumstances of the purchase of those ill-omened boots. But his face and voice made so deep impression that during the next few minutes I ordered many pairs. Nemesis fell! They lasted more terribly than ever. And I was not able conscientiously to go to him for nearly two years.

When at last I went I was surprised to find that outside one of the two little windows of his shop another name was painted, also that of a bootmaker—making, of course, for the Royal Family. The old familiar boots, no longer in dignified isolation, were huddled in the single window. Inside, the now contracted well of the one little shop was more scented and darker than ever. And it was longer than usual, too, before a face peered down, and the tip-tap of the bast slippers began. At last he stood before me, and, gazing through those rusty iron spectacles, said:

"Mr.——, isn'd it?"

"Ah! Mr. Gessler," I stammered, "but your boots are really *too* good, you know! See, these are quite decent still!" And I stretched out to him my foot. He looked at it.

"Yes," he said, "beople do nod wand good boods, id seems."

To get away from his reproachful eyes and voice I hastily remarked: "What have you done to your shop?"

He answered quietly: "Id was too exbensif. Do you wand some boods?"

I ordered three pairs, though I had only wanted two, and quickly left. I had, I do not know quite what feeling of being part, in his mind, of a conspiracy against him; or not perhaps so much against him as against his idea of boot. One does not, I suppose, care to feel like that; for it was again many months before my next visit to his shop, paid, I remember, with the feeling: "Oh! well, I can't leave the old boy—so here goes! Perhaps it'll be his elder brother!"

For his elder brother, I knew, had not character enough to reproach me, even dumbly.

And, to my relief, in the shop there did appear to be his elder brother, handling a piece of leather.

"Well, Mr. Gessler," I said, "how are you?"

He came close, and peered at me.

"I am breddy well," he said slowly; "but my elder brudder is dead."

And I saw that it was indeed himself—but how aged and wan! And never before had I heard him mention his brother. Much shocked, I murmured: "Oh! I am sorry!"

"Yes," he answered, "he was a good man, he made a good bood; but he is dead." And he touched the top of his head, where the hair had suddenly gone as thin as it had been on that of his poor brother, to indicate, I suppose, the cause of death. "He could nod ged over losing de oder shop. Do you wand any boods?" And he held up the leather in his hand: "Id's a beaudiful biece."

I ordered several pairs. It was very long before they came—but they were better than ever. One simply could not wear them out. And soon after that I went abroad.

It was over a year before I was again in London. And the first shop I went to was my old friend's. I had left a man of sixty, I came back to one of seventy-five, pinched and worn and tremulous, who genuinely, this time, did not at first know me.

"Oh! Mr. Gessler," I said, sick at heart; "how splendid your boots are! See, I've been wearing this pair nearly all the time I've been abroad; and they're not half worn out, are they?"

He looked long at my boots—a pair of Russia leather, and his face seemed to regain its steadiness. Putting his hand on my instep, he said:

"Do dey vid you here? I 'ad drouble wid dat bair, I remember."

I assured him that they had fitted beautifully.

"Do you wand any boods?" he said. "I can make dem quickly; id is a slack dime."

I answered: "Please, please! I want boots all round—every kind!"

"I will make a vresh model. Your food must be bigger." And with utter slowness, he traced round my foot, and felt my toes, only once looking up to say:

"Did I dell you my brudder was dead?"

To watch him was painful, so feeble had he grown; I was glad to get away.

I had given those boots up, when one evening they came. Opening the parcel, I set the four pairs out in a row. Then one by one I tried them on. There was no doubt about it. In shape and fit, in finish and quality of leather, they were the best he had ever made me. And in the mouth of one of the town walking-boots I found his bill. The amount was the same as usual, but it gave me quite a shock. He had never before sent it in till quarter day. I flew down-stairs, and wrote a check, and posted it at once with my own hand. A week later, passing the little street, I thought I would go in and tell him how splendidly the new boots fitted. But when I came to where his shop had been, his name was gone. Still there, in the window, were the slim pumps, the patent leathers with cloth tops, the sooty riding boots.

I went in, very much disturbed. In the two little shops—again made into one—was a young man with an English face.

"Mr. Gessler in?" I said.

He gave me a strange, ingratiating look.

"No, sir," he said, "no. But we can attend to anything with pleasure. We've taken the shop over. You've seen our name, no doubt, next door. We make for some very good people."

"Yes, yes," I said; "but Mr. Gessler?"

"Oh!" he answered; "dead."

"Dead! But I only received these boots from him last Wednesday week."

"Ah!" he said; "a shockin' go. Poor old man starved 'imself."

"Good God!"

"Slow starvation, the doctor called it! You see he went to work in such a way! Would keep the shop on; wouldn't have a soul touch his boots but himself. When he got an order, it took him such a time. People won't wait. He lost everybody. And there he'd sit, goin' on and on—I will say that for him—not a man in London made a better boot! But look at the competition! He never advertised! Would 'ave the best leather, too, and do it all 'imself. Well, there it is. What could you expect with his ideas?"

"But starvation——!"

"That may be a bit flowery, as the sayin' is—but I know myself he was sittin' over his boots day and night, to the very last. You see I used to watch him. Never gave 'imself time to eat; never had a penny in the house. All went in rent and leather. How he lived so long I don't know. He regular let his fire go out. He was a character. But he made good boots."

"Yes," I said, "he made good boots."

And I turned and went out quickly, for I did not want that youth to know that I could hardly see.

For Discussion:

1. What is the central idea that the author wishes to convey? Where is the theme first indicated? How is it related to the title of the story?
2. What effect does Galsworthy's choice of a first-person narrator have upon the story?
3. Is the tone of the story sentimental, critical, or both? Do you feel it is a propaganda piece? Explain.
4. Show how the author uses setting to point up character in his bootmaker.
5. What is the basic conflict in this story? How do the Gessler brothers meet it? Is this response consistent with the characters as they have been presented? Why or why not?
6. Are you satisfied with the ending? Why is it the logical one to expect? How were you prepared for it?

For Composition: "Producers today are more interested in quantity and efficiency than in quality and workmanship." Write a short composition explaining why you agree or disagree with this statement.

Her First Ball

KATHERINE MANSFIELD

Katherine Mansfield (1888–1924) applied her unusually sensitive literary ability solely to the writing of short stories. Experimenting with various prose styles, she arrived independently at her own particular form of the stream-of-consciousness technique which Virginia Woolf was using in the novel about the same time.

In her narratives, Miss Mansfield shows little concern for plot development. She is more interested in what is going on *within* her characters at any one moment. Her stories are about young girls and women who are sensitive, naive, and open-hearted. She selects the details that will catch most exactly the situation she is writing about, and then permits her characters to reveal themselves through their actions, their conversations, and their thoughts. To her, the emotionally charged moment of enchantment or disillusionment constitutes a sufficient span of time for a complete story, and she relates it with genuine understanding. Her object is to hold the fleeting moment just long enough for the reader to share it. She believes that the real objective of literature is that of "subjecting its readers to a real and at the same time illuminating experience."

———◆———

Exactly when the ball began Leila would have found it hard to say. Perhaps her first real partner was the cab. It did not matter that she shared the cab with the Sheridan girls and their brother. She sat back in her own little corner of it, and the bolster on which her hand rested felt like the sleeve of an unknown young man's dress suit; and away they bowled, past waltzing lamp-posts and houses and fences and trees.

"Have you really never been to a ball before, Leila? But, my child, how too weird—" cried the Sheridan girls.

"Our nearest neighbour was fifteen miles," said Leila softly, gently opening and shutting her fan.

Oh, dear, how hard it was to be indifferent like the others! She tried not to smile too much; she tried not to care. But every single thing was so new and exciting . . . Meg's tuberoses, Jose's long loop of amber, Laura's little dark head, pushing above her white fur like a flower through snow. She would remember for ever. It even gave her a pang to see her cousin Laurie throw away the wisps of tissue

145

paper he pulled from the fastenings of his new gloves. She would like to have kept those wisps as a keepsake, as a remembrance. Laurie leaned forward and put his hand on Laura's knee.

"Look here, darling," he said. "The third and the ninth as usual. Twig?"

Oh, how marvellous to have a brother! In her excitement Leila felt that if there had been time, if it hadn't been impossible, she couldn't have helped crying because she was an only child, and no brother had ever said "Twig?" to her; no sister would ever say, as Meg said to Jose that moment, "I've never known your hair go up more successfully than it has to-night!"

But, of course, there was no time. They were at the drill hall already; there were cabs in front of them and cabs behind. The road was bright on either side with moving fan-like lights, and on the pavement gay couples seemed to float through the air; little satin shoes chased each other like birds.

"Hold on to me, Leila; you'll get lost," said Laura.

"Come on, girls, let's make a dash for it," said Laurie.

Leila put two fingers on Laura's pink velvet cloak, and they were somehow lifted past the big golden lantern, carried along the passage, and pushed into the little room marked "Ladies." Here the crowd was so great there was hardly space to take off their things; the noise was deafening. Two benches on either side were stacked high with wraps. Two old women in white aprons ran up and down tossing fresh armfuls. And everybody was pressing forward trying to get at the little dressing-table and mirror at the far end.

A great quivering jet of gas lighted the ladies' room. It couldn't wait; it was dancing already. When the door opened again and there came a burst of tuning from the drill hall, it leaped almost to the ceiling.

Dark girls, fair girls were patting their hair, tying ribbons again, tucking handkerchiefs down the fronts of their bodices, smoothing marble-white gloves. And because they were all laughing it seemed to Leila that they were all lovely.

"Aren't there any invisible hair-pins?" cried a voice. "How most extraordinary! I can't see a single invisible hair-pin."

"Powder my back, there's a darling," cried someone else.

"But I must have a needle and cotton. I've torn simply miles and miles of the frill," wailed a third.

Then, "Pass them along, pass them along!" The straw basket of programmes was tossed from arm to arm. Darling little pink-and-silver programmes, with pink pencils and fluffy tassels. Leila's fingers shook as she took one out of the basket. She wanted to ask someone, "Am I meant to have one too?" but she had just time to read: "Waltz 3. *Two, Two in a Canoe.* Polka 4. *Making the Feathers Fly,*" when Meg cried, "Ready, Leila?" and they pressed their way through the crush in the passage towards the big double doors of the drill hall.

Dancing had not begun yet, but the band had stopped tuning, and the noise was so great it seemed that when it did begin to play it would never be heard. Leila, pressing close to Meg, looking over Meg's shoulder, felt that even the little quivering coloured flags strung across the ceiling were talking. She quite forgot to be shy; she forgot how in the middle of dressing she had sat down on the bed with one shoe off and one shoe on and begged her mother to ring up her cousins and say she couldn't go after all. And the rush of longing she had had to be sitting on the veranda of their forsaken up-country home, listening to the baby owls crying "More pork" in the moonlight, was changed to a rush of joy so sweet that it was hard to bear alone. She clutched her fan, and, gazing at the gleaming, golden floor, the azaleas, the lanterns, the stage at one end with its red carpet and gilt chairs and the band in a corner, she thought breathlessly, "How heavenly; how simply heavenly!"

All the girls stood grouped together at one side of the doors, the men at the other, and the chaperones in dark dresses, smiling rather foolishly, walked with little careful steps over the polished floor towards the stage.

"This is my little country cousin Leila. Be nice to her. Find her partners; she's under my wing," said Meg, going up to one girl after another.

Strange faces smiled at Leila—sweetly, vaguely. Strange voices answered, "Of course, my dear." But Leila felt the girls didn't really see her. They were looking towards the men. Why didn't the men begin? What were they waiting for? There they stood, smoothing their gloves, patting their glossy hair and smiling among themselves. Then, quite suddenly, as if they had only just made up their minds that that was what they had to do, the men came gliding over the parquet. There was a joyful flutter among the girls. A tall, fair man flew up to Meg, seized her programme, scribbled something; Meg passed him on to Leila. "May I have the pleasure?" He ducked and smiled. There came a dark man wearing an eyeglass, then cousin

Laurie with a friend, and Laura with a little freckled fellow whose tie was crooked. Then quite an old man—fat, with a big bald patch on his head—took her programme and murmured, "Let me see, let me see!" And he was a long time comparing his programme, which looked black with names, with hers. It seemed to give him so much trouble that Leila was ashamed. "Oh, please don't bother," she said eagerly. But instead of replying the fat man wrote something, glanced at her again. "Do I remember this bright little face?" he said softly. "Is it known to me of yore?" At that moment the band began playing; the fat man disappeared. He was tossed away on a great wave of music that came flying over the gleaming floor, breaking the groups up into couples, scattering them, sending them spinning. . . .

Leila had learned to dance at boarding school. Every Saturday afternoon the boarders were hurried off to a little corrugated iron mission hall where Miss Eccles (of London) held her "select" classes. But the difference between that dusty-smelling hall—with calico texts on the walls, the poor terrified little woman in a brown velvet toque with rabbit's ears thumping the cold piano, Miss Eccles poking the girls' feet with her long white wand—and this was so tremendous that Leila was sure if her partner didn't come and she had to listen to that marvellous music and to watch the others sliding, gliding over the golden floor, she would die at least, or faint, or lift her arms and fly out of one of those dark windows that showed the stars.

"Ours, I think—" Some one bowed, smiled, and offered her his arm; she hadn't to die after all. Some one's hand pressed her waist, and she floated away like a flower that is tossed into a pool.

"Quite a good floor, isn't it?" drawled a faint voice close to her ear.

"I think it's most beautifully slippery," said Leila.

"Pardon!" The faint voice sounded surprised. Leila said it again. And there was a tiny pause before the voice echoed, "Oh, quite!" and she was swung round again.

He steered so beautifully. That was the great difference between dancing with girls and men, Leila decided. Girls banged into each other, and stamped on each other's feet; the girl who was gentleman always clutched you so.

The azaleas were separate flowers no longer; they were pink and white flags streaming by.

"Were you at the Bells' last week?" the voice came again. It sounded tired. Leila wondered whether she ought to ask him if he would like to stop.

"No, this is my first dance," said she.

Her partner gave a little gasping laugh. "Oh, I say," he protested.

"Yes, it is really the first dance I've ever been to." Leila was most fervent. It was such a relief to be able to tell somebody. "You see, I've lived in the country all my life up until now. . . ."

At that moment the music stopped, and they went to sit on two chairs against the wall. Leila tucked her pink satin feet under and fanned herself, while she blissfully watched the other couples passing and disappearing through the swing doors.

"Enjoying yourself, Leila?" asked Jose, nodding her golden head.

Laura passed and gave her the faintest little wink; it made Leila wonder for a moment whether she was quite grown up after all. Certainly her partner did not say very much. He coughed, tucked his handkerchief away, pulled down his waistcoat, took a minute thread off his sleeve. But it didn't matter. Almost immediately the band started, and her second partner seemed to spring from the ceiling.

"Floor's not bad," said the new voice. Did one always begin with the floor? And then, "Were you at the Neaves' on Tuesday?" And again Leila explained. Perhaps it was a little strange that her partners were not more interested. For it was thrilling. Her first ball! She was only at the beginning of everything. It seemed to her that she had never known what the night was like before. Up till now it had been dark, silent, beautiful very often—oh, yes—but mournful somehow. Solemn. And now it would never be like that again—it had opened dazzling bright.

"Care for an ice?" said her partner. And they went through the swing doors, down the passage, to the supper room. Her cheeks burned, she was fearfully thirsty. How sweet the ices looked on little glass plates, and how cold the frosted spoon was, iced too! And when they came back to the hall there was the fat man waiting for her by the door. It gave her quite a shock again to see how old he was; he ought to have been on the stage with the fathers and mothers. And when Leila compared him with her other partners he looked shabby. His waistcoat was creased, there was a button off his glove, his coat looked as if it was dusty with French chalk.

"Come along, little lady," said the fat man. He scarcely troubled to clasp her, and they moved away so gently, it was more like walking than dancing. But he said not a word about the floor. "Your first dance, isn't it?" he murmured.

"How *did* you know?"

"Ah," said the fat man, "that's what it is to be old!" He wheezed faintly as he steered her past an awkward couple. "You see, I've been doing this kind of thing for the last thirty years."

"Thirty years?" cried Leila. Twelve years before she was born!

"It hardly bears thinking about, does it?" said the fat man gloomily. Leila looked at his bald head, and she felt quite sorry for him.

"I think it's marvellous to be still going on," she said kindly.

"Kind little lady," said the fat man, and he pressed her a little closer, and hummed a bar of the waltz. "Of course," he said, "you can't hope to last anything like as long as that. No-o," said the fat man, "long before that you'll be sitting up there on the stage, looking on, in your nice black velvet. And these pretty arms will have turned into little short fat ones, and you'll beat time with such a different kind of fan—a black bony one." The fat man seemed to shudder. "And you'll smile away like the poor old dears up there, and point to your daughter, and tell the elderly lady next to you how some dreadful man tried to kiss her at the club ball. And your heart will ache, ache"—the fat man squeezed her closer still, as if he really was sorry for that poor heart—"because no one wants to kiss you now. And you'll say how unpleasant these polished floors are to walk on, how dangerous they are. Eh, Mademoiselle Twinkletoes?" said the fat man softly.

Leila gave a light little laugh, but she did not feel like laughing. Was it—could it all be true? It sounded terribly true. Was this first ball only the beginning of her last ball after all? At that the music seemed to change; it sounded sad, sad; it rose upon a great sigh. Oh, how quickly things changed! Why didn't happiness last forever? Forever wasn't a bit too long.

"I want to stop," she said in a breathless voice. The fat man led her to the door.

"No," she said, "I won't go outside. I won't sit down. I'll just stand here, thank you." She leaned against the wall, tapping with her foot, pulling up her gloves and trying to smile. But deep inside her a little girl threw her pinafore over her head and sobbed. Why had he spoiled it all?

"I say, you know," said the fat man, "you mustn't take me seriously, little lady."

"As if I should!" said Leila, tossing her small dark head and sucking her underlip. . . .

Again the couples paraded. The swing doors opened and shut.

Now new music was given out by the bandmaster. But Leila didn't want to dance any more. She wanted to be home, or sitting on the veranda listening to those baby owls. When she looked through the dark windows at the stars, they had long beams like wings. . . .

But presently a soft, melting, ravishing tune began, and a young man with curly hair bowed before her. She would have to dance, out of politeness, until she could find Meg. Very stiffly she walked into the middle; very haughtily she put her hand on his sleeve. But in one minute, in one turn, her feet glided, glided. The lights, the azaleas, the dresses, the pink faces, the velvet chairs, all became one beautiful flying wheel. And when her next partner bumped her into the fat man and he said, "Par*don*," she smiled at him more radiantly than ever. She didn't even recognize him again.

For Discussion:

1. How has Katherine Mansfield's choice of details helped her to create the mood of this story? What advantage is there in relating the story from Leila's point of view? What effect would have been achieved if it had been told from an adult point of view?
2. Although the conflict is suggested very subtly by the author, it is a real one. What is it? How does Leila meet it?
3. Point out those incidents that reveal the kind of girl Leila is. Do you believe she is ready for the experience she has at the ball? Explain.
4. Prove that this story is developed through a third person stream-of-consciousness technique. You will have to re-read the story to collect your evidence.

For Composition: Everyone experiences important "firsts." Relate one of your "first" experiences. Make clear what was new about it and what circumstances caused it to be unique. Pay special attention to the details that will re-create the emotional tone of the situation.

Araby

JAMES JOYCE

James Joyce (1882–1941), one of the most controversial of modern writers, was born in Dublin, Ireland. In 1902, after taking his degree from Jesuit University College in Dublin, he turned his back upon the country of his birth and rejected his faith. The emotional ties with his past remained, however. These constitute the basis of his first successful work *The Dubliners*, a volume of short stories. Although now considered by many to be his best book, it was refused by more than a dozen publishers before it appeared. They hesitated to accept responsibility for the supposedly "treasonous" passages which drew a picture of Dublin life with its frustrated men and women and its seamy and sordid background.

Joyce was particularly concerned with describing the inner life of his characters and the way their thoughts and feelings actually occurred from moment to moment. For this purpose, the stream-of-consciousness technique was ideally suited to him. He worked tirelessly to develop it through a careful use of words that would convey most precisely and subtly to his readers this inner state of his characters. In his passionate search for fresh language, he used exotic, foreign, and archaic words, and even made up words where he felt they would serve his purpose. At its best, this made for a rich and musical prose. In his last works, however, it resulted in an increasingly difficult and complex prose style.

His early short story "Araby" from *The Dubliners* is one of his most direct. In it he uses the stream-of-consciousness technique delicately and effectively to convey the thoughts and feelings of a young Irish boy.

North Richmond Street, being blind, was a quiet street except at the hour when the Christian Brothers' School set the boys free. An uninhabited house of two storeys stood at the blind end, detached from its neighbours in a square ground. The other houses of the street, conscious of decent lives within them, gazed at one another with brown imperturbable faces.

The former tenant of our house, a priest, had died in the back drawing-room. Air, musty from having been long enclosed, hung in all the rooms, and the waste room behind the kitchen was littered with old useless papers. Among these I found a few paper-covered books, the pages of which were curled and damp: *The Abbot*, by Walter Scott, *The Devout Communicant* and *The Memoirs of*

Vidocq. I liked the last best because its leaves were yellow. The wild garden behind the house contained a central apple-tree and a few straggling bushes under one of which I found the late tenant's rusty bicycle-pump. He had been a very charitable priest; in his will he had left all his money to institutions and the furniture of his house to his sister.

When the short days of winter came dusk fell before we had well eaten our dinners. When we met in the street the houses had grown sombre. The space of sky above us was the colour of ever-changing violet and towards it the lamps of the street lifted their feeble lanterns. The cold air stung us and we played till our bodies glowed. Our shouts echoed in the silent street. The career of our play brought us through the dark muddy lanes behind the houses where we ran the gauntlet of the rough tribes from the cottages, to the back doors of the dark dripping gardens where odours arose from the ashpits, to the dark odorous stables where a coachman smoothed and combed the horse or shook music from the buckled harness. When we returned to the street light from the kitchen windows had filled the areas. If my uncle was seen turning the corner we hid in the shadow until we had seen him safely housed. Or if Mangan's sister came out on the doorstep to call her brother in to his tea we watched her from our shadow peer up and down the street. We waited to see whether she would remain or go in and, if she remained, we left our shadow and walked up to Mangan's steps resignedly. She was waiting for us, her figure defined by the light from the half-opened door. Her brother always teased her before he obeyed and I stood by the railings looking at her. Her dress swung as she moved her body and the soft rope of her hair tossed from side to side.

Every morning I lay on the floor in the front parlour watching her door. The blind was pulled down to within an inch of the sash so that I could not be seen. When she came out on the doorstep my heart leaped. I ran to the hall, seized my books and followed her. I kept her brown figure always in my eye and, when we came near the point at which our ways diverged, I quickened my pace and passed her. This happened morning after morning. I had never spoken to her, except for a few casual words, and yet her name was like a summons to all my foolish blood.

Her image accompanied me even in places the most hostile to romance. On Saturday evenings when my aunt went marketing I had to go to carry some of the parcels. We walked through the flaring streets, jostled by drunken men and bargaining women, amid the curses of labourers, the shrill litanies of shop-boys who stood on guard by the barrels of pigs' cheeks, the nasal chanting of street-singers, who sang a *come-all-you* about O'Donovan Rossa, or a ballad about the troubles in our native land. These noises converged in a single sensation of life for me: I imagined that I bore my chalice safely through a throng of foes. Her name sprang to my lips at moments in strange prayers and praises which I myself did not understand. My eyes were often full of tears (I could not tell why) and at times a flood from my heart seemed to pour itself out into my bosom. I thought little of the future. I did not know whether I would ever speak to her or not or, if I spoke to her, how I could tell her of my confused adoration. But my body was like a harp and her words and gestures were like fingers running upon the wires.

One evening I went into the back drawing-room in which the priest had died. It was a dark rainy evening and there was no sound in the house. Through one of the broken panes I heard the rain impinge upon the earth, the fine incessant needles of water playing in the sodden beds. Some distant lamp or lighted window gleamed below me. I was thankful that I could see so little. All my senses seemed to desire to veil themselves and, feeling that I was about to slip from them, I pressed the palms of my hands together until they trembled, murmuring: "O love! O love!" many times.

At last she spoke to me. When she addressed the first words to me I was so confused that I did not know what to answer. She asked me was I going to *Araby*. I forgot whether I answered yes or no. It would be a splendid bazaar, she said she would love to go.

"And why can't you?" I asked.

While she spoke she turned a silver bracelet round and round her wrist. She could not go, she said, because there would be a retreat that week in her convent. Her brother and two other boys were fighting for their caps and I was alone at the railings. She held one of the spikes, bowing her head towards me. The light from the lamp opposite our door caught the white curve of her neck, lit up her hair that rested there and, falling, lit up the hand upon the railing. It fell over one side of her dress and caught the white border of a petticoat, just visible as she stood at ease.

"It's well for you," she said.

"If I go," I said, "I will bring you something."

What innumerable follies laid waste my waking and sleeping

thoughts after that evening! I wished to annihilate the tedious intervening days. I chafed against the work of school. At night in my bedroom and by day in the classroom her image came between me and the page I strove to read. The syllables of the word *Araby* were called to me through the silence in which my soul luxuriated and cast an Eastern enchantment over me. I asked for leave to go to the bazaar on Saturday night. My aunt was surprised and hoped it was not some Freemason affair. I answered few questions in class. I watched my master's face pass from amiability to sternness; he hoped I was not beginning to idle. I could not call my wandering thoughts together. I had hardly any patience with the serious work of life which, now that it stood between me and my desire, seemed to me child's play, ugly monotonous child's play.

On Saturday morning I reminded my uncle that I wished to go to the bazaar in the evening. He was fussing at the hallstand, looking for the hat-brush, and answered me curtly:

"Yes, boy, I know."

As he was in the hall I could not go into the front parlour and lie at the window. I left the house in bad humour and walked slowly towards the school. The air was pitilessly raw and already my heart misgave me.

When I came home to dinner my uncle had not yet been home. Still it was early. I sat staring at the clock for some time and, when its ticking began to irritate me, I left the room. I mounted the staircase and gained the upper part of the house. The high cold empty gloomy rooms liberated me and I went from room to room singing. From the front window I saw my companions playing below in the street. Their cries reached me weakened and indistinct and, leaning my forehead against the cool glass, I looked over at the dark house where she lived. I may have stood there for an hour, seeing nothing but the brown-clad figure cast by my imagination, touched discreetly by the lamplight at the curved neck, at the hand upon the railings and at the border below the dress.

When I came downstairs again I found Mrs. Mercer sitting at the fire. She was an old garrulous woman, a pawnbroker's widow, who collected used stamps for some pious purpose. I had to endure the gossip of the tea-table. The meal was prolonged beyond an hour and still my uncle did not come. Mrs. Mercer stood up to go: she was sorry she couldn't wait any longer, but it was after eight o'clock and she did not like to be out late, as the night air was bad for her.

When she had gone I began to walk up and down the room, clenching my fists. My aunt said:

"I'm afraid you may put off your bazaar for this night of Our Lord."

At nine o'clock I heard my uncle's latchkey in the halldoor. I heard him talking to himself and heard the hallstand rocking when it had received the weight of his overcoat. I could interpret these signs. When he was midway through his dinner I asked him to give me the money to go to the bazaar. He had forgotten.

"The people are in bed and after their first sleep now," he said. I did not smile. My aunt said to him energetically:

"Can't you give him the money and let him go? You've kept him late enough as it is."

My uncle said he was very sorry he had forgotten. He said he believed in the old saying: "All work and no play makes Jack a dull boy." He asked me where I was going and, when I had told him a second time he asked me did I know *The Arab's Farewell to his Steed*. When I left the kitchen he was about to recite the opening lines of the piece to my aunt.

I held a florin tightly in my hand as I strode down Buckingham Street towards the station. The sight of the streets thronged with buyers and glaring with gas recalled to me the purpose of my journey. I took my seat in a third-class carriage of a deserted train. After an intolerable delay the train moved out of the station slowly. It crept onward among ruinous houses and over the twinkling river. At Westland Row Station a crowd of people pressed to the carriage doors; but the porters moved them back, saying that it was a special train for the bazaar. I remained alone in the bare carriage. In a few minutes the train drew up beside an improvised wooden platform. I passed out on to the road and saw by the lighted dial of a clock that it was ten minutes to ten. In front of me was a large building which displayed the magical name.

I could not find any sixpenny entrance and, fearing that the bazaar would be closed, I passed in quickly through a turnstile, handing a shilling to a weary-looking man. I found myself in a big hall girdled at half its height by a gallery. Nearly all the stalls were closed and the greater part of the hall was in darkness. I recognised a silence like that which pervades a church after a service. I walked into the centre of the bazaar timidly. A few people were gathered about the stalls which were still open. Before a curtain, over which the words *Café Chantant* were written in coloured lamps, two men were counting money on a salver. I listened to the fall of the coins.

Remembering with difficulty why I had come I went over to one of the stalls and examined porcelain vases and flowered tea-sets. At the door of the stall a young lady was talking and laughing with two young gentlemen. I remarked their English accents and listened vaguely to their conversation.

"O, I never said such a thing!"

"O, but you did!"

"O, but I didn't!"

"Didn't she say that?"

"Yes. I heard her."

"O, there's a . . . fib!"

Observing me, the young lady came over and asked me did I wish to buy anything. The tone of her voice was not encouraging; she seemed to have spoken to me out of a sense of duty. I looked humbly at the great jars that stood like eastern guards at either side of the dark entrance to the stall and murmured:

"No, thank you."

The young lady changed the position of one of the vases and went back to the two young men. They began to talk of the same subject. Once or twice the young lady glanced at me over her shoulder.

I lingered before her stall, though I knew my stay was useless, to make my interest in her wares seem the more real. Then I turned away slowly and walked down the middle of the bazaar. I allowed the two pennies to fall against the sixpence in my pocket. I heard a voice call from one end of the gallery that the light was out. The upper part of the hall was now completely dark.

Gazing up into the darkness I saw myself as a creature driven and derided by vanity; and my eyes burned with anguish and anger.

For Discussion:

1. Does the title of this story have any particular significance? Is this a simple story of a boy's first love or does it tell something more than that? Explain.
2. State the theme of "Araby" in your own words, and point out passages to support your answer.

3. What means does the author use to make you aware that the incident occurs in a large city? How does his description of the house and street where the boy lives contribute to the theme?

4. From whose point of view is the story told? How long after its occurrence is it related? Find passages to support your answer. Are the person's feelings now the same as they were when the incident occurred? Explain.

5. Characterize the boy in this story. Point to specific sentences that reveal these traits.

6. Comment on the relationship between the boy and each of the other important characters mentioned: the dead priest, his aunt, his uncle Mangan's sister. When describing his feelings toward the girl, the boy uses a particularly vivid figure of speech. What is its significance? What other striking images help to emphasize the central idea of the story?

7. The final sentence in this story exemplifies what Joyce called an "epiphany,"—a moment when some hitherto hidden truth is suddenly made clear. What does this epiphany reveal to the narrator?

For Composition: In a brief, third-person narrative, describe an epiphany that you have experienced.

The New Dress

VIRGINIA WOOLF

Early in her writing career, Virginia Woolf (1882–1941) grew impatient with writers of her time. She subjected three of them—H. G. Wells, John Galsworthy, and Arnold Bennett—to severe criticism in an essay entitled "Modern Fiction." She states that these writers seem to be "constrained . . . by some powerful and unscrupulous tyrant . . . to provide a plot . . . and an air of probability . . . so impeccable that if all the figures were to come to life they would find themselves dressed down to the last button of their coats in the fashion of the hour."

Such constraint irked Virginia Woolf. She believed that the incidents of life could not be shaped and presented so neatly; they must flow freely as they actually are experienced in the minds of people. According to her, each moment a person lives might well be a lifetime, for in every moment the mind is charged with a "shower of innumerable atoms." In short, men do not focus upon one idea at a time. Rather, each triggering of the senses, each idea grasped at by the mind starts up a reaction similar to that of a pebble in a pool. There is a sort of chain reaction as man's consciousness is touched.

This idea obsessed Mrs. Woolf. Her desire to penetrate to the consciousness of her characters rather than to portray their surface lives attracted her to the stream-of-consciousness technique. Her novels, notably *Mrs. Dalloway*, and her short stories are examples of this form of narrative. The reader finds neither plot, nor an exposition of the relationships among the characters, nor any description of the setting. He does find, rather, an accurate though complex presentation of interrelated sights, sounds, impressions, and thoughts as they are had by a character over a brief period of time. From this internal picture, he must construct what is happening to the character externally. "The New Dress" is a vivid example of this approach.

Mabel had her first serious suspicion that something was wrong as she took her cloak off and Mrs. Barnet, while handing her the mirror and touching the brushes and thus drawing her attention, perhaps rather markedly, to all the appliances for tidying and improving hair, complexion, clothes, which existed on the dressing table, confirmed the suspicion—that it was not right, not quite right, which growing stronger as she went upstairs and springing at her, with conviction as she greeted Clarissa Dalloway, she went straight to the far end of the room, to a shaded corner where a looking-glass hung and looked. No! It was not *right*. And at once the misery which she always tried to hide, the profound dissatisfaction—the sense she had had, ever since she was a child, of being inferior to other people—set upon her, relentlessly, remorselessly, with an intensity which she could not beat off, as she would when she woke at night at home, by reading Borrow or Scott; for oh these men, oh these women, all were thinking—"What's Mabel wearing? What a fright she looks! What a hideous new dress!"—their eyelids flickering as they came up and then their lids shutting rather tight. It was her own appalling inadequacy; her cowardice; her mean, water-sprinkled blood that depressed her. And at once the whole of the room where, for ever so many hours, she had planned with the little dressmaker how it was to go, seemed sordid, repulsive; and her own drawing-room so shabby, and herself, going out, puffed up with vanity as she touched the letters on the hall table and said: "How dull!" to show off—all this now seemed unutterably silly, paltry, and provincial. All this had been absolutely destroyed, shown up, exploded, the moment she came into Mrs. Dalloway's drawing-room.

What she had thought that evening when, sitting over the tea-cups, Mrs. Dalloway's invitation came, was that, of course, she could not be fashionable. It was absurd to pretend it even—fashion meant cut, meant style, meant thirty guineas at least—but why not be original? Why not be herself, anyhow? And, getting up, she had taken that old fashion book of her mother's, a Paris fashion book of the time of the Empire, and had thought how much prettier, more dignified, and more womanly they were then, and so set herself—oh, it was foolish—trying to be like them, pluming herself in fact, upon being modest and old-fashioned and very charming, giving herself up, no doubt about it, to an orgy of self-love, which deserved to be chastised, and so rigged herself out like this.

But she dared not look in the glass. She could not face the whole horror—the pale yellow, idiotically old-fashioned silk dress with its long skirt and its high sleeves and its waist and all the things that looked so charming in the fashion book, but not on her, not among all these ordinary people. She felt like a dressmaker's dummy standing there, for young people to stick pins into.

"But, my dear, it's perfectly charming!" Rose Shaw said, looking her up and down with that little satirical pucker of the lips which she expected—Rose herself being dressed in the height of the fashion, precisely like everybody else, always.

We are all like flies trying to crawl over the edge of the saucer, Mabel thought, and repeated the phrase as if she were crossing herself, as if she were trying to find some spell to annul this pain, to make this agony endurable. Tags of Shakespeare, lines from books she had read ages ago, suddenly came to her when she was in agony, and she repeated them over and over again. "Flies trying to crawl," she repeated. If she could say that over often enough and make herself see the flies, she would become numb, chill, frozen, dumb. Now she could see flies crawling slowly out of a saucer of milk with their wings stuck together; and she strained and strained (standing in front of the looking-glass, listening to Rose Shaw) to make herself see Rose Shaw and all the other people there as flies, trying to hoist themselves out of something, or into something, meagre, insignificant, toiling flies. But she could not see them like that, not other people. She saw herself like that—she was a fly, but the others were dragonflies, butterflies, beautiful insects, dancing, fluttering, skimming, while she alone dragged herself up out of the saucer. (Envy and spite, the most detestable of the vices, were her chief faults.)

"I feel like some dowdy, decrepit, horribly dingy old fly," she said, making Robert Haydon stop just to hear her say that, just to reassure herself by furbishing up a poor weak-kneed phrase and so showing how detached she was, how witty, that she did not feel in the least out of anything. And, of course, Robert Haydon answered something quite polite, quite insincere, which she saw through instantly, and said to herself, directly he went (again from some book), "Lies, lies, lies!" For a party makes things either much more real, or much less real, she thought; she saw in a flash to the bottom of Robert Haydon's heart; she saw through everything. She saw the truth. *This* was true, this drawing-room, this self, and the other false. Miss Milan's little work-room was really terribly hot, stuffy, sordid. It smelt of clothes and cabbage cooking; and yet, when Miss Milan put the glass in her hand, and she looked at herself with the dress on, finished, an extraordinary bliss shot through her heart. Suffused with light, she sprang into existence. Rid of cares and wrinkles, what she had dreamed of herself was there—a beautiful woman. Just for a second (she had not dared look longer, Miss Milan wanted to know about the length of the skirt), there looked at her, framed in the scrolloping mahogany, a grey-white, mysteriously smiling, charming girl, the core of herself, the soul of herself; and it was not vanity only, not only self-love that made her think it good, tender, and true. Miss Milan said that the skirt could not well be longer; if anything the skirt, said Miss Milan, puckering her forehead, considering with all her wits about her, must be shorter; and she felt, suddenly, honestly, full of love for Miss Milan, much, much fonder of Miss Milan than of any one in the whole world, and could have cried for pity that she should be crawling on the floor with her mouth full of pins, and her face red and her eyes bulging—that one human being should be doing this for another, and she saw them all as human beings merely, and herself going off to her party, and Miss Milan pulling the cover over the canary's cage, or letting him pick a hemp-seed from between her lips, and the thought of it, of this side of human nature and its patience and its endurance and its being content with such miserable, scanty, sordid, little pleasures filled her eyes with tears.

And now the whole thing had vanished. The dress, the room, the love, the pity, the scrolloping looking-glass, and the canary's cage—all had vanished, and here she was in a corner of Mrs. Dalloway's drawing-room, suffering tortures, woken wide awake to reality.

But it was all so paltry, weak-blooded, and petty-minded to care so much at her age with two children, to be still so utterly dependent on people's opinions and not have principles or convictions, not to be able to say as other people did, "There's Shakespeare! There's death! We're all weevils in a captain's biscuit"—or whatever it was that people did say.

She faced herself straight in the glass; she pecked at her left shoulder; she issued out into the room, as if spears were thrown at her yellow dress from all sides. But instead of looking fierce or tragic, as Rose Shaw would have done—Rose would have looked like Boadicea—she looked foolish and self-conscious, and simpered like a schoolgirl and slouched across the room, positively slinking, as if she were a beaten mongrel, and looked at a picture, an engraving. As if one went to a party to look at a picture! Everybody knew why she did it—it was from shame, from humiliation.

"Now the fly's in the saucer," she said to herself, "right in the middle, and can't get out, and the milk," she thought, rigidly staring at the picture, "is sticking its wings together."

"It's so old-fashioned," she said to Charles Burt, making him stop (which by itself he hated) on his way to talk to some one else. She meant, or she tried to make herself think that she meant, that it was the picture and not her dress, that was old-fashioned. And one word of praise, one word of affection from Charles would have made all the difference to her at the moment. If he had only said, "Mabel, you're looking charming to-night!" it would have changed her life. But then she ought to have been truthful and direct. Charles said nothing of the kind, of course. He was malice itself. He always saw through one, especially if one were feeling particularly mean, paltry, or feeble-minded.

"Mabel's got a new dress!" he said, and the poor fly was absolutely shoved into the middle of the saucer. Really, he would like her to drown, she believed. He had no heart, no fundamental kindness, only a veneer of friendliness. Miss Milan was much more real, much kinder. If only one could feel that and stick to it, always. "Why," she asked herself—replying to Charles much too pertly, letting him see that she was out of temper, or "ruffled" as he called it ("Rather ruffled?" he said and went on to laugh at her with some woman over there)—"Why," she asked herself, "can't I feel one thing always, feel quite sure that Miss Milan is right, and Charles wrong and stick to it, feel sure about the canary and pity and love and not be whipped all round in a second by coming into a room full of people?" It was her odious, weak, vacillating character again, always giving at the critical moment and not being seriously interested in conchology, etymology, botany, archeology, cutting up potatoes and watching them fructify like Mary Dennis, like Violet Searle.

Then Mrs. Holman, seeing her standing there, bore down upon her. Of course a thing like a dress was beneath Mrs. Holman's notice, with her family always tumbling downstairs or having the scarlet fever. Could Mabel tell her if Elmthorpe was ever let for August and September? Oh, it was a conversation that bored her unutterably!—it made her furious to be treated like a house agent or a messenger boy, to be made use of. Not to have value, that was it, she thought, trying to grasp something hard, something real, while she tried to answer sensibly about the bathroom and the south aspect and the hot water to the top of the house; and all the time she could see little bits of her yellow dress in the round looking-glass which made them all the size of boot-buttons or tadpoles; and it was amazing to think how much humiliation and agony and self-loathing and effort and passionate ups and downs of feeling were contained in a thing the size of a threepenny bit. And what was still odder, this thing, this Mabel Waring, was separate, quite disconnected; and

though Mrs. Holman (the black button) was leaning forward and
telling her how her eldest boy had strained his heart running, she
could see her, too, quite detached in the looking-glass, and it was
impossible that the black dot, leaning forward, gesticulating, should
make the yellow dot, sitting solitary, self-centred, feel what the black
dot was feeling, yet they pretended.

"So impossible to keep boys quiet"—that was the kind of thing
one said.

And Mrs. Holman, who could never get enough sympathy and
snatched what little there was greedily, as if it were her right (but
she deserved much more for there was her little girl who had come
down this morning with a swollen knee-joint), took this miserable
offering and looked at it suspiciously, grudgingly, as if it were a half-
penny when it ought to have been a pound and put it away in her
purse, must put up with it, mean and miserly though it was, times
being hard, so very hard; and on she went, creaking, injured Mrs.
Holman, about the girl with the swollen joints. Ah, it was tragic,
this greed, this clamour of human beings, like a row of cormorants,
barking and flapping their wings for sympathy—it was tragic, could
one have felt it and not merely pretended to feel it!

But in her yellow dress to-night she could not wring out one drop
more; she wanted it all, all for herself. She knew (she kept on looking into the glass, dipping into that dreadfully showing-up blue pool)
that she was condemned, despised, left like this in a backwater, because of her being like this a feeble, vacillating creature; and it seemed
to her that the yellow dress was a penance which she had deserved,
and if she had been dressed like Rose Shaw, in lovely, clinging green
with a ruffle of swansdown, she would have deserved that; and she
thought that there was no escape for her—none whatever. But it was
not her fault altogether, after all. It was being one of a family of
ten; never having money enough, always skimping and paring; and
her mother carrying great cans, and the linoleum worn on the stair
edges, and one sordid little domestic tragedy after another—nothing
catastrophic, the sheep farm failing, but not utterly; her eldest
brother marrying beneath him but not very much—there was no romance, nothing extreme about them all. They petered out respectably
in seaside resorts; every watering-place had one of her aunts even
now asleep in some lodging with the front windows not quite facing
the sea. That was so like them—they had to squint at things always.
And she had done the same—she was just like her aunts. For all her

dreams of living in India, married to some hero like Sir Henry Lawrence, some empire builder (still the sight of a native in a turban filled her with romance), she had failed utterly. She had married Hubert, with his safe, permanent underling's job in the Law Courts, and they managed tolerably in a smallish house, without proper maids, and hash when she was alone or just bread and butter, but now and then—Mrs. Holman was off, thinking her the most dried-up, unsympathetic twig she had ever met, absurdly dressed, too, and would tell every one about Mabel's fantastic appearance—now and then, thought Mabel Waring, left alone on the blue sofa, punching the cushion in order to look occupied, for she would not join Charles Burt and Rose Shaw, chattering like magpies and perhaps laughing at her by the fireplace—now and then, there did come to her delicious moments, reading the other night in bed, for instance, or down by the sea on the sand in the sun, at Easter—let her recall it—a great tuft of pale sand-grass standing all twisted like a shock of spears against the sky, which was blue like a smooth china egg, so firm, so hard, and then the melody of the waves—"Hush, hush," they said, and the children's shouts paddling—yes, it was a divine moment, and there she lay, she felt, in the hand of the Goddess who was the world; rather a hard-hearted, but very beautiful Goddess, a little lamb laid on the altar (one did think these silly things, and it didn't matter so long as one never said them). And also with Hubert sometimes she had quite unexpectedly—carving the mutton for Sunday lunch, for no reason, opening a letter, coming into a room—divine moments, when she said to herself (for she would never say this to anybody else), "This is it. This has happened. This is it!" And the other way about it was equally surprising—that is, when everything was arranged—music, weather, holidays, every reason for happiness was there—then nothing happened at all. One wasn't happy. It was flat, just flat, that was all.

Her wretched self again, no doubt! She had always been a fretful, weak, unsatisfactory mother, a wobbly wife, lolling about in a kind of twilight existence with nothing very clear or very bold, or more one thing than another, like all her brothers and sisters, except perhaps Herbert—they were all the same poor water-veined creatures who did nothing. Then in the midst of this creeping, crawling life, suddenly she was on the crest of a wave. That wretched fly—where had she read the story that kept coming into her mind about the fly and the saucer?—struggled out. Yes, she had those moments. But now that she was forty, they might come more and more seldom. By degrees she would cease to struggle any more. But that was deplorable! That was not to be endured! That made her feel ashamed of herself!

She would go to the London Library to-morrow. She would find some wonderful, helpful, astonishing book, quite by chance, a book by a clergyman, by an American no one had ever heard of; or she would walk down the Strand and drop, accidentally, into a hall where a miner was telling about the life in the pit, and suddenly she would become a new person. She would be absolutely transformed. She would wear a uniform; she would be called Sister Somebody; she would never give a thought to clothes again. And for ever after she would be perfectly clear about Charles Burt and Miss Milan and this room and that room; and it would be always, day after day, as if she were lying in the sun or carving the mutton. It would be it!

So she got up from the blue sofa, and the yellow button in the looking-glass got up too, and she waved her hand to Charles and Rose to show them she did not depend on them one scrap, and the yellow button moved out of the looking-glass, and all the spears were gathered into her breast as she walked towards Mrs. Dalloway and said, "Good night."

"But it's too early to go," said Mrs. Dalloway, who was always so charming.

"I'm afraid I must," said Mabel Waring. "But," she added in her weak, wobbly voice which only sounded ridiculous when she tried to strengthen it, "I have enjoyed myself enormously."

"I have enjoyed myself," she said to Mr. Dalloway, whom she met on the stairs.

"Lies, lies, lies!" she said to herself, going downstairs, and "Right in the saucer!" she said to herself as she thanked Mrs. Barnet for helping her and wrapped herself, round and round and round, in the Chinese cloak she had worn these twenty years.

For Discussion:

1. How does the author help you to know Mabel's past? What hints are given about her family? How do these affect the problem presented in the story?
2. What was Mabel's reason for choosing this particular style of dress? Is it, as she claims, "idiotically old-fashioned"? If not, why do those who meet her act as if it were? Or do they?

3. Mabel is characterized chiefly by her thoughts and actions. What exactly are her character traits? What forces motivate her actions?
4. From whose point of view is the story told? Does this perspective provide you with a true picture of life as represented in Mrs. Dalloway's drawing room? Do all the incidents related by Mabel really occur? If not, which episodes are real, which are not?
5. Is Mabel, a "social-climber," snubbed by her acquaintances, or is she accepted by the group in which she moves? Are the guests aware of Mabel's feelings or are they unfeeling people?
6. What is your reaction to each of the following statements of Mabel:
   (a) "We are all like flies trying to crawl over the saucer."
   (b) "Lies, lies, lies!"
   (c) ". . . a party makes things much more real or much less real."
7. While reading the story you have probably felt as ill at ease and embarrassed as Mabel; it is with relief you accompany her to the cloakroom. How do you account for her change of feeling as she prepares to go home? Is there any significance that on leaving she wraps herself "round and round, in the Chinese cloak she had worn these twenty years"?
8. State the theme of this story in your own words and cite sentences or passages which express this idea.

For Composition

1. Doubtless you have had occasion to feel inadequate to a situation in which you found yourself. In a short narrative, describe such a situation and your feelings at that time.
2. Imagine you are one of the men or women who attended Mrs. Dalloway's party. Write an entry in your diary after returning home, describing your reaction to Mabel and what you thought of her.

The Verger*

W. SOMERSET MAUGHAM

William Somerset Maugham (1874–   ), one of the most accomplished prose writers of the twentieth century, is also one of the most productive. He has written 40 novels, many collections of short stories, books of literary criticism, a travel book, an autobiography, and some 20 plays. Though his novel *Of Human Bondage* won him fame, he prefers to be known as a storyteller rather than as a novelist.

Critics are divided in their opinion of his work. Some hail him as a great writer of modern fiction, and a brilliant creator of stories with a polished classical style; others see him merely as a clever and extremely competent craftsman.

Maugham stands clear of the argument and enunciates his own "Credo of a Storyteller." He believes the best kind of story is one that "relates an unusual incident. The scene is set . . . briefly and clearly . . . with just the detail needed to make facts plain. You are told only what you need to know about the characters involved."

Maugham's frequent travels throughout the world have furnished him with the materials for many of his tales, often set in an exotic background. A keen observer of human nature, he has a flair for collecting dramatic and original types caught in a web of their own making. Often his view of life is cynical, and his characters are not the most admirable, but just as often he presents these people with humor and power.

———◆———

There had been a christening that afternoon at St. Peter's, Neville Square, and Albert Edward Foreman still wore his verger's gown. He kept his new one, its folds as full and stiff as though it were made not of alpaca but of perennial bronze, for funerals and weddings (St. Peter's, Neville Square, was a church much favored by the fashionable for these ceremonies), and now he wore only his second best. He wore it with complacence; for it was the dignified symbol of his office, and without it (when he took it off to go home) he had the disconcerting sensation of being somewhat insufficiently clad. He took pains with it; he pressed it and ironed it himself. During the sixteen years he had been verger of this church he had had a succession of such gowns; but he had never been able to throw them away when

verger: a person who takes care of the interior of a church

168

they were worn out, and the complete series, neatly wrapped up in brown paper, lay in the bottom drawer of the wardrobe in his bed-room.

The verger busied himself quietly, replacing the painted wooden cover on the marble font, taking away a chair that had been brought for an infirm old lady, and waited for the vicar to have finished in the vestry so that he could tidy up in there and go home. Presently he saw him walk across the chancel, genuflect in front of the high altar, and come down the aisle; but he still wore his cassock.

"What's he 'anging about for?" the verger said to himself. "Don't 'e know I want my tea?"

The vicar had been but recently appointed, a red-faced, energetic man in his early forties, and Albert Edward still regretted his prede-cessor, a clergyman of the old school who preached leisurely sermons in a silvery voice and dined out a great deal with his more aristocratic parishioners. He liked things in church to be just so, but he never fussed; he was not like this new man who wanted to have his finger in every pie. But Albert Edward was tolerant. St. Peter's was in a very good neighborhood and the parishioners were a very nice class of people. The new vicar had come from the East End, and he couldn't be expected to fall in all at once with the discreet ways of his fashion-able congregation.

"All this 'ustle," said Albert Edward. "But give 'im time; he'll learn."

When the vicar had walked down the aisle so far that he could address the verger without raising his voice more than was becoming in a place of worship, he stopped.

"Foreman, will you come into the vestry for a minute? I have something to say to you."

"Very good, sir."

The vicar waited for him to come up and they walked up the church together.

"A very nice christening, I thought, sir. Funny 'ow the baby stopped cryin' the moment you took him."

"I've noticed they very often do," said the vicar, with a little smile. "After all, I've had a good deal of practice with them."

It was a source of subdued pride to him that he could nearly al-ways quiet a whimpering infant by the manner in which he held it, and he was not unconscious of the amused admiration with which mothers and nurses watched him settle the baby in the crook of his surpliced arm. The verger knew that it pleased him to be complimented on his talent.

The vicar preceded Albert Edward into the vestry. Albert Edward was a trifle surprised to find the two churchwardens there. He had not seen them come in. They gave him pleasant nods.

"Good afternoon, my lord. Good afternoon, sir," he said to one after the other.

They were elderly men, both of them, and they had been churchwardens almost as long as Albert Edward had been verger. They were sitting now at a handsome refectory table that the old vicar had brought many years before from Italy, and the vicar sat down in the vacant chair between them. Albert Edward faced them, the table between him and them, and wondered with slight uneasiness what was the matter. He remembered still the occasion on which the organist had got into trouble and the bother they had had to hush things up. In a church like St. Peter's, Neville Square, they couldn't afford a scandal. On the vicar's red face was a look of resolute benignity, but the others bore an expression that was slightly troubled.

"He's been naggin' them, he 'as," said the verger to himself. "He's jockeyed them into doin' something, but they don't 'alf like it. That's what it is; you mark my words."

But his thoughts did not appear on Albert Edward's clean-cut and distinguished features. He stood in a respectful but not obsequious attitude. He had been in service before he was appointed to his ecclesiastical office, but only in very good houses, and his deportment was irreproachable. Starting as a page boy in the household of a merchant prince, he had risen by due degrees from the position of fourth to first footman; for a year he had been singlehanded butler to a widowed peeress and, till the vacancy occurred at St. Peter's, butler with two men under him in the house of a retired ambassador. He was tall, spare, grave, and dignified. He looked, if not like a duke, at least like an actor of the old school who specialized in dukes' parts. He had tact, firmness, and self-assurance. His character was unimpeachable.

The vicar began briskly.

"Foreman, we've got something rather unpleasant to say to you. You've been here a great many years, and I think his lordship and the general agree with me that you've fulfilled the duties of your office to the satisfaction of everybody concerned."

The two churchwardens nodded.

"But a most extraordinary circumstance came to my knowledge the other day and I felt it my duty to impart it to the churchwardens. I discovered to my astonishment that you could neither read nor write."

The verger's face betrayed no sign of embarrassment.

"The last vicar knew that, sir," he replied. "He said it didn't make no difference. He always said there was a great deal too much education in the world for 'is taste."

"It's the most amazing thing I ever heard," cried the general. "Do you mean to say that you've been verger of this church for sixteen years and never learned to read or write?"

"I went into service when I was twelve, sir. The cook in the first place tried to teach me once; but I didn't seem to 'ave the knack for it, and then what with one thing and another I never seemed to 'ave the time. I've never really found the want of it. I think a lot of these young fellows waste a lot of time readin' when they might be doin' something useful."

"But don't you want to know the news?" said the other churchwarden. "Don't you ever want to write a letter?"

"No, me lord, I seem to manage very well without. And of late years, now they've all these pictures in the papers, I get to know what's goin' on pretty well. Me wife's quite a scholar, and if I want to write a letter she writes it for me. It's not as if I was a bettin' man."

The two churchwardens gave the vicar a troubled glance and then looked down at the table.

"Well, Foreman, I've talked the matter over with these gentlemen and they quite agree with me that the situation is impossible. At a church like St. Peter's, Neville Square, we cannot have a verger who can neither read nor write."

Albert Edward's thin, sallow face reddened and he moved uneasily on his feet, but he made no reply.

"Understand me, Foreman, I have no complaint to make against you. You do your work quite satisfactorily. I have the highest opinion both of your character and of your capacity, but we haven't the right to take the risk of some accident that might happen owing to your lamentable ignorance. It's a matter of prudence as well as of principle."

"But couldn't you learn, Foreman?" asked the general.

"No, sir, I'm afraid I couldn't—not now. You see, I'm not as young as I was, and, if I couldn't seem able to get the letters in me 'ead when I was a nipper, I don't think there's much chance of it now."

"We don't want to be harsh with you, Foreman," said the vicar. "But the churchwardens and I have quite made up our minds. We'll give you three months, and if at the end of that time you cannot read and write I'm afraid you'll have to go."

Albert Edward had never liked the new vicar. He'd said from the beginning that they'd made a mistake when they gave him St. Peter's. He wasn't the type of man they wanted with a classy congregation like that. And now he straightened himself a little. He knew his value and he wasn't going to allow himself to be put upon.

"I'm very sorry, sir; I'm afraid it's no good. I'm too old a dog to learn new tricks. I've lived a good many years without knowin' 'ow to read and write, and without wishin' to praise myself—self-praise is no recommendation—I don't mind sayin' I've done my duty in that state of life in which it 'as pleased a merciful providence to place me, and if I *could* learn now I don't know as I'd want to."

"In that case, Foreman, I'm afraid you must go."

"Yes, sir, I quite understand. I shall be 'appy to 'and in my resignation as soon as you've found somebody to take my place."

But when Albert Edward, with his usual politeness, had closed the church door behind the vicar and the two churchwardens, he could not sustain the air of unruffled dignity with which he had borne the blow inflicted upon him, and his lips quivered. He walked slowly back to the vestry and hung up on its proper peg his verger's gown. He sighed as he thought of all the grand funerals and smart weddings it had seen. He tidied everything up, put on his coat, and hat in hand walked down the aisle. He locked the church door behind him. He strolled across the square; but, deep in his sad thoughts, he did not take the street that led him home, where a nice strong cup of tea awaited him—he took the wrong turning.

He walked slowly along. His heart was heavy. He did not know what he should do with himself. He did not fancy the notion of going back to domestic service; after being his own master for so many years—for the vicar and churchwardens could say what they liked; it was he that had run St. Peter's, Neville Square—he could scarcely demean himself by accepting a situation. He had saved a tidy sum, but not enough to live on without doing something; and life seemed to cost more every year. He had never thought to be troubled with such questions. The vergers of St. Peter's, like the popes of Rome, were there for life. He had often thought of the pleasant reference the vicar would make, in his sermon at evensong the first Sunday after his death, to the long and faithful service and the exemplary character of their late verger Albert Edward Foreman.

He sighed deeply. Albert Edward was a nonsmoker and a total abstainer, but with a certain latitude; that is to say, he liked a glass of beer with his dinner and when he was tired he enjoyed a cigarette. It occurred to him now that one would comfort him and, since he did not carry them, he looked about him for a shop where he could buy a packet of Gold Flakes. He did not at once see one and walked on a little. It was a long street, with all sorts of shops in it; but there was not a single one where you could buy cigarettes.

"That's strange," said Albert Edward.

To make sure, he walked right up the street again. No, there was no doubt about it. He stopped and looked reflectively up and down.

"I can't be the only man as walks along this street and wants a fag," he said. "I shouldn't wonder but what a fellow might do very well with a little shop here. Tobacco and sweets, you know."

He gave a sudden start.

"That's an idea," he said. "Strange 'ow things come to you when you least expect it."

He turned, walked home, and had his tea.

"You're very silent this afternoon, Albert," his wife remarked.

"I'm thinkin'," he said.

He considered the matter from every point of view, and next day he went along the street and by good luck found a little shop to let that looked as though it would exactly suit him. Twenty-four hours later he had taken it and, when a month after that he left St. Peter's, Neville Square, forever, Albert Edward Foreman set up in business as a tobacconist and newsagent. His wife said it was a dreadful comedown after being verger of St. Peter's; but he answered that you had to move with the times, the church wasn't what it was, and 'enceforward he was going to render unto Caesar what was Caesar's. Albert Edward did very well. He did so well that in a year or so it struck him that he might take a second shop and put a manager in. He looked for another long street that hadn't got a tobacconist in it and when he found it, and a shop to let, took it and stocked it. This was a success too. Then it occurred to him that if he could run two he could run half a dozen; so he began walking about London, and whenever he found a long street that had no tobacconist, and a shop to let, he took it. In the course of ten years he had acquired no less than ten shops and he was making money hand over fist. He went round to all of them himself every Monday, collected the week's takings and took them to the bank.

One morning when he was there, paying in a bundle of notes and a heavy bag of silver, the cashier told him that the manager would like to see him. He was shown into an office and the manager shook hands with him.

"Mr. Foreman, I wanted to have a talk to you about the money you've got on deposit with us. D'you know exactly how much it is?"

"Not within a pound or two, sir; but I've got a pretty rough idea."

"Apart from what you paid in this morning, it's a little over thirty thousand pounds. That's a very large sum to have on deposit and I should have thought you'd do better to invest it."

"I wouldn't want to take no risk, sir. I know it's safe in the bank."

"You needn't have the least anxiety. We'll make you out a list of absolutely gilt-edged securities. They'll bring you in a better rate of interest than we can possibly afford to give you."

A troubled look settled on Mr. Foreman's distinguished face.

"I've never 'ad anything to do with stocks and shares and I'd 'ave to leave it all in your 'ands," he said.

The manager smiled.

"We'll do everything. All you'll have to do next time you come in is just to sign the transfers."

"I could do that all right," said Albert uncertainly. "But 'ow should I know what I was signin'?"

"I suppose you can read," said the manager a trifle sharply.

Mr. Foreman gave him a disarming smile.

"Well, sir, that's just it. I can't. I know it sounds funny like, but there it is! I can't read or write—only me name, an' I only learned to do that when I went into business."

The manager was so surprised that he jumped up from his chair.

"That's the most extraordinary thing I ever heard."

"You see, it's like this, sir—I never 'ad the opportunity until it was too late, and then some'ow I wouldn't. I got obstinate like."

The manager stared at him as though he were a prehistoric monster.

"And do you mean to say that you've built up this important business and amassed a fortune of thirty thousand pounds without being able to read or write? Good God, man, what would you be now if you had been able to?"

"I can tell you that, sir," said Mr. Foreman, a little smile on his still aristocratic features. "I'd be verger of St. Peter's, Neville Square."

For Discussion:

1. What is the conflict in this story? How does the resolution of the conflict shed new light on your sense of values?
2. Account for the ability of the verger to please the former vicar and his inability to please the present one. Do you believe it is really the verger's illiteracy that costs him his position? Explain your answer.
3. How important is setting to the total impact of the story? What is the importance of characterization?
4. How would you characterize the verger? Point out specific passages to support your opinion. What one statement seems to sum up his character?
5. Look up the definition of the word *irony* in the dictionary. How does this story fit the definition?

For Composition: Write a short theme on the influence of environment and family traditions on a man's choice of a life occupation.

A Queer Heart

ELIZABETH BOWEN

Elizabeth Bowen (1899–   ) writes with the sensitivity of Katherine Mansfield and the psychological insight of Virginia Woolf. Still, she is the master of a style uniquely her own.

Possessed of an unusually vivid awareness of the visible world, Miss Bowen often makes her settings as important as her characters. In fact, setting at times seem to *be* character. She blends light and shade, spirit and matter with the technique of an impressionistic landscape painter.

Preoccupied as she is with the relationship between an individual and his environment, and the impact of one character on another in that environment, she gives little attention to plot. It evolves only as tensions mount within a character facing the challenge of his daily living.

Elizabeth Bowen is very much alive to the small unimportant details cluttering the surface of life over which her characters skim. She considers these impediments carefully, while aware of deeper forces working in the people. This is to be seen with particular impact in her story "The Queer Heart."

———◆———

Mrs. Cadman got out of the bus backwards. No amount of practice ever made her more agile; the trouble she had with her big bulk amused everyone, and herself. Gripping the handles each side of the bus door so tightly that the seams of her gloves cracked, she lowered herself cautiously, like a climber, while her feet, overlapping her smart shoes, uneasily scrabbled at each step. One or two people asked why the bus made, for one passenger, such a long, dead stop. But on the whole she was famous on this line, for she was constantly in and out of town. The conductor waited behind her, smiling, holding her basket, arms wide to catch her if she should slip.

Having got safe to the ground, Mrs. Cadman shook herself like a satisfied bird. She took back her shopping basket from the conductor and gave him a smile instead. The big kind scarlet bus once more ground into movement, off up the main road hill: it made a fading blur in the premature autumn dusk. Mrs. Cadman almost waved after it, for with it went the happy part of her day. She turned down the side road that led to her gate.

A wet wind of autumn, smelling of sodden gardens, blew in her face and tilted her hat. Leaves whirled along it, and one lime leaf, as though imploring shelter, lodged in her fur collar. Every gust did more to sadden the poor trees. This was one of those roads outside growing provincial cities that still keep their rural mystery. They seem to lead into something still not known. Traffic roars past one end, but the other end is in silence: you see a wood, a spire, a haughty manor gate, or your view ends with the turn of an old wall. Here some new raw-looking villas stood with spaces between them; in the spaces were orchards and market-gardens. A glasshouse roof reflected the wet grey light; there was a shut chapel farther along. And, each standing back in half an acre of ground, there were two or three stucco houses with dark windows, sombre but at the same time ornate, built years ago in this then retired spot. Dead lime leaves showered over their grass plots and evergreens. Mrs. Cadman's house, Granville, was one of these: its name was engraved in scrolls over the porch. The solid house was not large, and Mrs. Cadman's daughter, Lucille, could look after it with a daily help.

The widow and her daughter lived here in the state of cheerless meekness Lucille considered suitable for them now. *Mr.* Cadman had liked to have everything done in style. But twelve years ago he had died, travelling on business, in an hotel up in the North. Always the gentleman, he had been glad to spare them this upset at home. He had been brought back to the Midlands for his impressive funeral, whose size showed him a popular man. How unlike Mr. Cadman was Rosa proving herself. One can be most unfriendly on one's way of dying. Ah, well, one chooses one's husband; one's sister is dealt out to one by fate.

Mrs. Cadman, thumb on the latch of her own gate, looked for a minute longer up and down the road—deeply, deeply unwilling to go in. She looked back at the corner where the bus had vanished, and an immense sigh heaved up her coat lapels and made a cotton carnation, pinned to the fur, brush a fold of her chin. Laced, hooked, buttoned so tightly into her clothes, she seemed to need to deflate herself by these sudden sighs, by yawns or by those explosions of laughter that often vexed Lucille. Through her face—embedded in fat but still very lively, as exposed, as ingenuous as a little girl's—you could see some emotional fermentation always at work in her. Her smiles were frequent, hopeful and quick. Her pitching walk was due to her tight shoes.

When she did go in, she went in with a sort of rush. She let the door bang back on the hall wall, so that the chain rattled and an outraged clatter came from the letter-box. Immediately she knew she had done wrong. Lucille, appalled, looked out of the dining-room. "*Shisssssh!* How can you, mother!" she said.

"Ever so sorry, dear," said Mrs. Cadman, cast down.

"She'd just dropped off," said Lucille. "After her bad night and everything. It really does seem hard."

Mrs. Cadman quite saw that it did. She glanced nervously up the stairs, then edged into the dining-room. It was not cheerful in here: a monkey puzzle, too close to the window, drank the last of the light up; the room still smelt of dinner; the fire smouldered resentfully, starved for coal. The big mahogany furniture lowered, with no shine. Mrs. Cadman, putting her basket down on the table, sent an uncertain smile across at Lucille, whose glasses blankly gleamed high up on her long face. She often asked herself where Lucille could have come from. *Could* this be the baby daughter she had borne, and tied pink bows on, and christened a pretty name? In the sun in this very bow window she had gurgled into the sweet-smelling creases of Lucille's neck—one summer lost in time.

"You *have* been an age," Lucille said.

"Well, the shops were quite busy. I never *saw*," she said with irrepressible pleasure, "I never *saw* so many people in town!"

Lucille, lips tighter than ever shut, was routing about, unpacking the shopping basket, handling the packages. Chemist's and grocer's parcels. Mrs. Cadman watched her with apprehension. Then Lucille pounced; she held up a small soft parcel in frivolous wrappings. "Oho," she said. "So you've been in at Babbington's?"

"Well, I missed one bus, so I had to wait for the next. So I just popped in there a minute out of the cold. And, you see, I've been wanting a little scarf——"

"Little scarf!" said Lucille. "I don't know what to make of you, mother. I don't really. How *could* you, at such a time? How you ever could have the heart!" Lucille, standing the other side of the table, leaned across it, her thin weight on her knuckles. This brought her face near her mother's. "Can't you understand?" she said. "Can't you take *anything* in? The next little scarf *you'll* need to buy will be black!"

"What a thing to say!" exclaimed Mrs. Cadman, profoundly offended. "With that poor thing upstairs now, waiting to have her tea."

"Tea? She can't take her tea. Why, since this morning she can't keep a thing down."

Mrs. Cadman blenched and began unbuttoning her coat. Lucille seemed to feel that her own prestige and Aunt Rosa's entirely hung on Aunt Rosa's approaching death. You could feel that she and her aunt had thought up this plan together. These last days had been the climax of their complicity. And there was Mrs. Cadman—as ever, as usual—put in the wrong, frowned upon, out of things. Whenever Rosa arrived to stay Mrs. Cadman had no fun in her home, and now Rosa was leaving for ever it seemed worse. A perverse kick of the heart, a flicker of naughtiness, made Mrs. Cadman say: "Oh, well, while there's life there's hope."

Lucille said: "If you won't face it, you won't. But I just say it does fall heavy on me. . . . We had the vicar round here this afternoon. He was up with Aunt for a bit, then he looked in and said he did feel I needed a prayer too. He said he thought I was wonderful. He asked where you were, and he seemed to wonder you find the heart to stay out so long. I thought from his manner he wondered a good deal."

Mrs. Cadman, with an irrepressible titter, said: "Give him something to think about! Why if I'd ha' shown up that vicar'd have popped out as fast as he popped in. Thinks I'd make a mouthful of him. Why, I've made him bolt down the street. Well, well. He's not *my* idea of a vicar. When your father and I first came here we had a rural dean. Oh, he was as pleasant as anything."

Lucille, with the air of praying for Christian patience, folded her lips. Jabbing her fingers down the inside of her waistbelt, she more tightly tucked in her tight blouse. She liked looking like Mrs. Noah —no, *Miss* Noah. "The doctor's not been again. We're to let him know of any change."

"Well, let's do the best we can," said Mrs. Cadman. "But don't keep on *talking*. You don't make things any better, keeping on going on. My opinion is one should keep bright to the last. When my time comes, oh, I would like a cheery face."

"It's well for you . . ." began Lucille. She bit the remark off and, gathering up the parcels, stalked scornfully out of the dining-room. Without comment she left exposed on the table a small carton of goodies Mrs. Cadman had bought to cheer herself up with and had concealed in the toe of the shopping bag. Soon, from the kitchen came the carefully muffled noises of Lucille putting away provisions and tearing the wrappings off the chemist's things. Mrs. Cadman, reaching out for the carton, put a peppermint into each cheek. She, oh so badly, wanted a cup of tea but dared not follow Lucille into the kitchen in order to put the kettle on.

Though, after all, Granville *was* her house. . . .

You would not think it was her house—not when Rosa was there. While Lucille and her mother were *tête à tête* Lucille's disapproval was at least fairly tacit. But as soon as Rosa arrived on one of these yearly autumn visits—always choosing the season when Mrs. Cadman felt in her least good form, the fall of the leaf—the aunt and niece got together and found everything wrong. Their two cold natures ran together. They found Mrs. Cadman lacking; they forbade the affection she would have offered them. They censured her the whole time. Mrs. Cadman could date her real alienation from Lucille from the year when Rosa's visits began. During Mr. Cadman's lifetime Rosa had never come for more than an afternoon. Mr. Cadman had been his wife's defence from her sister—a great red kind of rumbustious fortification. He had been a man who kept every chill wind out. Rosa, during those stilted afternoon visits, had adequately succeeded in conveying that she found marriage *low*. She might just have suffered a pious marriage; she openly deprecated this high living, this state of fleshly bliss. In order not to witness it too closely she lived on in lodgings in her native town. . . . But once widowhood left her sister exposed, Rosa started flapping round Granville like a doomful bird. She instituted these yearly visits, which, she made plain at the same time, gave her not much pleasure. The journey was tedious, and by breaking her habits, leaving her lodgings, Rosa was, out of duty, putting herself about. Her joyless and intimidating visits had, therefore, only one object—to protect the interests of Lucille.

Mrs. Cadman had suspected for some time that Rosa had something the matter with her. No one looks as yellow as that for nothing. But she was not sufficiently intimate with her sister to get down to the cosy subject of insides. This time, Rosa arrived looking worse than ever, and three days afterwards had collapsed. Lucille said now she had known her aunt was poorly. Lucille said now she had always known. "But of course you wouldn't notice, mother," she said.

Mrs. Cadman sat down by the fire and, gratefully, kicked off her tight shoes. In the warmth her plump feet uncurled, relaxed, expanded like sea-anemones. She stretched her legs out, propped her heels on the fender and wiggled her toes voluptuously. They went on wiggling of their own accord: they seemed to have an independent existence. Here, in her home, where she felt so "put wrong" and chilly, they were like ten stout confidential friends. She said, out loud: "Well, *I* don't know what I've done."

The fact was: Lucille and Rosa resented her. (She'd feel better when she had had her tea.) She should *not* have talked as she had about the vicar. But it seemed so silly, Lucille having just him. She did wish Lucille had a better time. No young man so much as paused at the gate. Lucille's aunt had wrapped her own dank virginity round her like someone sharing a mackintosh.

Mrs. Cadman had had a good time. A real good time always lasts: you have it with all your nature and all your nature stays living with it. She had been a pretty child with long, blonde hair that her sister Rosa, who was her elder sister, used to tweak when they were alone in their room. She had grown used, in that childish attic bedroom, to Rosa's malevolent silences. Then one had grown up, full of great uppish curves. Hilda Cadman could sing. She had sung at parties and sung at charity concerts, too. She had been invited from town to town, much fêted in business society. She had sung in a dress cut low at the bosom, with a rose or carnation tucked into her hair. She had drunk port wine in great red rooms blazing with chandeliers. Mr. Cadman had whisked her away from her other gentlemen friends, and not for a moment had she regretted it. Nothing had been too good for her: she had gone on singing. She had felt warm air on her bare shoulders; she still saw the kind, flushed faces crowding round. Mr. Cadman and she belonged to the jolly set. They all thought the world of her, and she thought the world of them.

Mrs. Cadman, picking up the poker, jabbed the fire into a spurt of light. It does not do any good to sit and think in the dark.

The town was not the same now. They had all died, or lost their money, or gone. But you kept on loving the town for its dear old sake. She sometimes thought: Why not move and live at the seaside, where there would be a promenade and a band? But she knew her nature clung to the old scenes; where you had lived, you lived—your nature clung like a cat. While there was *something* to look at she was not one to repine. It kept you going to keep out and about. Things went, but then new things came in their place. You can't cure yourself of the habit of loving life. So she drank up the new pleasures—the big cafés, the barging buses, the cinemas, the shops dripping with colour, almost all built of glass. She could be perfectly happy all alone in a café, digging into a cream bun with a fork, the band playing, smiling faces all round. The old faces had not gone: they had dissolved, diluted into the ruddy blur through which she saw everything.

Meanwhile, Lucille was hard put to it, living her mother down. Mother looked ridiculous, always round town like that.

Mrs. Cadman heard Lucille come out of the kitchen and go upstairs with something rattling on a tray. She waited a minute more, then sidled into the kitchen, where she cautiously started to make tea. The gas-ring, as though it were a spy of Lucille's, popped loudly when she applied the match.

"Mother, she's asking for you."

"Oh, dear—do you mean she's——?"

"She's much more herself this evening," Lucille said implacably.

Mrs. Cadman, at the kitchen table, had been stirring sugar into her third cup. She pushed her chair back, brushed crumbs from her bosom and followed Lucille like a big unhappy lamb. The light was on in the hall, but the stairs led up into shadow: she had one more start of reluctance at their foot. Autumn draughts ran about in the top story: up there the powers of darkness all seemed to mobilize. Mrs. Cadman put her hand on the banister knob. "Are you sure she *does* want to see me? Oughtn't she to stay quiet?"

"You should go when she's asking. You never know. . . ."

Breathless, breathing unevenly on the top landing, Mrs. Cadman pushed open the spare-room—that was the sick-room—door. In there —in here—the air was dead, and at first it seemed very dark. On the ceiling an oil-stove printed its flower-pattern; a hooded lamp, low down, was turned away from the bed. On that dark side of the lamp she could just distinguish Rosa, propped up, with the sheet drawn to her chin.

"Rosa?"

"Oh, it's you?"

"Yes; it's me, dear. Feeling better this evening?"

"Seemed funny, you not coming near me."

"They said for you to keep quiet."

"My own sister. . . . You never liked sickness, did you? Well, I'm going. I shan't trouble you long."

"Oh, don't talk like that!"

"I'm glad to be going. Keeping on lying here. . . . We all come to it. Oh, give over crying, Hilda. Doesn't do any good."

Mrs. Cadman sat down, to steady herself. She fumbled in her lap with her handkerchief, perpetually, clumsily knocking her elbows against the arms of the wicker chair. "It's such a shame," she said. "It's such a pity. You and me, after all . . ."

"Well, it's late for all that now. Each took our own ways." Rosa's voice went up in a sort of ghostly sharpness. "There were things that couldn't be otherwise. I've tried to do right by Lucille. Lucille's a good girl, Hilda. You should ask yourself if you've done right by her."

"Oh, for shame, Rosa," said Mrs. Cadman, turning her face through the dark towards that disembodied voice. "For shame, Rosa, even if you *are* going. You know best what's come between her and me. It's been you and her, you and her. I don't know where to turn sometimes——"

Rosa said: "You've got such a shallow heart."

"How should you know? Why, you've kept at a distance from me ever since we were tots. Oh, I know I'm a great silly, always after my fun, but I never took what was yours; I never did harm to you. I don't see what call we have got to judge each other. You didn't want my life that I've had."

Rosa's chin moved: she was lying looking up at her sister's big rippling shadow, splodged up there by the light of the low lamp. It is frightening, having your shadow watched. Mrs. Cadman said: "But what did I do to you?"

"I *could* have had a wicked heart," said Rosa. "A vain, silly heart like yours. I could have fretted, seeing you take everything. One thing, then another. But I was shown. God taught me to pity you. God taught me my lesson. . . . You wouldn't even remember that Christmas tree."

"What Christmas tree?"

"No, you wouldn't even remember. Oh, I thought it was lovely. I could have cried when they pulled the curtains open, and there it was, all blazing away with candles and silver and everything——"

"Well, isn't that funny. I——"

"No; you've had all that pleasure since. All of us older children couldn't take it in, hardly, for quite a minute or two. It didn't look real. Then I looked up, and there was a fairy doll fixed on the top, right on the top spike, fixed on to a star. I set my heart on her. She had wings and long fair hair, and she was shining away. I couldn't take my eyes off her. They cut the presents down; but she wasn't for anyone. In my childish blindness I kept praying to God. If I am not to have her, I prayed, let her stay there."

"And what did God do?" Hilda said eagerly.

"Oh, He taught me and saved me. You were a little thing in a blue sash; you piped up and asked might you have the doll."

"Fancy me! Aren't children awful!" said Mrs. Cadman. "Asking like that."

"They said: 'Make her sing for it.' They were taken with you. So you piped up again, singing. You got her, all right. I went off where they kept the coats. I've thanked God ever since for what I had to go through! I turned my face from vanity from that very night. I had been shown."

"Oh, what a shame!" said Hilda. "Oh, I think it was cruel; you poor little mite."

"No; I used to see that doll all draggled about the house till no one could bear the sight of it. I said to myself: that's how those things end. Why, I'd learnt more in one evening than you've ever learnt in your life. Oh, yes, I've watched you, Hilda. Yes, and I've pitied you."

"Well, you showed me no pity."

"You asked for no pity—all vain and set up."

"No wonder you've been against me. Fancy me not knowing. I didn't *mean* any harm—why, I was quite a little thing. I don't even remember."

"Well, you'll remember one day. When you lie as I'm lying you'll find that everything comes back. And you'll see what it adds up to."

"Well, if I do?" said Hilda. "I haven't been such a baby; I've seen things out in my own way; I've had my ups and downs. It hasn't been all jam." She got herself out of the armchair and came and stood uncertainly by the foot of the bed. She had a great wish to reach out and turn the hooded lamp round, so that its light could fall on her sister's face. She felt she should *see* her sister, perhaps for the first time. Inside the flat, still form did implacable disappointment, then, stay locked? She wished she could give Rosa some little present. Too late to give Rosa anything pretty now: she looked back —it had always, then, been too late? She thought: you poor queer heart; you queer heart, eating yourself out, thanking God for the pain. She thought: I did that to her; then what have I done to Lucille?

She said: "You're ever so like me, Rosa, really, aren't you? Setting our hearts on things. When you've got them you don't notice. No wonder you wanted Lucille. . . . You did ought to have had that fairy doll."

For Discussion:

1. Both Mr. and Mrs. Cadman belonged to the "jolly set." In view of this, how do you explain the traits of their daughter?
2. The author says of Mrs. Cadman that after her descent from the bus "she shook herself like a satisfied bird." Of her sister Rosa, the writer comments that she "started flapping around Granville like a doomed bird." What do these quotations suggest about the character traits of the two sisters?
3. Why do the downtown folks and the bus conductor good-naturedly accept Mrs. Cadman? Why doesn't her daughter respond in the same way?
4. At the conclusion of the story, Mrs. Cadman says, "You're ever so like me, Rosa, really aren't you?" Do you agree that the sisters were basically alike? Explain your answer.
5. Rosa has spent her life pitying her sister. From the way the story is told, whom do you pity? Why?
6. What is the basic conflict in the story? Whose conflict is it? How does she meet it? How would you express the main idea of the story?

For Composition: Write a short composition entitled "Elizabeth Bowen's Use of Setting in 'A Queer Heart'."

The Fur Coat

SEAN O'FAOLAIN

Sean O'Faolain (1900–   ), like James Joyce, was born in Dublin, and is one of the distinguished short-story writers of our time. Americans take special pride in the success he has achieved. A Commonwealth Fellow at Harvard, he taught Gaelic and Anglo-Irish literature. Later he became visiting lecturer and professor at Boston College. Looking back to these years he recalls that it was then he "began writing in the real sense of the word."

O'Faolain applies high standards to his writing. Technique, for him, "is the least part of the business." What he wants in his stories is "punch and poetry," a combination of "reality, in the simple sense of plausibility, and personal voltage." It is the "personal voltage" which lights up each of his stories, making the reader remember it "even when we have forgotten the details of the yarn."

His stories deal chiefly with the Irish he knows and loves: life among the lower middle classes or among the fast-disappearing peasantry. Usually the picture he presents is not flattering. Like Joyce he is openly critical of people, but unlike Joyce he views their frustrations and confusions, not with cynicism but with compassion and humor.

———◆———

When Maguire became Parliamentary Secretary to the Minister for Roads and Railways his wife wound her arms around his neck, lifted herself on her toes, gazed into his eyes and said, adoringly:

"Now, Paddy, I must have a fur coat."

"Of course, of course, me dear," Maguire cried, holding her out from him admiringly; for she was a handsome little woman still, in spite of the graying hair and the first hint of a stoop. "Get two fur coats! Switzer's will give us any amount of tick from now on."

Molly sat back into her chair with her fingers clasped between her knees and said, chidingly:

"You think I'm extravagant!"

"Indeed, then, I do not. We've had some thin times together and it's about time we had a bit of comfort in our old age. I'd like to see my wife in a fur coat. I'd love to see my wife take a shine out of some of those straps in Grafton Street—painted jades that never lifted a finger for God or man, not to as much as mention the word

Ireland. By all means get a fur coat. Go down to Switzer's tomorrow morning," he cried with all the innocence of a warm-hearted, inexperienced man, "and order the best fur coat that money can buy."

Molly Maguire looked at him with affection and irritation. The years had polished her hard—politics, revolution, husband in and out of prison, children reared with the help of relatives and Prisoners' Dependents' Funds. You could see the years on her fingertips, too pink, too coarse, and in her diamond-bright eyes.

"Paddy, you big fool, do you know what you'd pay for a mink coat? Not to mention a sable? And not as much as to whisper the word broadtail?"

"Say a hundred quid," said Paddy, manfully. "What's a hundred quid? I'll be handling millions of public money from now on. I have to think big."

She replied in her warm Limerick singsong; sedately and proudly as befitted a woman who had often, in her father's country store, handled thousands of pound notes.

"Do you know, Paddy Maguire, what a really bang-up fur coat could cost you? It could cost you a thousand guineas, and more."

"One thousand guineas? For a coat? Sure, that's a whole year's salary."

"It is."

Paddy drew into himself. "And," he said, in a cautious voice, "is that the kind of coat you had in mind?"

She laughed, satisfied at having taken him off his perch.

"Yerrah, not at all. I thought I might pick up a nice little coat for, maybe, thirty or forty or, at the outside, fifty quid. Would that be too much?"

"Go down to Switzer's in the morning and bring it home on your back."

But, even there, she thought she detected a touch of the bravo, as if he was still feeling himself a great fellow. She let it pass. She said she might have a look around. There was no hurry. She did not bring up the matter again for quite fifteen minutes.

"Paddy! About that fur coat. I sincerely hope you don't think I'm being *vulgar*?"

"How could you be vulgar?"

"Oh, sort of *nouveau riche*. I don't want a fur coat for show-off." She leaned forward eagerly. "Do you know the reason why I want a fur coat?"

"To keep you warm. What else?"

"Oh, well, that too, I suppose, yes," she agreed shortly. "But you must realize that from this on we'll be getting asked out to parties and receptions and so forth. And—well—I haven't a rag to wear!"

"I see," Paddy agreed; but she knew that he did not see.

"Look," she explained, "what I want is something I can wear any old time. I don't want a fur coat for grandeur." (This very scornfully.) "I want to be able to throw it on and go off and be as well dressed as anybody. You see, you can wear any old thing under a fur coat."

"That sounds a good idea." He considered the matter as judiciously as if he were considering a memorandum for a projected bypass. She leaned back, contented, with the air of a woman who has successfully laid her conscience to rest.

Then he spoiled it all by asking, "But, tell me, what do all the women do who haven't fur coats?"

"They dress."

"Dress? Don't ye all dress?"

"Paddy, don't be silly. They think of nothing else but dress. I have no time for dressing. I'm a busy housewife and, anyway, dressing costs a lot of money." (Here she caught a flicker in his eye which obviously meant that forty quid isn't to be sniffed at either.) "I mean they have costumes that cost twenty-five pounds. Half a dozen of 'em. They spend a lot of time and thought over it. They live for it. If you were married to one of 'em you'd soon know what it means to dress. The beauty of a fur coat is that you can just throw it on and you're as good as the best of them."

"Well, that's fine! Get the ould coat."

He was evidently no longer enthusiastic. A fur coat, he had learned, is not a grand thing—it is just a useful thing. He drew his brief case towards him. There was that pier down in Kerry to be looked at. "Mind you," he added, "it'd be nice and warm, too. Keep you from getting a cold."

"Oh, grand, yes, naturally, cozy, yes, all that, yes, yes!"

And she crashed out and banged the door after her and put the children to bed as if she were throwing sacks of turf into a cellar. When she came back he was poring over maps and specifications. She began to patch one of the boy's pajamas. After a while she held it up and looked at it in despair. She let it sink into her lap and looked at the pile of mending beside her.

"I suppose when I'm dead and gone they'll invent plastic pajamas that you can wash with a dishcloth and mend with a lump of glue."

She looked into the heart of the turf fire. A dozen pajamas . . . underwear for the whole house . . .

"Paddy!"

"Huh?"

"The last thing that I want anybody to start thinking is that I, by any possible chance, could be getting grand notions."

She watched him hopefully. He was lost in his plans.

"I can assure you, Paddy, that I loathe—I simply loathe all this modern show-off."

"That's right."

"Those wives that think they haven't climbed the social ladder until they've got a fur coat!"

He grunted at the map of the pier.

"Because I don't care what you or anybody else says, Paddy, there *is* something vulgar about a fur coat. There's no shape to them. Especially musquash. What I was thinking of was black Indian lamb. Of course, the real thing would be ocelot. But they're much too dear. The real ones. And I wouldn't be seen dead in an imitation ocelot."

He glanced sideways from the table. "You seem to know a lot about fur." He leaned back and smiled benevolently. "I never knew you were hankering all this time after a fur coat."

"Who said I'm hankering! I am *not*. What do you mean? Don't be silly. I just want something decent to wear when we go out to a show, or to wear over a dance frock, that's all. What do you mean—hankering?"

"Well, what's wrong with that thing you have with the fur on the sleeves? The shiny thing with the what-do-you-call-'ems—sequins, is it?"

"*That!* Do you mean *that?* For heaven's sake, don't be talking about what you don't know anything about. I've had *that* for fourteen years. It's like something me grandmother wore at her own funeral."

He laughed. "You used to like it."

"Of course, I liked it when I got it. Honestly, Paddy Maguire, there are times when . . ."

"Sorry, sorry, sorry. I was only trying to be helpful. How much is an ocelot?"

"Eighty-five or ninety—at the least."

"Well, why not?"

"Paddy, tell me honestly. Honestly, now! Do you seriously think that I could put eighty-five pounds on my back?"

With his pencil Maguire frugally drew a line on the map, reducing the pier by five yards, and wondered would the county surveyor let him get away with it.

"Well, the question is: will you be satisfied with the Indian lamb? What color did you say it is? Black? That's a very queer lamb."

Irritably he rubbed out the line. The wretched thing would be too shallow at low water if he cut five yards off it.

"It's dyed. You could get it brown, too," she cried. "You could get all sorts of lamb. Broadtail is the fur of unborn Persian lambs."

That woke him up: the good farmer stock in him was shocked.

"Unborn lambs!" he cried. "Do you mean to say that they . . ."

"Yes, isn't it awful? Honest to Heaven, Paddy, anyone that'd wear broadtail ought to be put in prison. Paddy, I've made up my mind. I just couldn't buy a fur coat. I just won't buy it. That's the end of it."

She picked up the pajamas again and looked at them with moist eyes. He turned to devote his full attention to her problem.

"Molly, darling, I'm afraid I don't understand what you're after. I mean, do you or do you not want a fur coat? I mean, supposing you didn't buy a fur coat, what else could you do?"

"Just exactly what do you mean?"—very coldly.

"I mean, it isn't apparently necessary that you should buy a fur coat. I mean, not if you don't really want to. There must be some other way of dressing besides fur coats? If you have a scunner against fur coats, why not buy something else just as good? There's hundreds of millions of other women in the world and they all haven't fur coats."

"I've told you before that they dress! And I've no time to dress. I've explained all that to you."

Maguire got up. He put his back to the fire, his hands behind him, a judicial look on him. He addressed the room.

"All the other women in the world can't all have time to dress. There must be some way out of it. For example, next month there'll be a garden party up at the President's house. How many of all these women will be wearing fur coats?" He addressed the armchair. "Has Mrs. de Valera time to dress?" He turned and leaned over the turf basket. "Has Mrs. General Mulcahy time to dress? There's ways and means of doing everything." (He shot a quick glance at the map of the pier; you could always knock a couple of feet off the width of it.) "After all, you've told me yourself that you could purchase a black costume for twenty-five guineas. Is that or is that not a fact? Very well then," triumphantly, "why not buy a black costume for twenty-five guineas?"

"Because, you big fathead, I'd have to have shoes and a blouse and hat and gloves and a fur and a purse and everything to match it, and I'd spend far more in the heel of the hunt, and I haven't time for that sort of thing and I'd have to have two or three costumes—Heaven above, I can't appear day after day in the same old rig, can I?"

"Good! Good! That's settled. Now, the question is: shall we or shall we not purchase a fur coat? Now! What is to be said for a fur coat?" He marked off the points on his fingers. "Number one: it is warm. Number two: it will keep you from getting cold. Number three . . ."

Molly jumped up, let a scream out of her, and hurled the basket of mending at him.

"Stop it! I told you I don't want a fur coat! And you don't want me to get a fur coat! You're too mean, that's what it is! And, like all the Irish, you have the peasant streak in you. You're all alike, every bloody wan of ye. Keep your rotten fur coat. I never wanted it . . ."

And she ran from the room sobbing with fury and disappointment.

"Mean?" gasped Maguire to himself. "To think that anybody could say that I . . . Mean!"

She burst open the door to sob:

"I'll go to the garden party in a mackintosh. And I hope that'll satisfy you!" and ran out again.

He sat miserably at his table, cold with anger. He murmured the hateful word over and over, and wondered could there be any truth in it. He added ten yards to the pier. He reduced the ten to five, and then, seeing what he had done, swept the whole thing off the table.

It took them three days to make it up. She had hit him below the belt, and they both knew it. On the fourth morning she found a check for a hundred and fifty pounds on her dressing table. For a moment her heart leaped. The next moment it died in her. She went down and put her arms about his neck and laid the check, torn in four, into his hand.

"I'm sorry, Paddy," she begged, crying like a kid. "You're not mean. You never were. It's me that's mean."

"You! Mean?" he said, fondly holding her in his arms.

"No, I'm not mean. It's not that. I just haven't the heart, Paddy. It was knocked out of me donkeys' years ago." He looked at her sadly. "You know what I'm trying to say?"

He nodded. But she saw that he didn't. She was not sure that she knew herself. He took a deep, resolving breath, held her out from him by the shoulders, and looked her straight in the eyes. "Molly, tell me the truth. You want this coat?"

"I do. O God, I do!"

"Then go out and buy it."

"I couldn't, Paddy. I just couldn't."

He looked at her for a long time. Then he asked:

"Why?"

She looked straight at him and, shaking her head sadly, she said in a little sobbing voice:

"I don't know."

For Discussion:

1. This story demonstrates how a comparatively slight plot may be used to give a vivid insight into life. How would you express the theme of the story?

2. How do the physical setting and the emotional atmosphere contribute to the sense of reality in this story?

3. What do Maguire's changing attitudes toward a fur coat tell you about him?

4. Examine and account for the various stages through which Molly moves to deny herself the coat. Are these stages consistent with Molly's character? What does the coat represent to her?

5. What is the conflict in the story? What sentence in the story most vividly reveals Molly's inner struggle?

6. Even though in the end Molly says she doesn't know why she can't buy the coat, you do know. How would you state the reason?

For Composition: Compare and contrast "Araby" (page 152) and this story, showing the attitude of Joyce and O'Faolain toward the people of Ireland.

Across the Bridge

GRAHAM GREENE

Graham Greene (1904–   ) is an author of diverse accomplishments. He has written with equal ease thrillers, serious novels, short stories, essays, and travel books. His thrillers, or "entertainments" as he prefers to call them, such as *This Gun for Hire*, *The Ministry of Fear*, and *Our Man in Havana*, are psychological tales of mystery, intrigue, and suspense. His serious novels, however, are more quiet, somber studies which reveal the fear, failure, and the awful isolation of the unloved human being. Yet these novels are written so deftly and in a style that is so cool and swift, that the immediate response of the reader is one of pleasure.

Like most modern writers, Greene is less concerned with plot than with character. To him the solution of the problem of evil lies not so much in man's actions as in man's thoughts and motives. Relentlessly he uncovers the weaknesses, even the sins, of his characters, but never without that compassion which man looks for from others. Greene insists upon the necessity for pity and the hope of mercy. He resembles Joseph Conrad in his interest in the human heart. Unlike Conrad, however, Greene suggests that evil and sin can be an occasion for grace and redemption.

◆

"They say he's worth a million," Lucia said. He sat there in the little hot damp Mexican square, a dog at his feet, with an air of immense and forlorn patience. The dog attracted your attention at once; for it was very nearly an English setter, only something had gone wrong with the tail and the feathering. Palms wilted over his head, it was all shade and stuffiness round the bandstand, radios talked loudly in Spanish from the little wooden sheds where they changed your pesos into dollars at a loss. I could tell he didn't understand a word from the way he read his newspaper—as I did myself, picking out the words which were like English ones. "He's been here a month," Lucia said. "They turned him out of Guatemala and Honduras."

You couldn't keep any secrets for five hours in this border town. Lucia had only been twenty-four hours in the place, but she knew all about Mr. Joseph Calloway. The only reason I didn't know about him (and I'd been in the place two weeks) was because I couldn't

193

talk the language any more than Mr. Calloway could. There wasn't another soul in the place who didn't know the story—the whole story of the Halling Investment Trust and the proceedings for extradition. Any man doing dusty business in any of the wooden booths in the town is better fitted by long observation to tell Mr. Calloway's tale than I am, except that I was in—literally—at the finish. They all watched the drama proceed with immense interest, sympathy and respect. For, after all, he had a million.

Every once in a while through the long steamy day, a boy came and cleaned Mr. Calloway's shoes: he hadn't the right words to resist them—they pretended not to know his English. He must have had his shoes cleaned the day Lucia and I watched him at least half a dozen times. At midday he took a stroll across the square to the Antonio Bar and had a bottle of beer, the setter sticking to heel as if they were out for a country walk in England (he had, you may remember, one of the biggest estates in Norfolk). After his bottle of beer, he would walk down between the money-changers' huts to the Rio Grande and look across the bridge into the United States: people came and went constantly in cars. Then back to the square till lunch-time. He was staying in the best hotel, but you don't get good hotels in this border town: nobody stays in them more than a night. The good hotels were on the other side of the bridge: you could see their electric signs twenty stories high from the little square at night, like lighthouses marking the United States.

You may ask what I'd been doing in so drab a spot for a fortnight. There was no interest in the place for any one; it was just damp and dust and poverty, a kind of shabby replica of the town across the river: both had squares in the same spots; both had the same number of cinemas. One was cleaner than the other, that was all, and more expensive, much more expensive. I'd stayed across there a couple of nights waiting for a man a tourist bureau said was driving down from Detroit to Yucatan and would sell a place in his car for some fantastically small figure—twenty dollars, I think it was. I don't know if he existed or was invented by the optimistic half-caste in the agency; anyway, he never turned up and so I waited, not much caring, on the cheap side of the river. It didn't much matter; I was living. One day I meant to give up the man from Detroit and go home or go south, but it was easier not to decide anything in a hurry. Lucia was just waiting for a car going the other way, but she didn't have to wait so long. We waited together and watched Mr. Calloway waiting —for God knows what.

I don't know how to treat this story—it was a tragedy for Mr. Calloway, it was poetic retribution, I suppose, in the eyes of the shareholders he'd ruined with his bogus transactions, and to Lucia and me, at this stage, it was pure comedy—except when he kicked the dog. I'm not a sentimentalist about dogs, I prefer people to be cruel to animals rather than to human beings, but I couldn't help being revolted at the way he'd kick that animal—with a hint of cold-blooded venom, not in anger but as if he were getting even for some trick it had played him a long while ago. That generally happened when he returned from the bridge: it was the only sign of anything resembling emotion he showed. Otherwise he looked a small, set, gentle creature with silver hair and a silver moustache, and gold-rimmed glasses, and one gold tooth like a flaw in character.

Lucia hadn't been accurate when she said he'd been turned out of Guatemala and Honduras; he'd left voluntarily when the extradition proceedings seemed likely to go through and moved north. Mexico is still not a very centralized state, and it is possible to get round governors as you can't get round cabinet ministers or judges. And so he waited there on the border for the next move. That earlier part of the story is, I suppose, dramatic, but I didn't watch it and I can't invent what I haven't seen—the long waiting in ante-rooms, the bribes taken and refused, the growing fear of arrest, and then the flight—in gold-rimmed glasses—covering his tracks as well as he could, but this wasn't finance and he was an amateur at escape. And so he'd washed up here, under my eyes and Lucia's eyes, sitting all day under the bandstand, nothing to read but a Mexican paper, nothing to do but look across the river at the United States, quite unaware, I suppose, that everyone knew everything about him, once a day kicking his dog. Perhaps in its semi-setter way it reminded him too much of the Norfolk estate—though that too, I suppose, was the reason he kept it.

And the next act again was pure comedy. I hesitate to think what this man worth a million was costing his country as they edged him out from this land and that. Perhaps somebody was getting tired of the business, careless; anyway, they sent across two detectives, with an old photograph. He'd grown his silvery moustache since that had been taken, and he'd aged a lot, and they couldn't catch sight of him.

They hadn't been across the bridge two hours when everybody knew that there were two foreign detectives in town looking for Mr. Calloway—everybody knew, that is to say, except Mr. Calloway, who couldn't talk Spanish. There were plenty of people who could have told him in English, but they didn't. It wasn't cruelty, it was a sort of awe and respect: like a bull, he was on show, sitting there mournfully in the plaza with his dog, a magnificent spectacle for which we all had ring-side seats.

I ran into one of the policemen in the Bar Antonio. He was disgusted; he had had some idea that when he crossed the bridge life was going to be different, so much more colour and sun, and—I suspect—love, and all he found were wide mud streets where the nocturnal rain lay in pools, and mangy dogs, smells and cockroaches in his bedroom, and the nearest to love, the open door of the Academia Comercial, where pretty mestizo girls sat all the morning learning to typewrite. Tip-tap-tip-tap-tip—perhaps they had a dream, too—jobs on the other side of the bridge, where life was going to be so much more luxurious, refined and amusing.

We got into conversation; he seemed surprised that I knew who they both were and what they wanted. He said, "We've got information this man Calloway's in town."

"He's knocking around somewhere," I said.

"Could you point him out?"

"Oh, I don't know him by sight," I said.

He drank his beer and thought a while. "I'll go out and sit in the plaza. He's sure to pass sometime."

I finished my beer and went quickly off and found Lucia. I said, "Hurry, we're going to see an arrest." We didn't care a thing about Mr. Calloway, he was just an elderly man who kicked his dog and swindled the poor, and who deserved anything he got. So we made for the plaza; we knew Calloway would be there, but it had never occurred to either of us that the detectives wouldn't recognize him. There was quite a surge of people round the place; all the fruit-sellers and boot-blacks in town seemed to have arrived together; we had to force our way through, and there in the little green stuffy centre of the place, sitting on adjoining seats, were the two plainclothes men and Mr. Calloway. I've never known the place so silent; everybody was on tiptoe, and the plainclothes men were staring at the crowd looking for Mr. Calloway, and Mr. Calloway sat on his usual seat staring out over the money-changing booths at the United States.

"It can't go on. It just can't," Lucia said. But it did. It got more fantastic still. Somebody ought to write a play about it. We sat as close as we dared. We were afraid all the time we were going to laugh. The semi-setter scratched for fleas and Mr. Calloway watched the U.S.A. The two detectives watched the crowd, and the crowd watched the show with solemn satisfaction. Then one of the detectives got up and went over to Mr. Calloway. That's the end, I thought. But it wasn't, it was the beginning. For some reason they had eliminated him from their list of suspects. I shall never know why.

The man said, "You speak English?"

"I *am* English," Mr. Calloway said.

Even that didn't tear it, and the strangest thing of all was the way Mr. Calloway came alive. I don't think anybody had spoken to him like that for weeks. The Mexicans were too respectful—he was a man with a million—and it had never occurred to Lucia and me to treat him casually like a human being; even in our eyes he had been magnified by the colossal theft and the world-wide pursuit.

He said, "This is rather a dreadful place, don't you think?"

"It is," the policeman said.

"I can't think what brings anybody across the bridge."

"Duty," the policeman said gloomily. "I suppose you are passing through."

"Yes," Mr. Calloway said.

"I'd have expected over here there'd have been—you know what I mean—life. You read things about Mexico."

"Oh, life," Mr. Calloway said. He spoke firmly and precisely, as if to a committee of shareholders. "That begins on the other side."

"You don't appreciate your own country until you leave it."

"That's very true," Mr. Calloway said. "Very true."

At first it was difficult not to laugh, and then after a while there didn't seem to be much to laugh at; an old man imagining all the fine things going on beyond the international bridge. I think he thought of the town opposite as a combination of London and Norfolk—theatres and cocktail bars, a little shooting and a walk round the field at evening with the dog—that miserable imitation of a setter—poking the ditches. He'd never been across, he couldn't know that it was just the same thing over again—even the same layout; only the streets were paved and the hotels had ten more stories, and life was more expensive, and everything was a little bit cleaner. There wasn't anything Mr. Calloway would have called living—no galleries, no book-shops, just *Film Fun* and the local paper, and *Click* and *Focus* and the tabloids.

"Well," said Mr. Calloway, "I think I'll take a stroll before lunch. You need an appetite to swallow the food here. I generally go down and look at the bridge about now. Care to come too?"

The detective shook his head. "No," he said, "I'm on duty. I'm looking for a fellow." And that, of course, gave *him* away. As far as Mr. Calloway could understand, there was only one "fellow" in the world anyone was looking for—his brain had eliminated friends who were seeking their friends, husbands who might be waiting for their wives, all objectives of any search but just the one. The power of elimination was what had made him a financier—he could forget the people behind the shares.

That was the last we saw of him for a while. We didn't see him going into the Botica Paris to get his aspirin, or walking back from the bridge with his dog. He simply disappeared, and when he disappeared, people began to talk, and the detectives heard the talk. They looked silly enough, and they got busy after the very man they'd been sitting next to in the garden. Then they too disappeared. They, as well as Mr. Calloway, had gone to the state capital to see the Governor and the Chief of Police, and it must have been an amusing sight there too, as they bumped into Mr. Calloway and sat with him in the waiting-rooms. I suspect Mr. Calloway was generally shown in first, for everyone knew he was worth a million. Only in Europe is it possible for a man to be a criminal as well as a rich man.

Anyway, after about a week the whole pack of them returned by the same train. Mr. Calloway travelled Pullman, and the two policemen travelled in the day coach. It was evident that they hadn't got their extradition order.

Lucia had left by that time. The car came and went across the bridge. I stood in Mexico and watched her get out at the United States Customs. She wasn't anything in particular but she looked beautiful at a distance as she gave me a wave out of the United States and got back into the car. And I suddenly felt sympathy for Mr. Calloway, as if there were something over there which you couldn't find here, and turning round I saw him back on his old beat, with the dog at his heels.

I said "Good afternoon," as if it had been all along our habit to greet each other. He looked tired and ill and dusty, and I felt sorry for him—to think of the kind of victory he'd been winning, with so much expenditure of cash and care—the prize this dirty and dreary town, the booths of the money-changers, the awful little beauty parlours with their wicker chairs and sofas looking like the reception rooms of brothels, that hot and stuffy garden by the bandstand.

He replied gloomily, "Good morning," and the dog started to sniff at some ordure and he turned and kicked it with fury, with depression, with despair.

And at that moment a taxi with the two policemen in it passed us on its way to the bridge. They must have seen that kick; perhaps they were cleverer than I had given them credit for, perhaps they were just sentimental about animals, and thought they'd do a good deed, and the rest happened by accident. But the fact remains—those two pillars of the law set about the stealing of Mr. Calloway's dog.

He watched them go by. Then he said, "Why don't you go across?"

"It's cheaper here," I said.

"I mean just for an evening. Have a meal at that place we can see at night in the sky. Go to the theatre."

"There isn't a chance."

He said angrily, sucking his gold tooth, "Well, anyway, get away from here." He stared down the hill and up the other side. He couldn't see that that street climbing up from the bridge contained only the same money-changers' booths as this one.

I said, "Why don't *you* go?"

He said evasively, "Oh—business."

I said, "It's only a question of money. You don't *have* to pass by the bridge."

He said with faint interest, "I don't talk Spanish."

"There isn't a soul here," I said, "who doesn't talk English."

He looked at me with surprise. "Is that so?" he said. "Is that so?"

It's as I have said; he'd never tried to talk to anyone, and they respected him too much to talk to him—he was worth a million. I don't know whether I'm glad or sorry that I told him that. If I hadn't, he might be there now, sitting by the bandstand having his shoes cleaned—alive and suffering.

Three days later his dog disappeared. I found him looking for it, calling it softly and shamefacedly between the palms of the garden. He looked embarrassed. He said in a low angry voice, "I *hate* that dog. The beastly mongrel," and called "Rover, Rover" in a voice which didn't carry five yards. He said, "I bred setters once. I'd have shot a dog like that." It reminded him, I *was* right, of Norfolk, and he lived in the memory, and he hated it for its imperfection. He was a man without a family and without friends, and his only enemy was that dog. You couldn't call the law an enemy; you have to be intimate with an enemy.

Late that afternoon someone told him they'd seen the dog walking across the bridge. It wasn't true, of course, but we didn't know that then—they'd paid a Mexican five pesos to smuggle it across. So all that afternoon and the next Mr. Calloway sat in the garden having his shoes cleaned over and over again, and thinking how a dog could just walk across like that, and a human being, an immortal soul, was bound here in the awful routine of the little walk and the unspeakable meals and the aspirin at the *botica*. That dog was seeing things he couldn't see—that hateful dog. It made him mad—I think literally mad. You must remember the man had been going on for months. He had a million and he was living on two pounds a week, with nothing to spend his money on. He sat there and brooded on the hideous injustice of it. I think he'd have crossed over one day in any case, but the dog was the last straw.

Next day when he wasn't to be seen I guessed he'd gone across, and I went too. The American town is as small as the Mexican. I knew I couldn't miss him if he was there, and I was still curious. A little sorry for him, but not much.

I caught sight of him first in the only drug-store, having a Coca-Cola, and then once outside a cinema looking at the posters; he had dressed with extreme neatness, as if for a party, but there was no party. On my third time round, I came on the detectives—they were having Coca-Colas in the drug-store, and they must have missed Mr. Calloway by inches. I went in and sat down at the bar.

"Hello," I said, "you still about?" I suddenly felt anxious for Mr. Calloway, I didn't want them to meet.

One of them said, "Where's Calloway?"

"Oh," I said, "he's hanging on."

"But not his dog," he said, and laughed. The other looked a little shocked, he didn't like anyone to *talk* cynically about a dog. Then they got up—they had a car outside.

"Have another?" I said.

"No, thanks. We've got to keep moving."

The man bent close and confided to me, "Calloway's on this side."

"No!" I said.

"And his dog."

"He's looking for it," the other said.

"I'm damned if he is," I said, and again one of them looked a little shocked, as if I'd insulted the dog.

I don't think Mr. Calloway was looking for his dog, but his dog certainly found him. There was a sudden hilarious yapping from the car and out plunged the semi-setter and gambolled furiously down the street. One of the detectives—the sentimental one—was into the car before we got to the door and was off after the dog. Near the bottom of the long road to the bridge was Mr. Calloway—I do believe he'd come down to look at the Mexican side when he found there was nothing but the drug-store and the cinemas and the paper shops on the American. He saw the dog coming and yelled at it to go home —"home, home, home," as if they were in Norfolk—it took no notice at all, pelting towards him. Then he saw the police car coming and ran. After that, everything happened too quickly, but I think the order of events was this—the dog started across the road right in front of the car, and Mr. Calloway yelled, at the dog or the car, I don't know which. Anyway, the detective swerved—he said later, weakly, at the inquiry, that he couldn't run over a dog, and down went Mr. Calloway, in a mess of broken glass and gold rims and silver hair, and blood. The dog was on to him before any of us could reach him, licking and whimpering and licking. I saw Mr. Calloway put up his hand, and down it went across the dog's neck and the whimper rose to a stupid bark of triumph, but Mr. Calloway was dead—shock and a weak heart.

"Poor old geezer," the detective said, "I bet he really loved that dog," and it's true that the attitude in which he lay looked more like a caress than a blow. I thought it was meant to be a blow, but the detective may have been right. It all seemed to me a little too touching to be true as the old crook lay there with his arm over the dog's neck, dead with his million between the money-changers' huts, but it's as well to be humble in the face of human nature. He had come across the river for something, and it may, after all, have been the dog he was looking for. It sat there, baying its stupid and mongrel triumph across his body, like a piece of sentimental statuary. The nearest he could get to the fields, ditches, the horizon of his home. It was comic and it was pitiable; but it wasn't less comic because the man was dead. Death doesn't change comedy to tragedy, and if that

last gesture was one of affection, I suppose it was only one more in-
dication of a human being's capacity for self-deception, our baseless
optimism that is so much more appalling than our despair.

For Discussion:

1. What is the basic conflict in this story? Cite evidence to prove your
   point.
2. Of what importance are physical setting and atmosphere to the theme
   of the story? What moods do they evoke? How do they help you to
   understand the characters and their actions?
3. Compare the towns connected by the bridge. What elements do they
   have in common? What is obviously lacking in each? Why does the
   author give the American town a vague, dreamlike quality?
4. What is your reaction when Greene describes Calloway as "dead
   with his million between the money-changers' huts"? Is there any
   significance in this?
5. The narrator views Calloway's experience as a comedy. Explain why
   you agree or do not agree with him.
6. The detective pitied the dead man as he "lay there with his arm
   over the dog's neck." He believes Calloway's gesture was meant as a
   caress. The narrator is not sure, but "thought it was meant to be a
   blow." With whom do you agree? Why?
7. What irony is involved in Calloway's earlier mistreatment of the dog?
   Where do you find other examples of irony and humor in the story?
8. Explain what Calloway had hoped to find across the bridge. Why did
   he fail to find it?

For Composition: Using evidence from the story, write a short composition showing how Graham Greene achieves suspense in "Across the
Bridge."

Modern Essays

The term "essay" conveys to many people a literary form which was written only in past centuries characterized by leisure, fine manners, and delicate feelings. Nothing could be further from the truth. Many articles appearing in today's better magazines can be rightly called essays, and the best of them have sometimes appeared later in book form. A periodical today seldom uses the term "essay" in its table of contents; consequently, readers have come to classify all short pieces of nonfiction as articles. But the article and the essay are closely related.

The essay, like the article, is brief and may be on any topic. An article, however, is usually limited to a factual and impersonal account of some timely subject, while the essay is broader in range. Though it may be topical, the essay is more often concerned with *general* ideas which are the result of the writer's own thinking and reflection. It is these ideas which the essayist wishes to explain and convince the reader of. The essay, then, is a short, *reflective* piece of prose, dealing with almost any subject, and written in a personal or informal style.

Some of the essays that follow in this book, such as "St. Thomas More" by Barbara Ward, are serious and attempt to convince the reader of some truth. Others, while serious in their intention, are approached by the writer more indirectly under the guise of humor or satire. This is true of such informal or personal essays as "The Crime" by Max Beerbohm and "The United States" by E. M. Forster. In both the serious and informal essay, however, there is not only the interpretation of facts and life, but also a reflection of the attitudes of the author himself. Particularly in the informal essay, the reader feels as if he is having an entertaining chat with a friend.

As in the past, the essay continues to impart briefly, effectively, and often charmingly, the opinions, criticisms, hopes, and fears of men. Like the great essayists of the past—Bacon, Addison and Steele, Lamb, Hazlitt, Macaulay, and Newman—today's essayists have broad and varied interests, and they have opened up new avenues of thought for the reader, inviting him to explore further and to come to his own honest conclusions.

The Fear of the Past

G. K. CHESTERTON

Shortly after Matthew Arnold and the skeptics of the late nineteenth century had loudly proclaimed that the modern world held ". . . neither joy, nor love, nor light," a champion arose to dispel the gloom and to enlighten the "ignorant armies" that were clashing in darkness.

Gilbert Keith Chesterton (1874–1936), dubbed "Knight of the Holy Ghost" by Walter de la Mare, had prepared for a journalistic career but in 1905, on the publication of his book *Heretics*, he emerged as a Christian apologist. This brilliant and amusing work challenged the position of the leading English writers of the time: Rudyard Kipling, George Bernard Shaw, H. G. Wells. It stirred readers to ask, "Heretics from what?" and to pose anew the question of the ages, "What is the truth?"

To answer, Chesterton published *Orthodoxy*. In it he accepted the Christian position on truth, giving his reasons with needling wit and great good humor. The laughter of the skeptics melted before a flood of Christian gaiety and joy. Chesterton's pages sparkled with brilliant ideas, crisply worded and delightfully presented. *Heretics* and *Orthodoxy* were forerunners of a huge productivity for Chesterton. Over a period of forty years, he published three or four volumes annually, showing his versatility in the fields of history, biography, drama, criticism, poetry, the short story, the novel and the essay.

———◆———

The last few decades have been marked by a special cultivation of the romance of the future. We seem to have made up our minds to misunderstand what has happened; and we turn, with a sort of relief, to stating what will happen—which is (apparently) much easier. The modern man no longer preserves the memoirs of his great-grandfather; but he is engaged in writing a detailed and authoritative biography of his great-grandson. Instead of trembling before the specters of the dead, we shudder abjectly under the shadow of the babe unborn. This spirit is apparent everywhere, even to the creation of a form of futurist romance. Sir Walter Scott stands at the dawn of the nineteenth century for the novel of the past; Mr. H. G. Wells stands at the dawn of the twentieth century for the novel of the future. The old story, we know, was supposed to begin: "Late on a winter's evening two horsemen might have been seen——." The new story has to begin: "Late on a winter's evening two aviators will be seen——." The movement is not without its elements of charm; there is something spirited, if eccentric, in the sight of so many people fighting over again the fights that have not yet happened; of people still glowing with the memory of tomorrow morning. A man in advance of the age is a familiar phrase enough. An age in advance of the age is really rather odd.

But when full allowance has been made for this harmless element of poetry and pretty human perversity in the thing, I shall not hesitate to maintain here that this cult of the future is not only a weakness but a cowardice of the age. It is the peculiar evil of this epoch that even its pugnacity is fundamentally frightened; and the Jingo is contemptible not because he is impudent, but because he is timid. The reason why modern armaments do not inflame the imagination like the arms and emblazonments of the Crusades is a reason quite apart from optical ugliness or beauty. Some battleships are as beautiful as the sea; and many Norman nosepieces were as ugly as Norman noses. The atmospheric ugliness that surrounds our scientific war is an emanation from that evil panic which is at the heart of it. The charge of the Crusades was a charge; it was charging towards God, the wild consolation of the braver. The charge of the modern armaments is not a charge at all. It is a rout, a retreat, a flight from the devil, who will catch the hindmost. It is impossible to imagine a mediæval knight talking of longer and longer French lances, with precisely the quivering employed about larger and larger German ships. The man who called the Blue Water School the "Blue Funk School" uttered a psychological truth which that school itself would scarcely essentially deny. Even the two-power standard, if it be a necessity, is in a sense a degrading necessity. Nothing has more alienated many magnanimous minds from Imperial enterprises than the fact that they are always exhibited as stealthy or sudden defenses against a world of cold rapacity and fear. The Boer War, for instance, was colored not so much by the creed that we were doing something right, as by the creed that Boers and Germans were probably doing something wrong; driving us (as it was said) to the sea. Mr. Chamberlain, I think, said that the war was a feather in his cap; and so it was: a white feather.

Now this same primary panic that I feel in our rush towards patriotic armaments I feel also in our rush towards future visions of society. The modern mind is forced towards the future by a certain sense of fatigue, not unmixed with terror, with which it regards the past. It is propelled towards the coming time; it is, in the exact words of the popular phrase, knocked into the middle of next week. And the goad which drives it on thus eagerly is not an affectation for futurity. Futurity does not exist, because it is still future. Rather it is a fear of the past; a fear not merely of the evil in the past, but of the good in the past also. The brain breaks down under the unbearable virtue of mankind. There have been so many flaming faiths that we cannot hold; so many harsh heroisms that we cannot imitate; so many great efforts of monumental building or of military glory which seem to us at once sublime and pathetic. The future is a refuge from the fierce competition of our forefathers. The older generation, not the younger, is knocking at our door. It is agreeable to escape, as Henley said, into the Street of By-and-Bye, where stands the Hostelry of Never. It is pleasant to play with children, especially unborn children. The future is a blank wall on which every man can write his own name as large as he likes; the past I find already covered with illegible scribbles, such as Plato, Isaiah, Shakespeare, Michelangelo, Napoleon. I can make the future as narrow as myself; the past is obliged to be as broad and turbulent as humanity. And the upshot of this modern attitude is really this: that men invent new ideals because they dare not attempt old ideals. They look forward with enthusiasm, because they are afraid to look back.

Now in history there is no Revolution that is not a Restoration. Among the many things that leave me doubtful about the modern habit of fixing eyes on the future, none is stronger than this: that all the men in history who have really done anything with the future have had their eyes fixed upon the past. I need not mention the Renaissance, the very word proves my case. The originality of Michelangelo and Shakespeare began with the digging up of old vases and manuscripts. The mildness of poets absolutely arose out of the mildness of antiquaries. So the great mediæval revival was a memory of the Roman Empire. So the Reformation looked back to the Bible and Bible times. So the modern Catholic movement has looked back to patristic times. But that modern movement which many would count the most anarchic of all is in this sense the most conservative of all. Never was the past more venerated by men than it was by the French Revolutionists. They invoked the little republics of antiquity with the complete confidence of one who invokes the gods. The Sans-culottes believed (as their name might imply) in a return to simplicity. They believed most piously in a remote past; some might call it a mythical past. For some strange reason man must always thus plant his fruit trees in a graveyard. Man can only find life among the dead. Man is a misshapen monster, with his feet set forward and his face turned back. He can make the future luxuriant and gigantic, so long as he is thinking about the past. When he tries to think about the future itself, his mind diminishes to a pin point with imbecility, which some call Nirvana. To-morrow is the Gorgon; a man must only see it mirrored in the shining shield of yesterday. If he sees it directly he is turned to stone. This has been the fate of all those who have really seen fate and futurity as clear and inevitable. The Calvinists, with their perfect creed of predestination, were turned to stone. The modern sociological scientists (with their excruciating Eugenics) are turned to stone. The only difference is that the Puritans make dignified, and the Eugenists * somewhat amusing, statues.

But there is one feature in the past which more than all the rest defies and depresses the moderns and drives them towards this featureless future. I mean the presence in the past of huge ideals, unfulfilled and sometimes abandoned. The sight of these splendid failures is melancholy to a restless and rather morbid generation; and they maintain a strange silence about them—sometimes amounting to an unscrupulous silence. They keep them entirely out of their newspapers and almost entirely out of their history books. For example, they will often tell you (in their praises of the coming age) that we are moving on towards a United States of Europe. But they carefully omit to tell you that we are moving away from a United States of Europe; that such a thing existed literally in Roman and essentially in mediæval times. They never admit that the international hatreds (which they call barbaric) are really very recent, the mere breakdown of the ideal of the Holy Roman Empire. Or again, they will tell you that there is going to be a social revolution, a great rising of the poor against the rich; but they never rub it in that France made that magnificent attempt, unaided, and that we and all the world allowed it to be trampled out and forgotten. I say decisively that nothing is so marked in

Eugenists: those who believe that the human race can be improved through the control of hereditary factors

modern writing as the prediction of such ideals in the future combined with the ignoring of them in the past. Anyone can test this
for himself. Read any thirty or forty pages of pamphlets advocating
peace in Europe and see how many of them praise the old Popes
or Emperors for keeping the peace in Europe. Read any armful
of essays and poems in praise of social democracy, and see how
many of them praise the old Jacobins who created democracy
and died for it. These colossal ruins are to the modern only enormous
eyesores. He looks back along the valley of the past and sees a
perspective of splendid but unfinished cities. They are unfinished,
not always through enmity or accident, but often through fickleness,
mental fatigue, and the lust for alien philosophies. We have not
only left undone those things that we ought to have done, but we
have even left undone those things that we wanted to do.

It is very currently suggested that the modern man is the heir
of all the ages, that he has got the good out of these successive
human experiments. I know not what to say in answer to this, except
to ask the reader to look at the modern man, as I have just looked
at the modern man—in the looking-glass. Is it really true that you
and I are two starry towers built up of all the most towering
visions of the past? Have we really fulfilled all the great historic
ideals one after the other, from our naked ancestor who was brave
enough to kill a mammoth with a stone knife, through the Greek
citizen and the Christian saint to our own grandfather or great-
grandfather, who may have been sabred by the Manchester Yeo-
manry or shot in the '48? Are we still strong enough to spear
mammoths, but now tender enough to spare them? Does the
cosmos contain any mammoth that we have either speared or
spared? When we decline (in a marked manner) to fly the red flag
and fire across a barricade like our grandfathers, are we really de-
clining in deference to sociologists—or to soldiers? Have we indeed
outstripped the warrior and passed the ascetical saint? I fear we
only outstrip the warrior in the sense that we should probably run
away from him. And if we have passed the saint, I fear we have
passed him without bowing.

This is, first and foremost, what I mean by the narrowness of
the new ideas, the limiting effect of the future. Our modern
prophetic idealism is narrow because it has undergone a persistent
process of elimination. We must ask for new things because we are
not allowed to ask for old things. The whole position is based on

this idea that we have got all the good that can be got out of the ideas of the past. But we have not got all the good out of them, perhaps at this moment not any of the good out of them. And the need here is a need of complete freedom for restoration as well as revolution.

We often read nowadays of the valor or audacity with which some rebel attacks a hoary tyranny or an antiquated superstition. There is not really any courage at all in attacking hoary or antiquated things, any more than in offering to fight one's grandmother. The really courageous man is he who defies tyrannies young as the morning and superstitions fresh as the first flowers. The only true free-thinker is he whose intellect is as much free from the future as from the past. He cares as little for what will be as for what has been; he cares only for what ought to be. And for my present purpose I specially insist on this abstract independence. If I am to discuss what is wrong, one of the first things that are wrong is this: the deep and silent modern assumption that past things have become impossible. There is one metaphor of which the moderns are very fond; they are always saying, "You can't put the clock back." The simple and obvious answer is "You can." A clock, being a piece of human construction, can be restored by the human finger to any figure or hour. In the same way society, being a piece of human construction, can be reconstructed upon any plan that has ever existed.

There is another proverb, "As you have made your bed, so you must lie on it"; which again is simply a lie. If I have made my bed uncomfortable, please God I will make it again. We could restore the Heptarchy or the stage coaches if we chose. It might take some time to do, and it might be very inadvisable to do it; but certainly it is not impossible as bringing back last Friday is impossible. This is, as I say, the first freedom that I claim: the freedom to restore. I claim a right to propose as a solution the old patriarchal system of a Highland clan, if that should seem to eliminate the largest number of evils. It certainly would eliminate some evils; for instance, the unnatural sense of obeying cold and harsh strangers, mere bureaucrats and policemen. I claim the right to propose the complete independence of the small Greek or Italian towns, a sovereign city of Brixton or Brompton, if that seems the best way out of our troubles. It would be a way out of some of our troubles; we could not have in a small state, for instance, those enormous illusions about men or measures which are nourished by the great national or international newspapers. You could not persuade a city state that Mr. Beit was an Englishman, or Mr. Dillon a desperado, any more than you could persuade a Hampshire village that the village drunkard was a teetotaler or the village idiot a statesman. Nevertheless, I do not as a fact propose that the Browns and the Smiths should be collected under separate tartans. Nor do I even propose that Clapham should declare its independence. I merely declare my independence. I merely claim my choice of all the tools in the universe; and I shall not admit that any of them are blunted merely because they have been used.

For Discussion:

1. Does this essay engage in serious controversy or express a purely personal opinion?
2. Show how Chesterton in his defense of the past is defending or attacking history.
3. Locate the sentence in each paragraph that sums up the idea contained in it. How does each sentence help you to understand the central idea?
4. What is the meaning of Chesterton's statement: "The charge of the modern armaments is not a charge at all"?
5. Chesterton says, ". . . in history there is no Revolution that is not a Restoration." Are revolution and restoration part of the same process?
6. This essay contains many epigrammatic statements that cause a reader to think. Select several that you particularly like and say why.

For Composition: Select a statement from the essay with which you *disagree* and write a short refutation of it.

David Copperfield

VIRGINIA WOOLF

Virginia Woolf's education and family background prepared her for the distinctive place she was to occupy in the world of English letters. She was the daughter of Sir Leslie Stephen, scholar and editor of the *Dictionary of National Biography*. School for her meant exploring her father's great library where she was free to follow her interests: the great literature of the world, Greek, French, music, and art. It also meant learning from the artists, musicians, poets, and novelists who frequented her home.

These interests and associations continued after her marriage to Leonard Woolf. They set up the Hogarth Press dedicated to publishing books of quality. They were the first to present to the public the works of such young unknown writers as T. S. Eliot and Katherine Mansfield.

Virginia Woolf not only wrote novels and short stories, but also many essays in which she expressed her keen, penetrating criticisms of literature. This essay on Dickens' *David Copperfield* is a splendid example of her broad knowledge of literature and her understanding of a work of art.

———◆———

Like the ripening of strawberries, the swelling of apples, and all other natural processes, new editions of Dickens—cheap, pleasant-looking, well printed—are born into the world and call for no more notice than the season's plums and strawberries, save when by some chance the emergence of one of these masterpieces in its fresh green binding suggests an odd and overwhelming enterprise— that one should read *David Copperfield* for the second time. There is perhaps no person living who can remember reading *David Copperfield* for the first time. Like *Robinson Crusoe* and *Grimm's Fairy Tales* and the Waverley Novels, *Pickwick* and *David Copperfield* are not books, but stories communicated by word of mouth in those tender years when fact and fiction merge, and thus belong to the memories and myths of life, and not to its esthetic experience. When we lift it from this hazy atmosphere, when we consider it as a book, bound and printed and ordered by the rules of art, what impression does *David Copperfield* make upon us? As Peggotty and Barkis, the rooks and the workbox with the picture of St. Paul's, Traddles who drew skeletons, the donkeys who would cross the green, Mr. Dick and the Memorial,

Betsey Trotwood and Jip and Dora and Agnes and the Heeps and the Micawbers once more come to life with all their appurtenances and peculiarities, are they still possessed of the old fascination or have they in the interval been attacked by that parching wind which blows about books and, without our reading them, remodels them and changes their features while we sleep? The rumour about Dickens is to the effect that his sentiment is disgusting and his style commonplace; that in reading him every refinement must be hidden and every sensibility kept under glass; but that with these precautions and reservations he is of course Shakespearean; like Scott, a born creator; like Balzac, prodigious in his fecundity; but, rumour adds, it is strange that while one reads Shakespeare and one reads Scott, the precise moment for reading Dickens seldom comes our way.

This last charge may be resolved into this—that he lacks charm and idiosyncrasy, is everybody's writer and no one's in particular, is an institution, a monument, a public thoroughfare trodden dusty by a million feet. It is based largely upon the fact that of all great writers Dickens is both the least personally charming and the least personally present in his books. No one has ever loved Dickens as he loves Shakespeare and Scott. Both in his life and in his work the impression that he makes is the same. He has to perfection the virtues conventionally ascribed to the male; he is self-assertive, self-reliant, self-assured; energetic in the extreme. His message, when he parts the veil of the story and steps forward in person, is plain and forcible; he preaches the value of "plain hardworking qualities," of punctuality, order, diligence, of doing what lies before one with all one's might. Agitated as he was by the most violent passions, ablaze with indignation, teeming with queer characters, unable to keep the dreams out of his head at night, nobody appears, as we read him, more free from the foibles and eccentricities and charms of genius. He comes before us, as one of his biographers described him, "like a prosperous sea captain," stalwart, weather-beaten, self-reliant, with a great contempt for the finicky, the inefficient, or the effeminate. His sympathies indeed have strict limitations. Speaking roughly, they fail him whenever a man or woman has more than two thousand a year, has been to the university, or can count his ancestors back to the third generation. They fail him when he has to treat of the mature emotions—the seduction of Emily, for example, or the death of Dora; whenever it is no longer possible to keep moving and creating, but it is necessary to stand still and search into things and penetrate to the depths of what is there. Then, indeed, he fails grotesquely, and the pages in which he describes what in our convention are the peaks and pinnacles of human life, the explanation of Mrs. Strong, the despair of Mrs. Steerforth, or the anguish of Ham, are of an indescribable unreality—of that uncomfortable complexion which, if we heard Dickens talking so in real life, would either make us blush to the roots of our hair or dash out of the room to conceal our laughter. ". . . Tell him then," says Emily, "that when I hear the wind blowing at night I feel as if it was passing angrily from seeing him and uncle, and was going up to God against me." Miss Dartle raves—about carrion and pollution and earthworms, and worthless spangles and broken toys, and how she will have Emily "proclaimed on the common stair." The failure is akin to that other failure to think deeply, to describe beautifully. Of the men who go to make up the perfect novelist and should live in amity under his hat, two—the poet and philosopher—failed to come when Dickens called them.

But the greater the creator the more derelict the regions where his powers fail him; all about their fertile lands are deserts where not a blade of grass grows, swamps where the foot sinks deep in mud. Nevertheless, while we are under their spell these great geniuses make us see the world any shape they choose. We remodel our psychological geography when we read Dickens; we forget that we have ever felt the delights of solitude or observed with wonder the intricate emotions of our friends, or luxuriated in the beauty of nature. What we remember is the ardour, the excitement, the humour, the oddity of people's characters; the smell and savour and soot of London; the incredible coincidences which hook the most remote lives together; the city, the law courts; this man's nose, that man's limp; some scene under an archway or on the high road; and above all some gigantic and dominating figure, so stuffed and swollen with life that he does not exist singly and solitarily, but seems to need for his own realisation a host of others, to call into existence the severed parts that complete him, so that wherever he goes he is the centre of conviviality and merriment and punch-making; the room is full, the lights are bright; there are Mrs. Micawber, the twins, Traddles, Betsey Trotwood—all in full swing.

This is the power which cannot fade or fail in its effect—the power not to analyse or to interpret, but to produce, apparently without thought or effort or calculation of the effect upon the story, characters who exist not in detail, not accurately or exactly, but abundantly in a cluster of wild and yet extraordinarily revealing remarks, bubble climbing on the top of bubble as the breath of the creator fills them. And the fecundity and apparently irreflectiveness have a strange effect. They make creators of us, and not merely readers and spectators. As we listen to Micawber pouring himself forth and venturing perpetually some new flight of astonishing imagination, we see, unknown to Mr. Micawber, into the depths of his soul. We say, as Dickens himself says while Micawber holds forth: "How wonderfully like Mr. Micawber that is!" Why trouble, then, if the scenes where emotion and psychology are to be expected fail us completely? Subtlety and complexity are all there if we know where to look for them, if we can get over the surprise of finding them—as it seems to us, who have another convention in these matters—in the wrong places. As a creator of character his peculiarity is that he creates wherever his eyes rest—he has the visualising power in the extreme. His people are branded upon our eyeballs before we hear them speak, by what he sees them doing, and it seems as if it were the sight that sets his thought in action. He saw Uriah Heep "breathing into the pony's nostrils and immediately covering them with his hand"; he saw David Copperfield looking in the glass to see how red his eyes were after his mother's death; he saw oddities and blemishes, gestures and incidents, scars, eyebrows, everything that was in the room, in a second. His eye brings in almost too rich a harvest for him to deal with, and gives him an aloofness and a hardness which freeze his sentimentalism and make it seem a concession to the public, a veil thrown over the penetrating glance which left to itself pierced to the bone. With such a power at his command Dickens made his books blaze up, not by tightening the plot or sharpening the wit, but by throwing another handful of people upon the fire. The interest flags and he creates Miss Mowcher, completely alive, equipped in every detail as if she were to play a great part in the story, whereas once the dull stretch of road is passed by her help, she disappears; she is needed no longer. Hence a Dickens novel is apt to become a bunch of separate characters loosely held together, often by the most arbitrary conventions, who tend to fly asunder and split our attention into so many different parts that we drop the book in despair. But that danger is surmounted in *David Copperfield*. There, though characters swarm and life flows into every creek and cranny, some common feeling—youth, gaiety, hope—envelops the tumult, brings the scattered parts together, and invests the most perfect of all the Dickens novels with an atmosphere of beauty.

For Discussion:

1. What is Virginia Woolf's attitude toward the book she is criticizing? What is her attitude toward its author?
2. What does she mean when she writes ". . . no person living can remember reading *David Copperfield* for the first time"? Why does she call a second reading of the book an "odd and overwhelming enterprise"?
3. According to the author, why does the "precise moment for reading Dickens seldom come our way"? Does this indicate that his works are unpopular? Explain.
4. With what great artistic power does Mrs. Woolf credit Dickens? Explain her accusation that he uses this gift improperly.
5. In another of her essays, Mrs. Woolf says to the reader: "Do not dictate to your author; try to become him." Do you think she succeeded in doing this when she read Dickens? Prove your point.
6. In the end, how does the author evaluate *David Copperfield?* What reason does she give?

For Composition: Using one of the novels you have read recently, write a short essay expressing your attitude toward it and the novelist.

Henry V

HILAIRE BELLOC

In 1903, French-born Hilaire Belloc (1870–1953) became a British subject. Three years later he became a member of Parliament and won a reputation for his brilliant oratory. Ultimately he became a part of the group known as "The Big Four," which included Shaw, Wells, Chesterton, and Belloc. Chesterton and Belloc defended an antimaterialistic philosophy against the Fabian socialism of Shaw and Wells. The pages of periodicals crackled with their exchanges; lecture halls thundered with their debates; and conversations bristled with their barbed repartee.

Belloc's contributions, however, were not solely on controversial subjects. His love of learning, his concern for men, and his militant faith resulted in a remarkable literary output. He was a poet, essayist, biographer, historian, and apologist. His essays have been extremely popular and follow the leisurely half-nostalgic pace of the best of the Victorians. His earliest work displays a great interest in history and the men who made it, as can be seen in his essay "Henry V."

———◆———

I read the other day that the hilt and blade of Henry V's conquering sword, preserved at Westminster, had been more fully identified through some manuscript or other. Perhaps they will be shown in the future alongside with his saddle and his shield. He would have liked that. He was a great soldier.

It is true of all men, public or private, that their real selves are different from their labels and their legends; that is inevitable. It is especially true of national heroes. It is more especially true of such few among the national heroes of the English as died before the prodigious moral revolution of the later sixteenth and earlier seventeenth centuries had transformed the country. Henry V has suffered (or enjoyed) this contrast between reality and myth more than any other figure I can recall out of the English Middle Ages.

There are many reasons for this. He came at a moment when the language of the upper class was gradually changing from French to what to-day is English. He came of a cadet branch which had violently usurped the Throne by revolution and murder, and which, none the less, was able to transmit its own legend through the Tudors and to establish a sort of Lancastrian official version of that century wherein the ancient England perished. He was a great warrior and a successful warrior, dying at the height of his success; and a great warrior and a successful warrior at a moment when the new religion of nationalism was beginning to pierce through the old religion of Christendom.

He had the good fortune to fire the imagination of William Shakespeare, and so to rise from the dead in a personality very different from his own, much simpler, immensely more popular.

To all this I would add another point deriving from the one I have just mentioned. I have said that he had the luck to die at the height of his military success. Now, from this there derived, necessarily, an exalted legend concerning him. Think what Napoleon would be to the French if he had died before the Russian expedition, and if the subsequent failures were attached to the names of apparently incompetent successors! Such was Henry V's admirable fate. In many a tavern of England, during the thirties and early forties of the fifteenth century, men scarred from the French wars told the deeds they could remember in their youth under such a captain, and cursed the bunglers who (in some way they did not understand) were throwing away the fruits of the earlier reign. I fancy it was from such a tradition, long preserved, that the spectacular figure, presented to the world one hundred and fifty years later on the stage, owed its eminence.

What was he? He was spare, diseased, indomitable; with a very sharp, prominent profile, narrow head, cold but keen eyes; possessed of two qualities which formed his whole story—a very high military aptitude and an isolated will. These qualities were supported by other qualities less rare; he could appreciate a political situation, domestic or foreign; he could determine its larger lines; he could frame a policy suitable to each. It is probable that had he lived he could have carried out such policies in full, at home and abroad.

What then? Then we should have had a dominating Western realm from the Scotch border to the Mediterranean, with its capital in Paris, weighing as much as the Empire, or more, deciding the fate of the Church during the great quarrel between the Councils and the Papacy, and presumably affecting the development of Spain. The centre of gravity of the whole West would have lain in Northern France, and there would have been reconstituted a Diocese of the Gauls.

He did not live. He died of his insufficient body; its dissolution hastened by, burnt out with, campaigning and intense planning and intriguing. He was barely thirty-five when he so died in that old stonework dungeon of Vincennes; and, dying, he knew (it must have been an agony for him to know) that he could only leave instructions which might be bungled, lacking his personal command.

He was filled with religion, but religion of a twisted kind. When he rode into Paris down the rue St. Martin, the Roman road through the city (reversing Cæsar's order), when he kissed all the way the relics which the priests held up to him, it was no mere show. He was fervent in these things; and the whole world knows how he whispered, as he died, that his soul had hungered to retake Jerusalem. It is rhetorical but not unjust to say that he was, in spirit, the last of the Crusading kings. He was abominably cruel. He said that war without burning was like beef without mustard. He added fuel to what needed no addition—the strict and organised repression of heresy in the crisis which ended with the disruption of Christendom. It is true that the Church in England had fallen into the hands of those great lords who cared first for their revenues and very much less for doctrine. It is true that the Lancastrian usurpation needed to rely upon such Lords Ecclesiastical, as it needed to rely upon their brothers and cousins, the Lords Temporal. But we must not read into that truth the repeated falsehood that the Lancastrians only used the Church by way of policy. They were intense in their worship, and no one of them more than this one, the greatest of them.

Henry V came as a lad into an inheritance which he must have known to be most unsafe. Its instability spurred him to the famous effort he made. His father (that broad-faced, russet-bearded man, foredoomed to death from a taint in blood, but at the moment of his crime still vigorous) had ousted his cousin Richard with the vilest forms of treason, hypocrisy and lying, and then—surely without doubt—had murdered him. To the men of his own time, and (as I believe) to Henry IV's own soul, it was an abomination. The popular conscience judged the thing aright, and the criminal himself was haunted by the necessity for expiation. The story, doubtful or true (perhaps disproved but still arguable), that this king's body was thrown overboard by the sailors taking it down the Thames in their terror lest it should bring shipwreck, is at any rate symbolic of how Henry IV was looked upon by the common people. Now, his son may have argued that, with Richard dead, and no male heir of the Plantagenet blood surviving with better right than his own, the evil had been conjured. Even so the foreign war was undertaken by that young man (though by advice) with the desire to make his line founded and secure.

Having undertaken the adventure, with what genius does he not complete it! There is, of course, a major element of chance in all military affairs; but mark his way of accepting gratefully every favour which Fortune gave him and in mastering her when she teased him with obstacles. I think she, being a woman, must have loved him before the end.

He marched out from Harfleur with something less than a division—11,000 men. It was his business to get to Calais immediately, by rapid marches. In his eyes it must have seemed not only his business but a necessity. He found the passages of the Somme blocked; first the lower fords, then bridge after bridge. He still marched upstream. What qualities there must have been in that young commander (he was but twenty-eight) to keep discipline and even enthusiasm alive within the little army; to carry them on, covering more than fifteen miles a day, across the great bend of the river, determined to force a passage somewhere, even if he had to turn the obstacle by getting right down south and round across the shallow sources of the stream—with Calais (to which his back was turned) his objective all the time! What a handling of men to preserve that force without serious losses in days when common provision failed and they were gathering nuts for sustenance!

They turned northward, not challenging the walled towns: they heard of the great host gathered against them beyond the crossing of the Ternoise. They went up on the October evening, through the drenched fields, to the huts and tall trees of Maisoncelles. They slept in what barns they could or bivouacked in the rain. The next dull autumn dawn was Agincourt.

Agincourt did not give him that Anglo-French realm which had been the dream of the Plantagenets, inherited from the House of Normandy for now more than three hundred years. If he came at last to plucking the fruit (which rotted after his death) it was not directly through that Picard victory, but by a masterly diplomatic play between the warring factions of the Capetian House. Here again fate helped him; but how admirably he seized opportunity!

And all this done, he died. And the folly of others and the turn of fate, and the intervention of revelation, of vision and of whatever accompanies the Higher Powers undid it all.

The Maid rode over it: against that riding no mere mortal could make calculation.

Yet even as he died, murmuring of the Holy City, Henry must have known what a tangle he left, though he could not have known how the undoing of his effort would come. It is very often so with those who achieve much. They cannot but foresee that their achievement will fail at last, but they cannot conceive by what unexpected agency it will fail; they only know that nothing men plan is fully and finally performed.

For Discussion:

1. How does Belloc's opening paragraph set the tone for this essay? Does he maintain this tone to the end? Explain.
2. The essay is called "Henry V." Do you think the author is trying to give you something more than a message about the king? Explain.
3. If Belloc is sincere in his admiration for Henry V, why does he say, "He had the good fortune to fire the imagination of William Shakespeare, . . . the luck to die at the height of his military success"?
4. Analyze the character of Henry V as Belloc presents him. Do his vices outweigh his virtues or does he seem to have them in the same proportion as other men?
5. Do you feel that the final paragraph repeats Belloc's point in another way? Explain your answer.

For Composition: Choose one of the following titles and write several well-developed paragraphs on it: (a) Labels Are Not Always Exact, (b) A Hero in Spite of Himself, (c) Private Life vs. Public Life.

The Crime

MAX BEERBOHM

Sir Max Beerbohm (1872–1956), known as the "Incomparable Max," is as famous for his sly caricatures as he is for his witty and satirical essays. Both as an artist and a writer, he poked fun at people, not caring how important they seemed to be. This was done with such elegance and good humor, however, that his work has produced nothing but genial laughter.

A master of the familiar essay, Beerbohm touched lightly but accurately on various weaknesses and shortcomings of people, including himself, and on English life in general. He hated humbug and he attacked it wherever he saw it, though his ridicule is always good-natured. No modern-day essayist has been so sharply critical while writing such graceful, sophisticated prose. The combination has been the delight of his many readers. In "The Crime," Beerbohm pokes fun at women novelists and his attitude to their books.

On a bleak wet stormy afternoon at the outset of last year's Spring, I was in a cottage, all alone, and knowing that I must be all alone till evening. It was a remote cottage, in a remote county, and had been "let furnished" by its owner. My spirits are easily affected by weather, and I hate solitude. And I dislike to be master of things that are not mine. "Be careful not break us," say the glass and china. "You'd better not spill ink on *me*," growls the carpet. "None of your dog's-earing, thumb-marking, backbreaking tricks *here!*" snarl the books.

The books in this cottage looked particularly disagreeable— horrid little upstarts of this and that scarlet or cerulean "series" of "standard" authors. Having gloomily surveyed them, I turned my back on them, and watched the rain streaming down the latticed window, whose panes seemed likely to be shattered at any moment by the wind. I have known men who constantly visit the Central Criminal Court, visit also the scenes where famous crimes were committed, form their own theories of those crimes, collect souvenirs of those crimes, and call themselves Criminologists. As for me, my interest in crime is, alas, merely morbid. I did not know, as those others would doubtless have known, that the situation in which I found myself was precisely of the kind most conducive to the darkest deeds. I did but bemoan it, and think of Lear in the hovel on the heath. The wind howled in the chimney, and the rain had begun to sputter right down it, so that the fire was beginning to hiss in a very sinister manner. Suppose the fire went out! It looked as if it meant to. I snatched the pair of bellows that hung beside it. I plied them vigorously. "Now mind!—not *too* vigorously. We aren't yours!" they wheezed. I handled them more gently. But I did not release them till they had secured me a steady blaze. I sat down before that blaze. Despair had been warded off. Gloom, however, remained; and gloom grew. I felt that I should prefer any one's thoughts to mine. I rose, I returned to the books. A dozen or so of those which were on the lowest of the three shelves were full-sized, were octavo, looked as though they had been bought to be read. I would exercise my undoubted right to read one of them. Which of them? I gradually decided on a novel by a well-known writer whose works, though I had several times had the honour of meeting her, were known to me only by repute.

I knew nothing of them that was not good. The lady's "output" had not been at all huge, and it was agreed that her "level" was high. I had always gathered that the chief characteristic of her work was its great "vitality." The book in my hand was a third edition of her latest novel, and at the end of it were numerous press-notices, at which I glanced for confirmation. "Immense vitality," yes, said one critic. "Full," said another, "of an intense vitality." "A book that will live," said a third. How on earth did he know that? I was, however, very willing to believe in the vitality of this writer for all present purposes. Vitality was a thing in which she herself, her talk, her glance, her gestures, abounded. She and they had been, I remembered, rather too much for me. The first time I met her, she said something that I lightly and mildly disputed. On no future occasion did I stem any opinion of hers. Not that she had been rude. Far from it. She had but in a sisterly, brotherly way, and yet in a way that was filially eager too, asked me to explain my point. I did my best. She was all attention. But I was conscious that my best, under her eye, was not good. She was quick to help me: she said for me just what I had tried to say, and proceeded to show me just why it was wrong. I smiled the gallant smile of a man who regards women as all the more adorable because logic is *not* their strong point, bless them! She asked—not aggressively, but strenuously, as one who dearly loves a joke—what I was smiling at. Altogether, a chastening encounter; and my memory of it was tinged with a feeble resentment. How she had scored. No man likes to be worsted in argument by a woman. And I fancy that to be vanquished by a feminine writer is the kind of defeat least of all agreeable to a man who writes. A "sex war," we are often told is to be one of the features of the world's future—women demanding the right to do men's work, and men refusing, resisting, counter-attacking. It seems likely enough. One can believe anything of the world's future. Yet one conceives that not all men, if this particular evil come to pass, will stand packed shoulder to shoulder against all women. One does not feel that the dockers will be very bitter against such women as want to be miners, or the plumbers frown much upon the would-be steeple-jills. I myself have never had my sense of fitness jarred, nor a spark of animosity roused in me, by a woman practicing any of the fine arts—except the art of writing. That she should write a few little poems or *pensées*, or some impressions of a trip in a dahabieh as far as (say) Biskra, or even a short story or two, seems to me not wholly amiss, even though she do such things for publication. But that she should be an habitual, professional author, with a passion for her art, and a fountainpen and an agent, and sums down in advance of royalties on sales in Canada and Australia, and a profound knowledge of human character, and an essentially sane outlook, is somehow incongruous with my notions—my mistaken notions, if you will—of what she ought to be.

"Has a profound knowledge of human character, and an essentially sane outlook" said one of the critics quoted at the end of the book I had chosen. The wind and the rain in the chimney had not abated, but the fire was bearing up bravely. So would I. I would read cheerfully and without prejudice. I poked the fire and, pushing my chair slightly back, lest the heat should warp the book's covers, began Chapter I. A woman sat writing in a summer-house at the end of a small garden that overlooked a great valley in Surrey. The description of her was calculated to make her very admirable—a thorough *woman*, not strictly beautiful, but likely to be thought beautiful by those who knew her well; not dressed as though she gave much heed to her clothes, but dressed in a fashion that exactly harmonised with her special type. Her pen "travelled" rapidly across the foolscap, and while it did so she was described in more and more detail. But at length she came to a "knotty point" in what she was writing. She paused, she pushed back the hair from her temples, she looked forth at the valley; and now the landscape was described, but not at all exhaustively, for the writer soon overcame her difficulty, and her pen travelled faster than ever, till suddenly there was a cry of "Mammy!" and in rushed a seven-year-old child, in conjunction with whom she was more than ever admirable; after which the narrative skipped back across eight years, and the woman became a girl giving as yet no token of future eminence in literature, but—I had an impulse which I obeyed almost before I was conscious of it.

Nobody could have been more surprised than I was at what I had done—done so neatly, so quietly and gently. The book stood closed, upright, with its back to me, just as on a book-shelf, behind the bars of the grate. There it was. And it gave forth, as the flames crept up the blue cloth sides of it, a pleasant though acrid smell. My astonishment had passed, giving place to an exquisite satisfaction. How pottering and fumbling a thing was even the best kind of written criticism! I understood the contempt felt by the man of action for the man of words. But what pleased me most was that at last, actually, I, at my age, I of all people, had committed a crime—was guilty of a crime. I had power to revoke it. I might write to my bookseller for an unburnt copy, and place it on the shelf where this one had stood—this gloriously glowing one. I would do nothing of the sort. What I had done I had done. I would wear forever on my conscience the white rose of theft and the red rose of arson. If hereafter the owner of this cottage happened to miss that volume—let him! If he were fool enough to write to me about it, would I share my grand secret with him? No. Gently, with his poker, I prodded that volume further among the coals. The all-but-consumed binding shot forth little tongues of bright colour—flamelets of sapphire, amethyst, emerald. Charming! Could even the author herself not admire them? Perhaps. Poor woman!—I had scored now, scored so perfectly that I felt myself to be almost a brute while I poked off the loosened black outer pages and led the fire on to pages that were but pale brown.

These were quickly devoured. But it seemed to me whenever I left the fire to forage for itself it made little headway. I pushed the book over on its side. The flames closed on it, but presently, licking their lips, fell back, as though they had had enough. I took the tongs and put the book upright again, and raked it fore and aft. It seemed almost as thick as ever. With poker and tongs I carved it into two, three sections—the inner pages flashing white as when they were sent to the binders. Strange! Aforetime, a book was burnt now and again in the market-place by the common hangman. Was he, I wondered, paid by the hour? I had always supposed the thing quite easy for him—a bright little, brisk little conflagration, and so home. Perhaps other books were less resistant than this one? I began to feel that the critics were more right than they knew. Here was a book that had indeed an intense vitality, and an immense vitality. It was a book that would live—do what one might. I vowed it should not. I sub-divided it, spread it, redistributed it. Ever and anon my eye would be caught by some sentence or fragment of a sentence in the midst of a charred page before the flames crept over it. "lways loathed you, but," I remember; and "ning. Tolstoi was right." Who had always loathed whom? And what, what, had Tolstoi been right about? I had an absurd but genuine desire to know. Too late! Confound the woman!—she was scoring again. I furiously drove her pages into the yawning crimson jaws of the coals. Those jaws had lately been golden. Soon, to my horror, they seemed to be growing grey. They seemed to be closing—on nothing. Flakes of black paper, full-sized layers of paper brown and white, began to hide them from me altogether. I sprinkled a boxful of wax matches. I resumed the bellows. I lunged with the poker. I held a newspaper over the whole grate. I did all that inspiration could suggest, or skill accomplish. Vainly. The fire went out—darkly, dismally, gradually, quite out.

How she had scored again! But she did not know it. I felt no bitterness against her as I lay back in my chair, inert, listening to the storm that was still raging. I blamed only myself. I had done wrong. The small room became very cold. Whose fault was that but my own? I had done wrong hastily, but had done it and been glad of it. I had not remembered the words a wise king wrote long ago, that the lamp of the wicked shall be put out, and that the way of transgressors is hard.

For Discussion:

1. In this narrative essay, the setting is quite important. Explain.
2. The author pokes gentle fun at himself. How does each of the following contribute to this?
   (a) "I felt that I should prefer anyone's thoughts to mine."
   (b) "I smiled the gallant smile of a man who regards women as all the more adorable because logic is not their strong point, bless them!"

(c) "That she should write a few little poems, . . . or even a short story or two, seems to me not wholly amiss."

(d) "I would read cheerfully and without prejudice."

(e) "I understand the contempt felt by the man of action for the man of words."

3. Beerbohm is satirizing himself as a male and as a writer. In what way does his satire extend to all men and to all writers?

4. In this "sex war" the woman wins. Does she, however, come out entirely unscathed? Explain.

For Composition: Describe an experience of yours in which someone has scored on you without knowing it. Make the reader feel as you felt.

The Graf Spee

WINSTON CHURCHILL

Few political figures have as many claims to greatness as Sir Winston Churchill (1874–   ); fewer still have achieved their fame against greater odds. From the beginning, Churchill's genius as debator, tactician, and statesman was recognized, yet the very qualities that won him attention— brilliance, impetuosity, self-confidence, determination, and ambition— made him politically suspect. Through nearly forty years he battled the distrust and opposition of his countrymen in an intense struggle to become Prime Minister. His triumph came in England's darkest hour during World War II. As the German Army, which had broken through Holland and Belgium, stood poised for attack, England's three parties unanimously entrusted him with the care of the nation.

Temperament and experience, as well as personal interests fitted Churchill for his post. His temperament and experience were public knowledge, but only those who had read his works (some twenty-five volumes published during his stormy parliamentary career) were aware of his personal interests: an overwhelming desire to master military science and a consuming desire to become a part of the world of literature and of writing. The former provided the assurance he needed for moments of decision in World War II; the latter enabled him not only to rouse England and the world to new heights in periods of crisis, but also to leave to posterity an impressive record of the Western world's stand in the cause of humanity.

Churchill's prose is crisp, logically organized, carefully executed and frequently seasoned with the ready wit that won friends and vanquished foes. "The Graf Spee" is a selection from the first volume of his war memoirs, *The Gathering Storm*.

The *Deutschland*, which was to have harassed our lifeline across the Northwest Atlantic, interpreted her orders with comprehending caution. At no time during her two and a half months' cruise did she approach a convoy. Her determined efforts to avoid British forces prevented her from making more than two kills, one being a small Norwegian ship. A third ship, the United States *City of Flint*, carrying a cargo for Britain, was captured, but was eventually released by the Germans from a Norwegian port. Early in November, the

Deutschland slunk back to Germany, passing again through Arctic waters. The mere presence of this powerful ship upon our main trade route had, however, imposed, as was intended, a serious strain upon our escorts and hunting groups in the north Atlantic. We should in fact have preferred her activity to the vague menace she embodied.

The *Graf Spee* was more daring and imaginative, and soon became the centre of attention in the South Atlantic. In this vast area powerful Allied forces came into play by the middle of October. One group consisted of the aircraft carrier *Ark Royal* and the battle cruiser *Renown*, working from Freetown in conjunction with a French group of two heavy cruisers and the British aircraft carrier *Hermes*, based on Dakar. At the Cape of Good Hope were the two heavy cruisers *Sussex* and *Shropshire*, while on the east coast of South America, covering the vital traffic with the River Plate and Rio de Janeiro, ranged Commodore Harwood's group, comprising the *Cumberland, Exeter, Ajax*, and *Achilles*. The *Achilles* was a New Zealand ship manned mainly by New Zealanders.

The *Spee's* practice was to make a brief appearance at some point, claim a victim, and vanish again into the trackless ocean wastes. After a second appearance farther south on the Cape route, in which she sank only one ship, there was no further sign of her for nearly a month, during which our hunting groups were searching far and wide in all areas, and special vigilance was enjoined in the Indian Ocean. This was in fact her destination, and on November 15 she sank a small British tanker in the Mozambique Channel, between Madagascar and the mainland. Having thus registered her appearance as a feint in the Indian Ocean, in order to draw the hunt in that direction, her Captain—Langsdorff, a high-class person—promptly doubled back and, keeping well south of the Cape, re-entered the Atlantic. This move had not been unforeseen; but our plans to intercept him were foiled by the quickness of his withdrawal. It was by no means clear to the Admiralty whether in fact one raider was on the prowl or two, and exertions were made, both in the Indian and Atlantic Oceans. We also thought that the *Spee* was her sister ship, the *Scheer*. This disproportion between the strength of the enemy and the counter-measures forced upon us was vexatious. It recalled to me the anxious weeks before the actions at Coronel and later at the Falkland Islands in December, 1914, when we had to be prepared at seven or eight different points, in the

Pacific and South Atlantic, for the arrival of Admiral von Spee with the earlier edition of the *Scharnhorst* and *Gneisenau*. A quarter of a century had passed, but the puzzle was the same. It was with a definite sense of relief that we learnt that the *Spee* had appeared once more on the Cape-Freetown route, sinking two more ships on December 2 and one on the seventh.

*   *   *   *   *

From the beginning of the war, Commodore Harwood's special care and duty had been to cover British shipping off the River Plate and Rio de Janeiro. He was convinced that sooner or later the *Spee* would come towards the Plate, where the richest prizes were offered to her. He had carefully thought out the tactics which he would adopt in an encounter. Together, his eight-inch cruisers *Cumberland* and *Exeter*, and his six-inch cruisers *Ajax* and *Achilles*, could not only catch but kill. However, the needs of fuel and refit made it unlikely that all four would be present "on the day." If they were not, the issue was disputable. On hearing that the *Doric Star* had been sunk on December 2, Harwood guessed right. Although she was over three thousand miles away, he assumed that the *Spee* would come towards the Plate. He estimated with luck and wisdom that she might arrive by the thirteenth. He ordered all his available forces to concentrate there by December 12. Alas, the *Cumberland* was refitting at the Falklands; but on the morning of the thirteenth, *Exeter*, *Ajax*, and *Achilles* were in company at the centre of the shipping routes off the mouth of the river. Sure enough, at 6.14 A.M., smoke was sighted to the east. The longed-for collision had come.

Harwood in the *Ajax*, disposing his forces so as to attack the pocket battleship from widely divergent quarters and thus confuse her fire, advanced at the utmost speed of his small squadron. Captain Langsdorff thought at the first glance that he had only to deal with one light cruiser and two destroyers, and he too went full speed ahead; but a few moments later, he recognised the quality of his opponents, and knew that a mortal action impended. The two forces were now closing at nearly fifty miles an hour. Langsdorff had but a minute to make up his mind. His right course would have been to turn away immediately so as to keep his assailants as long as possible under the superior range and weight of his eleven-inch guns, to which the British could not at first have replied. He would thus have gained for his undisturbed firing the difference between adding speeds and subtracting them. He might well have crippled one of his foes before any could fire at him. He decided, on the contrary, to hold on his course and make for the *Exeter*. The action, therefore, began almost simultaneously on both sides.

Commodore Harwood's tactics proved advantageous. The eight-inch salvos from the *Exeter* struck the *Spee* from the earliest stages of the fight. Meanwhile, the six-inch cruisers were also hitting hard and effectively. Soon the *Exeter* received a hit which, besides knocking out B turret, destroyed all the communications on the bridge, killed or wounded nearly all upon it, and put the ship temporarily out of control. By this time, however, the six-inch cruisers could no longer be neglected by the enemy, and the *Spee* shifted her main armament to them, thus giving respite to the *Exeter* at a critical moment. The German battleship, plastered from three directions, found the British attack too hot, and soon afterwards turned away under a smoke screen with the apparent intention of making for the River Plate. Langsdorff had better have done this earlier.

After this turn the *Spee* once more engaged the *Exeter*, hard hit by the eleven-inch shells. All her forward guns were out of action. She was burning fiercely amidships and had a heavy list. Captain Bell, unscathed by the explosion on the bridge, gathered two or three officers round him in the after control station, and kept his ship in action with her sole remaining turret until at 7.30 failure of pressure put this, too, out of action. He could do no more. At 7.40 the *Exeter* turned away to effect repairs and took no further part in the fight.

The *Ajax* and *Achilles*, already in pursuit, continued the action in the most spirited manner. The *Spee* turned all her heavy guns upon them. By 7.25 the two after turrets in the *Ajax* had been knocked out, and the *Achilles* had also suffered damage. These two light cruisers were no match for the enemy in gun-power, and finding that his ammunition was running low, Harwood in the *Ajax* decided to break off the fight till dark, when he would have better chances of using his lighter armament effectively, and perhaps his torpedoes. He, therefore, turned away under cover of smoke, and the enemy did not follow. This fierce action had lasted an hour and twenty minutes. During all the rest of the day the *Spee* made for

Montevideo, the British cruisers hanging grimly on her heels with
only occasional interchanges of fire. Shortly after midnight, the *Spee*
entered Montevideo and lay there repairing damage, taking in
stores, landing wounded, transshipping personnel to a German
merchant ship, and reporting to the Fuehrer. *Ajax* and *Achilles* lay
outside, determined to dog her to her doom should she venture
forth. Meanwhile, on the night of the fourteenth, the *Cumberland*,
which had been steaming at full speed from the Falklands, took the
place of the utterly crippled *Exeter*. The arrival of this eight-inch-gun
cruiser restored to its narrow balance a doubtful situation.

It had been most exciting to follow the drama of this brilliant
action from the Admiralty War Room, where I spent a large part of the
thirteenth. Our anxieties did not end with the day. Mr. Chamberlain
was at that time in France on a visit to the Army. On the seventeenth I wrote to him:

December 17, 1939.

If the *Spee* breaks out, as she may do tonight, we hope to renew the
action of the thirteenth with the *Cumberland*, an *eight* eight-inch-gun
ship, in the place of the six-gun *Exeter*. The *Spee* knows now that
Renown and *Ark Royal* are oiling at Rio, so this is her best chance. The
Dorsetshire and *Shropshire*, who are coming across from the Cape, are
still three and four days away respectively. It is fortunate that the
Cumberland was handy at the Falklands, as *Exeter* was heavily damaged.
She was hit over a hundred times, one turret smashed, three guns knocked
out, and sixty officers and men killed and twenty wounded. Indeed the
Exeter fought one of the finest and most resolute actions against superior
range and metal on record. Every conceivable precaution has been
taken to prevent the *Spee* slipping out unobserved, and I have told
Harwood (who is now an Admiral and a K.C.B.) that he is free to attack
her anywhere outside the three-mile limit. We should prefer, however,
that she should be interned, as this will be less creditable to the German
Navy than being sunk in action. Moreover, a battle of this kind is full
of hazard, and needless bloodshed must never be sought.

The whole of the Canadians came in safely this morning under the
protection of the main fleet and [are] being welcomed by Anthony, Mas-
sey, and I trust a good part of the people of Greenock and Glasgow.
We plan to give them a cordial reception. They are to go to Aldershot,
where no doubt you will go and see them presently.

There have been ten air attacks today on individual ships along the
east coast from Wick to Dover, and some of the merchant ships have

been machine-gunned out of pure spite, some of our people being hit on their decks.

I am sure you must be having a most interesting time at the Front, and I expect you will find that change is the best kind of rest.

From the moment when we heard that action was joined, we instantly ordered powerful forces to concentrate off Montevideo, but our hunting groups were naturally widely dispersed and none was within two thousand miles of the scene. In the north, Force K, comprising the *Renown* and *Ark Royal*, was completing a sweep which had begun at Capetown ten days before and was now six hundred miles east of Pernambuco, and twenty-five hundred miles from Montevideo. Farther north still, the cruiser *Neptune* with three destroyers had just parted company with the French Force X and were coming south to join Force K. All these were ordered to Montevideo; they had first to fuel at Rio. However, we succeeded in creating the impression that they had already left Rio and were approaching Montevideo at thirty knots.

On the other side of the Atlantic, Force H was returning to the Cape for fuel after an extended sweep up the African coast. Only the *Dorsetshire* was immediately available at Capetown and was ordered at once to join Admiral Harwood, but she had over four thousand miles to travel. She was followed later by the *Shropshire*. In addition, to guard against the possible escape of the *Spee* to the eastward, Force I, comprising the *Cornwall*, *Gloucester*, and the aircraft carrier *Eagle*, from the East Indies station, which at this time was at Durban, was placed at the disposal of the Commander-in-Chief, South Atlantic.

*   *   *   *   *

Meanwhile, Captain Langsdorff telegraphed on December 16 to the German Admiralty as follows:

Strategic position off Montevideo. Besides the cruisers and destroyers, *Ark Royal* and *Renown*. Close blockade at night; escape into open sea and break-through to home waters hopeless. . . . Request decision on whether the ship should be scuttled in spite of insufficient depth in the Estuary of the Plate, or whether internment is to be preferred.

At a conference presided over by the Fuehrer, at which Raeder and Jodl were present, the following answer was decided on:

Attempt by all means to extend the time in neutral waters. . . . Fight your way through to Buenos Aires if possible. No internment in Uruguay. Attempt effective destruction, if ship is scuttled.

As the German envoy in Montevideo reported later that further attempts to extend the time limit of seventy-two hours were fruitless, these orders were confirmed by the German Supreme Command.

Accordingly, during the afternoon of the seventeenth the *Spee* transferred more than seven hundred men, with baggage and provisions, to the German merchant ship in the harbour. Shortly afterwards Admiral Harwood learnt that she was weighing anchor. At 6.15 P.M., watched by immense crowds, she left harbour and steamed slowly seaward, awaited hungrily by the British cruisers. At 8.54 P.M., as the sun sank, the *Ajax's* aircraft reported: "*Graf Spee* has blown herself up." The *Renown* and *Ark Royal* were still a thousand miles away.

Langsdorff was broken-hearted by the loss of his ship. In spite of the full authority he had received from his Government, he wrote on December 19:

I can now only prove by my death that the fighting services of the Third Reich are ready to die for the honour of the flag. I alone bear the responsibility for scuttling the pocket battleship *Admiral Graf Spee*. I am happy to pay with my life for any possible reflection on the honour of the flag. I shall face my fate with firm faith in the cause and the future of the nation and of my Fuehrer.

That night he shot himself.

Thus ended the first surface challenge to British trade on the oceans. No other raider appeared until the spring of 1940, when a new campaign opened, utilising disguised merchant ships. These could more easily avoid detection, but on the other hand could be mastered by lesser forces than those required to destroy a pocket battleship.

For Discussion:

1. The *Graf Spee* was important enough to warrant the use of 23 light and heavy craft in tracking her down. What constituted her chief danger to Britain?
2. Why did the *Spee* concentrate on putting the *Exeter* out of the battle? What would have been perhaps a better course of action?

3. Churchill says that the arrival of the *Cumberland* on the night of the 14th "restored to its narrow balance a doubtful situation." What does this mean and what does it indicate about the *Spee* and its command?

4. What is the "three-mile limit" mentioned in Churchill's letter to Mr. Chamberlain? What was the apparent position of Uruguay and Argentina at this time (December, 1939)?

5. Was there any chance for the *Spee* to escape once she entered Montivideo? Find a passage to support your answer.

6. What actually was responsible for the scuttling of the *Spee*? What has the phrase "we had succeeded in creating the impression . . ." mean?

For Composition: Listen to the recorded excerpts of Churchill's "Dunkirk Speech" on Edward Murrow's *I Can Hear It Now: Volume I*. Write your estimate of Churchill as a speaker or as a leader of men.

The United States

E. M. FORSTER

Many critics look upon E. M. Forster (1879–   ), English novelist and critic, as a key writer of this age. They find in him the moderation arrived at through self-discipline which marks the writer who has come to grips with life and has found a solution. Unlike the majority of modern writers, he refused to face an age of confusion with his own confusion. At the outset of his career he examined the drift of the times, set a purposeful course, and consistently followed it. His works, though few in number, have quality. His novel, *Passage to India*, has become a classic in his lifetime. Readers enjoy his careful, conscientious craftsmanship and appreciate his feeling for exact imagery.

All of his works—novels, short stories, essays—in one way or another reflect the same basic themes: appearance vs. reality, barriers to human contact vs. understanding, man's search for values vs. his way of living. Forster, had he lived earlier, is certain that the essay rather than the novel would have been his medium for expressing the sum of his belief, namely that "tolerance, good temper and sympathy—are what matter really, and if the human race is not to collapse they must come to the front before long."

———◆———

America is rather like life. You can usually find in it what you look for. If you look for skyscrapers or cowboys or cocktail parties or gangsters or business connections or political problems or women's clubs, they will certainly be there. You can be very hot there or very cold. You can explore the America of your choice by plane or train, by hitch-hike or on foot. It will probably be interesting, and it is sure to be large.

I went there for the first time at the age of sixty-eight. By sixty-eight one is so to speak a pilgrim grandfather who knows very clearly what to look for when he disembarks. I had no doubt as to what I wanted to discover in America. It was to provide me with scenery and individuals. The scenery was to be of two sorts—gigantic and homely. The individuals were not to be representative—I never could get on with representative individuals—but people who existed on their own account and with whom it might therefore be possible to be friends. That is the America I looked for and was to find. My visit was a complete success from my own point of view.

After a respectful glance at New York, I went a hundred miles north into the Berkshires. It was April. The trees were leafless—thousands and thousands of birch trees, their trunks whiter than the birch trees here, milk white, ghost white in the sharp sunshine, covering the sides of the valley and the crests of the hills; and among the birches pushed pine and hemlock—which is like a not very dark green yew. Was I in England? Almost, but not quite. That was again and again to be my sensation, and in the Arizona Desert I was to feel I was almost but not quite in India, and in the Yosemite Valley that it was not quite Switzerland. America is always throwing out these old-world hints, and then withdrawing them in favour of America. To return to the Berkshires: after a few days' quiet the snow descended and silence became absolute. The country became primeval and polar—endless purity, underspreading motionless trees. I can never be grateful enough for those opening days of silence and snow. They imposed proportion. They made me realise that America is not all town: such a generalization would be truer of England. It is country—controlled no doubt by mechanised gadgets, still it is country. I was glad I had not gaped too long at the New York skyscrapers. Exciting as they are, they mislead. They do not epitomise what lies behind them. Presently the snow melted. Where it had lain appeared dark brown earth and occasional pale lilac hepaticas, and the spring began—in double quick time compared to our spring.

The Berkshires are homely scenery. Gigantic scenery is more difficult to describe, but I will make an attempt. Suppose yourself walking on a Surrey common near Bagshot. There are a good many fir trees about, the soil is sandy, and the prospect rather dull. Suddenly the common stops, and you are standing without any warning on the brink of a precipice which is one mile deep. One mile into the tortured earth it goes, the other side of the chasm is miles away, and the chasm is filled with unbelievable deposits of rock which resemble sphinxes draped in crimson shawls. That, as far as I can get it into a single sentence, gives you my first impression of the Grand Canyon of the Colorado River, but the Grand Canyon would need many sentences to describe and many books. It is the most astounding natural object I have ever seen. It frightens. There are many colours in it besides crimson—strata of black and of white, and rocks of ochre and pale lilac. And the Colorado River itself is, when one gets down to it, still more sinister, for it is muddy white and very swift, and it rages like an infuriated maggot between precipices of granite, gnawing at them and cutting the Canyon deeper. It was strange after two days amongst these marvels, and terrors, to return to the surface of the earth, and go bowling away in a 'bus between little fir trees.

The second item I sought in America was the human, the individual. My work lay mainly in universities, and there and elsewhere I found the individuals I sought. I had expected generosity and hospitality. I had not expected so much tact, charm and sensitiveness; here was the delightful surprise. Wherever I went I found delicate understanding of our troubles in Britain over food and clothing, and a desire to help that was never patronising. This was not confined to the highly educated classes. I recall a cheap eating-house in Nevada where some strangers came up and asked what they could send. I remember the chambermaid in the hotel at Salt Lake City who when I offered her a tip replied, "I don't like to take your money, brother, you need it more than I do." That is the sort of remark which comes from the heart and goes to the heart, and in the light of it and the warmth of it I found difficulty in examining the defects of the American character. The defects are, I suspect, lack of discrimination, emotionalism, and a tendency to narrow the idea of freedom into freedom to make money. "What else have we fought the war for?" a business acquaintance enquired. But I cannot feel these defects are basic. My friends reassure me against this, and not only my friends; the faces of strangers lighting up everywhere, compassionate, respectful, anxious to help. The individuals I met were mostly of Anglo-Saxon stock; I also knew some Swedish and some Italian farming people, made some Oriental contacts, and had one or two Mexican friends. I did not have the good fortune to get to know any Negroes. On the whole I saw as much of the human landscape as an elderly traveller may reasonably expect, and I liked it.

But now comes a qualification. Although the Americans I encountered were full of charitable feelings towards Great Britain, I cannot say that they showed much interest in us otherwise. I have often been asked since my return home: "What do they think about us over there?" Indeed, it is often the only thing English people want to know. The answer, not very flattering to our pride, is that the Americans scarcely think about us at all. They are curious about our Royal Family, they are grateful and appreciative towards Mr. Churchill, they are—or were—enthusiastic over British films. That is all. They do not discuss our Empire. India, over which they have been so critical in the past, is now scarcely in the news and seems to bore them. Even Palestine was seldom mentioned. An explanation of this indifference is that they concentrate, as we all do, on home affairs, and that when they do think of foreign affairs they think of Russia. China to some extent, but mostly Russia. Russia is always weighing on their minds. They are afraid of war, or that their standard of life may be lowered. I shall never forget a dinner party, supposedly given in my honour, at which one of the guests, a journalist, urged that atomic bombs should be dropped upon the Soviet Union without notice, and quoted with approval a remark which he inaccurately ascribed to Oliver Cromwell: "Stone dead hath no fellow." "That's good, isn't it, Tom?" he called to another journalist. "Stone dead hath no fellow." Tom agreed that it was very good, and they shouted: "Stone dead hath no fellow" in unison or antiphonically for the rest of the evening. They were cultivated men, but as soon as the idea of Russia occurred to them, their faces became blood red; they ceased to be human. No one seemed appalled by the display but myself, no one was surprised and our hostess congratulated herself afterwards on the success of her party. This obsession over Russia should be realised by all who would understand America, and it explains in part her lack of interest in us.

I did not encounter such hysteria elsewhere, and maybe did not frequent the circles where it is likeliest to occur. Most of the people I was with were not influential or highly placed: many of them were teachers, and some of them were young—students, or they practised music or painting or acting or the ballet, or they were doing small commercial jobs or working on the land. My general impression was of good temper and goodwill and hopefulness. I could darken the picture, no doubt. I do not take the Statue of Liberty in New York harbour as seriously as she takes herself. And I did encounter hints of oppression and of violence, and of snobbery. But the main verdict is favourable, and I do beg anyone who happens to have fallen into the habit of nagging at America to drop it. Nagging is so insidious. It often resides not in what is said but in the tone of voice. It proceeds not from considered criticism but from envy and from discontent—and, of course, life out there is far more comfortable for the average man than it is here. The food is nicer, if dearer, the clothes are nicer and cheaper, the cold drinks are not lukewarm, and the railway carriages are not dirty. But these advantages over ourselves should not embitter us against the people who enjoy them. Nor should we charge it against all Americans that their politicians do what our politicians tell them, and tell us, they ought not to do.

I chanced to end my three months' visit in the same district of the Berkshires where it had begun. Now it was high summer. The little spring from which I fetched water every day had already begun to flag. The meadows were full of flowers—ox-eye daisies, black-eyed susans, orchids, and an under-carpet of creeping jenny; the meadows sloped down to a brook where the farm hands bathed. There were swallow-tail butterflies and fritillaries, and the bobolink, a very agreeable bird, skipped from post to post carolling, and another bird, the phoebe, repeated "phoebe, phoebe, phoebe," whence its name. At night there were fireflies to remind us that this was in the latitude of Madrid. Thunderstorms did not disconcert them, and I would watch their flash vanish in the superior brilliancy of lightning, and reappear. Some of them flew at the level of the grass, others across the curtain of birch trees. They were extraordinarily bright; it was a good year for fireflies, and the memory of them sparking in the warm rain and the thunder is the latest of my American impressions, and the loveliest.

For Discussion:

1. Forster wrote this delightful essay in 1947. If he visited the United States today, would he find the same things as he did in 1947? Why was his visit a complete success?
2. How much of Forster, the man, is revealed in his choices of things to do and people to meet during his visit?
3. Why does the author use the phrase "supposedly given in my honor," when he relates the episode of the dinner party? What features of the evening appalled him? Why?
4. Do you agree with Forster that the defects of the American character are "lack of discrimination, emotionalism, and a tendency to narrow the idea of freedom into freedom to make money"? Defend your position. If you disagree with him, perhaps you could point out how he might have made this error in judging Americans.

For Composition: Forster has the poet's eye in describing the Berkshires. Imitate his vivid power of picturing the birches, by describing some nature spot you have seen and enjoyed.

The Drama

HESKETH PEARSON

At fourteen, Hesketh Pearson (1887–   ) was writing summaries of famous men's lives for family and neighborhood enjoyment. People fascinated him. He wanted to know all about them: who they were, what they did, and why they did it. At school, life rather than books and studies attracted him. On leaving school, he entered the theatrical world where he acted, almost exclusively, in Shakespearean productions. As the theater turned more and more to the modern playwrights, his interest flagged. Occupation followed occupation in quick succession: soldier, salesman, journalist. Then his great interest in people took the form of biographical writing, and Pearson found his true career.

Pearson's biographies are not dry, factual works. His tone is warm, chatty, and informal. He attempts to give you a personal introduction to his subject. He invites you to stop and chat about this person whom he would like you to have as a mutual friend. Yet along with Pearson's delightful style, there is exceedingly careful scholarship. To read *Dizzy*, a biography of Disraeli, is to know the whole of Victorian England. To read *G. B. S.: A Full-Length Portrait* is to know, not only Shaw, but also Shakespeare, Ibsen, drama, art, music, manners, morals, and politics. The experience is exhilarating.

————◆————

Shaw had two very good reasons for attacking Shakespeare: firstly, he wished to draw attention to himself,[1] secondly, he wished to obtain a proper recognition of Ibsen's genius. He had been bowled over by Ibsen and had written a book, *The Quintessence of Ibsenism*, in order to bring Ibsen's philosophy into complete harmony with his own. Thus his reasons for smashing the idol Shakespeare were quite excusable because they were entirely personal. The enthusiastic and intelligent youths of every period like to discover their own gods and to kick the gods of their fathers, both discovery and kicking being healthy and enjoyable pursuits. Since Shaw fought for Ibsen, the younger generation has discovered Shaw and kicked Ibsen, or discovered Tchekov and kicked Shaw, or discovered someone and kicked

[1] This was not his view, for when I expressed it he gave me a volley: "What a horrid libel! I never thought about drawing attention to myself, because I could not help doing it every time I put pen to paper. Besides, my own Shakespearean output was then unwritten. I had nothing (to speak of) to draw attention to." "Except, as I said, yourself," was my reply.

someone else. It does not matter in the long run. The mental exercise of taking in and throwing out is thoroughly invigorating; youth grows up and achieves a more balanced view; while the immortals are all the better for the mud that has been thrown at them, because it has helped to protect them from the corrosion of time. No one to-day is so modern as Shakespeare, who owes a little of his freshness to Shaw's mud-slinging, which made it necessary for the succeeding age to clean him up and see what his features were really like.

Yet Shaw's line of attack on Shakespeare was as feeble as his reasons for it were sound. True he was not quite so stupid as Tolstoy, whose chief complaint was that Shakespeare had failed to face the question, "What are we alive for?", which any one but a fool would have to answer "In order to live" or "God alone knows!" But Shaw made the childish error, which a dramatist of all people should avoid, of confusing Shakespeare with his creations; and since his line of attack revealed his chief weakness as a man, and therefore as an artist, we must deal with it here.

One of Shakespeare's most famous characters is a witch-ridden, conscience-stricken, wife-chidden murderer, who wades through slaughter to a throne and shuts the gates of mercy on his friends, their wives and children, and who, following a course of ghostly apparitions and harrowing warnings from the infernal world, and surrounded on every side by conspiracy, rebellion and hatred, begins to be weary of life, takes refuge in self-pity, and regards the whole business of existence as a meaningless and sorry affair. "Out, out, brief candle," he says, reasonably enough under the circumstances. Shaw calmly took this as Shakespeare's considered attitude towards life, not as an expression of Macbeth's momentary emotion. "I want to be thoroughly used up when I die," he wrote, "for the harder I work, the more I live. I rejoice in life for its own sake. Life is no 'brief candle' for me. It is a sort of splendid torch, which I have got hold of for the moment; and I want to make it burn as brightly as possible before handing it on to future generations." Perhaps all that need be said about this impassioned outburst of rhetoric is that if Shakespeare had thought "splendid torch" a truer symbol of life from Macbeth's point of view, or a more exact expression of a superstitious and disillusioned dictator's feelings than "brief candle," he would no doubt have used it.

Shaw frequently made this error of condemning Shakespeare out of the mouths of his creations, and once he even did it when denying that the characters in a play of his own were so many projections of himself. "Some of the critics imagine I am contradicting myself when my characters contradict one another," he complained to an interviewer. "According to these innocents all the persons in *John Bull's Other Island* are only mouthpieces of Shaw . . . and the differences between these characters are therefore, if you please, my inconsistencies, my insincerities, my levities!" Having poured scorn on the critics for being such chumps, he then went on to say: "The business of a dramatist is to make experience intelligible. Shakespeare's notion that it was to hold the mirror up to nature was the blunder of a playwright who was a mere observer, not a thinker." It was, however, Hamlet, not his creator, who talked about holding the mirror up to nature; so Shakespeare's characters could be used in evidence against him, but Shaw's characters could not be so used.

The assumption that Shakespeare was expressing his own opinions through his creations shows that Shaw, while refusing to admit that his own characters expressed himself, could not really understand a dramatist who was able to attain complete objectivity. Shaw's chief failing as a dramatist was his inability to portray types with whom he had no sympathy, all his men and women betraying their blood-relationship, just as his chief failing as a man was his inability to understand people with whom he did not agree.

One of Shaw's objections to Shakespeare was that he did not write like Bunyan; in other words, that he pictured life as it was and is, not as Bunyan or Shaw would have liked it to be. Later we shall have an opportunity of placing Shakespeare's portrait of a great man of action against Shaw's conception of the same man, comparing them with recent samples of the species in real life. For the moment we may content ourselves with a typical specimen of Shavian absurdity on the theme of heroism.

The world was to Bunyan a more terrible place than it was to Shakespeare, said Shaw, "but he saw through it a path at the end of which a man might look not only forward to the Celestial City, but back on his life and say:—'Though with great difficulty I am got hither, yet now I do not repent me of all the trouble I have been at to arrive where I am. My sword I give to him that shall succeed me in my pilgrimage, and my courage and skill to him that can get it.' The heart vibrates like a bell to such an utterance as this: to turn from it to 'Out, out, brief candle,' and 'The rest is silence,' and 'We are such stuff as dreams are made of; and our little life is rounded by a sleep' is to turn from life, strength, resolution, morning air and eternal youth, to the terrors of a drunken nightmare."

Every single statement in this paragraph creates a totally false impression. The world could not have been a more terrible place to the author of *Pilgrim's Progress* than it was to the author of *King Lear.* The heart does not vibrate like a bell to the utterance of Bunyan's Mr. Valiant-for-truth, unless with the object of drowning the smug sentiments of a boastful prig. Shakespeare did not mean to convey a sense of life, strength, resolution, morning air or eternal youth when Macbeth was on his last legs, Hamlet was dying, and Prospero was about to retire from the world and lead a meditative life. Nor has any one except Shaw discovered the terrors of a drunken nightmare in the last words of those three characters. Nor is there the smallest evidence that those last words expressed Shakespeare's own feelings more accurately than the last words of Falstaff or any other of his great characters. Nor, for that matter, shall I be silly enough to call Bunyan a boastful prig solely on the strength of Mr. Valiant-for-truth's high opinion of himself, which is precisely what one would expect from a man so named. When, by the way, Shakespeare wished to sound the heroic note, he did not resort to the moral babble and pietistic twaddle of Bunyan. He put into the mouth of an average man a simple remark which told ordinary people what they had to do and what made it worth doing:

> Men must endure
> Their going hence even as their coming hither:
> Ripeness is all.

For Discussion:

1. Do the author's criticisms of Shaw indicate that he was a friend or an enemy? Explain.
2. Do you agree with the statement: "The immortals are all the better for the mud that has been thrown at them"?
3. Can you find proof in present-day America that "No one today is so modern as Shakespeare"?
4. What was the fatal mistake in Shaw's attack on Shakespeare?
5. Does Shaw differ from most men in being "unable to understand people with whom he did not agree"? Explain.
6. Does this essay provide a useful model for students interested in improving their own style? Why or why not?

Shooting an Elephant

GEORGE ORWELL

The provocative English writer George Orwell (1903–1950) was little known in America before the publication of his satirical *Animal Farm* and *1984*. These novels depict the political-social dilemma of today's world. *Animal Farm* satirizes dictatorships, while *1984* vividly shows the dehumanizing effect of a government-controlled country on the individual.

Orwell distrusted all "isms," and attacked both the Right and Left. His personal observation of, and keen insight into political situations in India, France, England, and Spain provided the raw materials for his works.

That these are more than propaganda pieces and journalistic articles results from Orwell's conviction that a literary work can justly have a political purpose behind it. He desired "to make political writing into an art." In his essay "Why I Write" he says, "Looking back through my work, I see that it is invariably where I lacked political purpose that I wrote lifeless books and was betrayed into purple passages, sentences without meaning, decorative adjectives and humbug generally."

Much of Orwell's power as a writer comes from his vigorous sentences and his use of understatement and irony. In "Shooting an Elephant," Orwell presents a dramatic and forceful picture of life in Burma, and of the position of the English official in that country when it was still under the rule of Great Britain.

———◆———

In Moulmein, in lower Burma, I was hated by large numbers of people—the only time in my life that I have been important enough for this to happen to me. I was subdivisional police officer of the town, and in an aimless, petty kind of way an anti-European feeling was very bitter. No one had the guts to raise a riot, but if a European woman went through the bazaars alone somebody would probably spit betel juice over her dress. As a police officer I was an obvious target and was baited whenever it seemed safe to do so. When a nimble Burman tripped me up on the football field and the referee (another Burman) looked the other way, the crowd yelled with hideous laughter. This happened more than once. In the end the sneering yellow faces of young men that met me everywhere, the insults hooted after me when I was at a safe distance, got badly on my

nerves. The young Buddhist priests were the worst of all. There were
several thousands of them in the town and none of them seemed to
have anything to do except stand on street corners and jeer at Europeans.

All this was perplexing and upsetting. For at that time I had already
made up my mind that imperialism was an evil thing and the sooner
I chucked up my job and got out of it the better. Theoretically—and
secretly, of course—I was all for the Burmese and all against their
oppressors, the British. As for the job I was doing, I hated it more
bitterly than I can perhaps make clear. In a job like that you see the
dirty work of Empire at close quarters. The wretched prisoners hud-
dling in the stinking cages of the lockups, the gray, cowed faces of
the long-term convicts, the scarred buttocks of the men who had been
flogged with bamboos—all these oppressed me with an intolerable
sense of guilt. But I could get nothing into perspective. I was young
and ill-educated and I had had to think out my problems in the utter
silence that is imposed on every Englishman in the East. I did not
even know that the British Empire is dying, still less did I know that
it is a great deal better than the younger empires that are going to sup-
plant it. All I knew was that I was stuck between my hatred of the
empire I served and my rage against the evil-spirited little beasts who
tried to make my job impossible. With one part of my mind I
thought of the British Raj as an unbreakable tryanny, as something
clamped down, in *saecula saeculorum*,* upon the will of prostrate
peoples; with another part I thought that the greatest joy in the world
would be to drive a bayonet into a Buddhist priest's guts. Feelings
like these are the normal by-product of imperialism; ask any Anglo-
Indian official, if you can catch him off duty.

One day something happened which in a roundabout way was
enlightening. It was a tiny incident in itself, but it gave me a better
glimpse than I had had before of the real nature of imperialism—the
real motives for which despotic governments act. Early one morning
the subinspector at a police station the other end of the town rang
me up on the phone and said that an elephant was ravaging the
bazaar. Would I please come and do something about it? I did not
know what I could do, but I wanted to see what was happening and
I got on to a pony and started out. I took my rifle, an old .44 Win-
chester and much too small to kill an elephant, but I thought the

in saecula saeculorum: for ages and ages

noise might be useful *in terrorem*.* Various Burmans stopped me on the way and told me about the elephant's doings. It was not, of course, a wild elephant, but a tame one which had gone "must." * It had been chained up, as tame elephants always are when their attack of "must" is due, but on the previous night it had broken its chain and escaped. Its mahout,* the only person who could manage it when it was in that state, had set out in pursuit, but had taken the wrong direction and was now twelve hours' journey away, and in the morning the elephant had suddenly reappeared in the town. The Burmese population had no weapons and were quite helpless against it. It had already destroyed somebody's bamboo hut, killed a cow and raided some fruit stalls and devoured the stock; also it had met the municipal rubbish van and, when the driver jumped out and took to his heels, had turned the van over and inflicted violences upon it.

The Burmese subinspector and some Indian constables were waiting for me in the quarter where the elephant had been seen. It was a very poor quarter, a labyrinth of squalid huts, thatched with palm leaf, winding all over a steep hillside. I remember that it was a cloudy, stuffy morning at the beginning of the rains. We began questioning the people as to where the elephant had gone and, as usual, failed to get any definite information. That is invariably the case in the East; a story always sounds clear enough at a distance, but the nearer you get to the scene of events the vaguer it becomes. Some of the people said that the elephant had gone in one direction, some said that he had gone in another, some professed not even to have heard of any elephant. I had almost made up my mind that the whole story was a pack of lies, when we heard yells a little distance away. There was a loud, scandalized cry of "Go away, child! Go away this instant!" and an old woman with a switch in her hand came round the corner of a hut, violently shooing away a crowd of naked children. Some more women followed, clicking their tongues and exclaiming; evidently there was something the children ought not to have seen. I rounded the hut and saw a man's dead body sprawling in the mud. He was an Indian, a black Dravidian * coolie, almost naked, and he could not have been dead many minutes. The people said that the elephant had come suddenly upon him round the corner of the hut, caught

in terrorem: in the event of fear
"must": mad
mahout: an elephant driver
Dravidian: an ancient race of India

him with its trunk, put its foot on his back, and ground him into the earth. This was the rainy season and the ground was soft, and his face had scored a trench a foot deep and a couple of yards long. He was lying on his belly with arms crucified and head sharply twisted to one side. His face was coated with mud, the eyes wide open, the teeth bared and grinning with an unendurable agony. (Never tell me, by the way, that the dead look peaceful. Most of the corpses I have seen looked devilish.) The friction of the great beast's foot had stripped the skin from his back as neatly as one skins a rabbit. As soon as I saw the dead man I sent an orderly to a friend's house nearby to borrow an elephant rifle. I had already sent back the pony, not wanting it to go mad with fright and throw me if it smelt the elephant.

The orderly came back in a few minutes with a rifle and five cartridges, and meanwhile some Burmans had arrived and told us that the elephant was in the paddy fields below, only a few hundred yards away. As I started forward, practically the whole population of the quarter flocked out of the houses and followed me. They had seen the rifle and were all shouting excitedly that I was going to shoot the elephant. They had not shown much interest in the elephant when he was merely ravaging their homes, but it was different now that he was going to be shot. It was a bit of fun to them, as it would be to an English crowd; besides they wanted the meat. It made me vaguely uneasy. I had no intention of shooting the elephant —I had merely sent for the rifle to defend myself if necessary—and it is always unnerving to have a crowd following you. I marched down the hill, looking and feeling a fool, with the rifle over my shoulder and an ever-growing army of people jostling at my heels. At the bottom, when you got away from the huts, there was a metaled road and beyond that a miry waste of paddy fields a thousand yards across, not yet plowed but soggy from the first rains and dotted with coarse grass. The elephant was standing eight yards from the road, his left side toward us. He took not the slightest notice of the crowd's approach. He was tearing up bunches of grass, beating them against his knees to clean them, and stuffing them into his mouth.

I had halted on the road. As soon as I saw the elephant I knew with perfect certainty that I ought not to shoot him. It is a serious matter to shoot a working elephant—it is comparable to destroying a huge and costly piece of machinery—and obviously one ought not to do it if it can possibly be avoided. And at that distance, peacefully eating, the elephant looked no more dangerous than a cow. I thought then and I think now that his attack of "must" was already passing off; in which case he would merely wander harmlessly about until the mahout came back and caught him. Moreover, I did not in the least want to shoot him. I decided that I would watch him for a little while to make sure that he did not turn savage again, and then go home.

But at that moment I glanced round at the crowd that had followed me. It was an immense crowd, two thousand at the least and growing every minute. It blocked the road for a long distance on either side. I looked at the sea of yellow faces above the garish clothes—faces all happy and excited over this bit of fun, all certain that the elephant was going to be shot. They were watching me as they would watch a conjurer about to perform a trick. They did not like me, but with the magical rifle in my hands I was momentarily worth watching. And suddenly I realized that I would have to shoot the elephant after all. The people expected it of me and I had got to do it; I could feel their two thousand wills pressing me forward irresistibly. And it was at this moment, as I stood there with the rifle in my hands, that I first grasped the hollowness, the futility of the white man's dominion in the East. Here was I, the white man with his gun, standing in front of the unarmed native crowd—seemingly the leading actor of the piece; but in reality I was only an absurd puppet pushed to and fro by the will of those yellow faces behind. I perceived in this moment that when the white man turns tyrant it is his own freedom that he destroys. He becomes a sort of hollow, posing dummy, the conventionalized figure of a sahib.* For it is the condition of his rule that he shall spend his life in trying to impress the "natives," and so in every crisis he has got to do what the "natives" expect of him. He wears a mask, and his face grows to fit it. I had got to shoot the elephant. I had committed myself to doing it when I sent for the rifle. A sahib has got to act like a sahib; he has got to appear resolute, to know his own mind and do definite things. To come all that way, rifle in hand, with two thousand people marching at my heels, and then to trail feebly away, having done nothing—no, that was impossible. The crowd would laugh at me. And my whole life, every white man's in the East, was one long struggle not to be laughed at.

But I did not want to shoot the elephant. I watched him beating his bunch of grass against his knees, with that preoccupied grand-

sahib: native expression for a European gentleman

motherly air that elephants have. It seemed to me that it would be murder to shoot him. At that age I was not squeamish about killing animals, but I had never shot an elephant and never wanted to. (Somehow it always seems worse to kill a *large* animal.) Besides, there was the beast's owner to be considered. Alive, the elephant was worth at least a hundred pounds; dead, he would only be worth the value of his tusks, five pounds, possibly. But I had got to act quickly. I turned to some experienced-looking Burmans who had been there when we arrived, and asked them how the elephant had been behaving. They all said the same thing; he took no notice of you if you left him alone, but he might charge if you went too close to him.

It was perfectly clear to me what I ought to do. I ought to walk up to within, say, twenty-five yards of the elephant and test his behavior. If he charged, I could shoot; if he took no notice of me, it would be safe to leave him until the mahout came back. But also I knew that I was going to do no such thing. I was a poor shot with a rifle and the ground was soft mud into which one would sink at every step. If the elephant charged and I missed him, I should have about as much chance as a toad under a steam roller. But even then I was not thinking particularly of my own skin, only of the watchful yellow faces behind. For at that moment, with the crowd watching me, I was not afraid in the ordinary sense, as I would have been if I had been alone. A white man mustn't be frightened in front of "natives"; and so, in general, he isn't frightened. The sole thought in my mind was that if anything went wrong those two thousand Burmans would see me pursued, caught, trampled on, and reduced to a grinning corpse like that Indian up the hill. And if that happened it was quite probable that some of them would laugh. That would never do. There was only one alternative. I shoved the cartridges into the magazine and lay down on the road to get a better aim.

The crowd grew very still, and a deep, low, happy sigh, as of people who see the theater curtain go up at last, breathed from innumerable throats. They were going to have their bit of fun after all. The rifle was a beautiful German thing with cross-hair sights. I did not then know that in shooting an elephant one would shoot to cut an imaginary bar running from earhole to earhole. I ought, therefore, as the elephant was sideways on, to have aimed straight at his earhole; actually I aimed several inches in front of this, thinking the brain would be further forward.

When I pulled the trigger I did not hear the bang or feel the kick—one never does when a shot goes home—but I heard the devilish roar of glee that went up from the crowd. In that instant, in too short a time, one would have thought, even for the bullet to get there, a mysterious, terrible change had come over the elephant. He neither stirred nor fell, but every line of his body had altered. He looked suddenly stricken, shrunken, immensely old, as though the frightful impact of the bullet had paralyzed him without knocking him down. At last, after what seemed a long time—it might have been five seconds, I dare say—he sagged flabbily to his knees. His mouth slobbered. An enormous senility seemed to have settled upon him. One could have imagined him thousands of years old. I fired again into the same spot. At the second shot he did not collapse but climbed with deperate slowness to his feet and stood weakly upright, with legs sagging and head drooping. I fired a third time. That was the shot that did for him. You could see the agony of it jolt his whole body and knock the last remnant of strength from his legs. But in falling he seemed for a moment to rise, for as his hind legs collapsed beneath him he seemed to tower upward like a huge rock toppling, his trunk reaching skywards like a tree. He trumpeted for the first and only time. And then down he came, his belly toward me, with a crash that seemed to shake the ground even where I lay.

I got up. The Burmans were already racing past me across the mud. It was obvious that the elephant would never rise again, but he was not dead. He was breathing very rhythmically with long rattling gasps, his great mound of a side painfully rising and falling. His mouth was wide open—I could see far down into caverns of pale pink throat. I waited a long time for him to die, but his breathing did not weaken. Finally I fired my two remaining shots into the spot where I thought his heart must be. The thick blood welled out of him like red velvet, but still he did not die. His body did not even jerk when the shots hit him, the tortured breathing continued without a pause. He was dying, very slowly and in great agony, but in some world remote from me where not even a bullet could damage him further. I felt that I had got to put an end to that dreadful noise. It seemed dreadful to see the great beast lying there, powerless to move and yet powerless to die, and not even to be able to finish him. I sent back for my small rifle and poured shot after shot into his heart and down his throat. They seemed to make no impression. The tortured gasps continued as steadily as the ticking of a clock.

In the end I could not stand it any longer and went away. I

heard later that it took him half an hour to die. Burmans were bringing dahs * and baskets even before I left, and I was told they had stripped his body almost to the bones by the afternoon.

Afterwards, of course, there were endless discussions about the shooting of the elephant. The owner was furious, but he was only an Indian and could do nothing. Besides, legally I had done the right thing, for a mad elephant has to be killed, like a mad dog, if its owner fails to control it. Among the Europeans, opinion was divided. The older men said I was right, the younger men said it was a shame to shoot an elephant for killing a coolie, because an elephant was worth more than any Coringhee coolie. And afterwards I was very glad that the coolie had been killed; it put me legally in the right and it gave me a sufficient pretext for shooting the elephant. I often wondered whether any of the others grasped that I had done it solely to avoid looking a fool.

dahs: bowls

For Discussion:

1. In this essay, Orwell states why the Burmese called on him to kill the elephant. Was this *his* reason for doing so? How is his reason related to his purpose in telling the incident? Quote sentences that support your answer.
2. Throughout the essay, Orwell attempts to win sympathy for the elephant. How does he do it? Why does he do it?
3. How does the essay corroborate the author's statement that, "He (the White Man in the East) wears a mask, and his face grows to fit it"?
4. After the episode, Europeans express various opinions. Explain the significance of these. Do you agree with any of them? If not, state your opinion.
5. An essay reveals much about its author. What does this essay reveal about Orwell?

For Composition

1. The statement "The owner (of the elephant that was shot) was furious, but he was only an Indian and could do nothing," shocks us as we read it. In the light of current events, write a short theme that demonstrates that such an attitude toward people does or does not exist in America.
2. Orwell states that "Laughter can be a deadly weapon." In a short narrative, describe an incident that you have experienced showing the truth of this statement.

St. Thomas More

BARBARA WARD

Americans know Barbara Ward (1914–   ), Britain's brilliant economist, both as a lecturer and as an author. Her first book, *The International Share-Out*, published when she was 24, impressed the editor of the London *Economist*, who invited her to join its staff. She held this position until increasing demands upon her time made it impossible for her to continue. Articles written by her were thoughtfully read and discussed, even as they are today.

Miss Ward writes as persuasively as she speaks. She presents her argument in clear, direct prose that makes even the most complex issues intelligible. The key to this lies in her simplicity of vision and the tremendous knowledge of history which forms the basis of her views. She is a realist whose sense of social responsibility is firmly rooted in Christian humanism. For her the connection between religion and politics is not an abstract one. It is as concrete as the connection between the dynamo and the light bulb. She has dedicated herself to work "hard against the current of a world that has lost the sense of the supernatural," a world that has "done violence to reality—the reality of history and the reality of men."

------◆------

In this troubled and angry world one of the great difficulties in approaching the saints is to be able to believe in their relevance. The title "saint" suggests the nun withdrawn in her cloister, the priest wholly dedicated to the service of God, the mystic, the ascetic—the works of Mary, not of Martha. The citizen of the twentieth century, struggling with income tax or the bill for his children's education, earning a living in the competitive world of law or commerce, or engulfed in the frustrations of government service, pays, no doubt, his tribute of respect to the idea of holiness—he is less likely than his grandfather to dismiss lives wholly consecrated to God and to prayer as "escapism"—but there is no change in his conviction that the daily business of living in office and home is what "real life" is about.

The most remarkable fact about St. Thomas More may therefore be the bare outline of his biography, which reads very like a modern entry in *Who's Who*. He was born in the City of London of a family prominent in the law and city affairs—his father, Sir John More, was a judge on the King's Bench. Thus his young son grew up with the law and the city in his bones. After reading classics at Oxford—in fact only Latin, Greek came later—he began his law studies at New Inn and Lincoln's Inn, was called to the bar young but already with a great reputation for scholarship, and quickly built up a very large and profitable practice as a result of immense knowledge and industry, equal speed and complete integrity.

As a rising young lawyer, he soon came to the notice of the City Fathers and was chosen as one of the burgesses—or members of parliament—for the City. In parliament, still a very young man—in fact, twenty-six—he made his mark at once, particularly in debates to reduce the Government's demands for fresh taxation. The City rewarded its able young burgess. At the age of thirty-two he was appointed Under-Sheriff, an office which made him the permanent legal officer to the Mayor and Corporation.

Meanwhile, More had married a Miss Colt of Netherhall in Essex. Three daughters and a son were born to them, but Mrs. More died only five years after her marriage. More then married a widowed lady, Mrs. Alice Middleton, who survived him.

The reputation which More had earned not only as a lawyer and a man of learning but also as an active politician in city affairs marked him out for further promotion. While still Under-Sheriff he was invited to take part in some difficult commercial negotiations with Britain's most important trading partner, the Netherlands, and it was during the months of discussion in Flanders that he found time to write his book *Utopia*, which at once became a best-seller throughout Europe. His contemporaries counted him, with Erasmus and Budé and Vives, the foremost scholar of his day.

The trade mission also enhanced his reputation for public business. A year or so later, promotion came again in the shape of an invitation to join the government. He was appointed to the Council, on which he served for eleven years. During this period he acted as Under-Treasurer, as Speaker in Parliament, as Chancellor of the Duchy of Lancaster and as High Steward of both Oxford and Cambridge Universities. At the same time his missions abroad continued, and he had the delicate and ungrateful task of retrieving what could be retrieved for England at the Cambrai Peace Conference. This high career of service was crowned by his appointment as Lord Chancellor—or as we might say now, Prime Minister.

So far, the biography reads like a typical success story in twentieth-century political life—the usual beginnings in the law, the gaining

of reputation in local politics, promotion to the national scene, ending with the highest political position in the land. Admittedly one
has to turn to Mr. Winston Churchill himself to find some analogy
with More's combination of statesmanship and great literary gifts.
Nevertheless, this scholarship apart, his career is not untypical of the
leading men of our own day. For the last years, however, we have to
turn our eyes from modern London—or modern Washington—to
post-war Budapest or Warsaw or Prague.

Faced with the Government's increasing claim to total power,
More resigned his Chancellorship. For a year, he is allowed to live at
peace in his own home. But the insistence on submission and on uni-
formity of opinion seeks him out in retirement. He is told to seal
with a public oath his complete acceptance of the "new order." His
refusal is followed first by fifteen months' imprisonment without a
trial, then by a mock-trial of complete illegality. The death sentence
is passed and More is executed as a traitor to the state.

The impression of modernity is surely remarkable. Yet once the
dates are filled in, More slips back again into the mists of the past.
Born in 1478, we read, member of parliament in 1504, married in
1505, Under-Sheriff in 1510, called to Henry VIII's Council in 1518
and served there until 1529, Henry's Lord Chancellor until 1532,
executed by the same Henry in 1535. Back flows the unreality of his-
torical picture-books—the gold chains and fur tippets, the rush-strewn
floors and household jesters—More had one, Henry Patenson, to
whom he was greatly attached—the odd language: "deus bone, deus
bone, man, will this gear never be left?"—the overwhelming authority of the King's good grace, the pageant of chivalry and medieval
magnificence of that Field of the Cloth of Gold which More himself attended. It is all very splendid and even moving, but it is infinitely remote. Looking at those men in their velvet caps and the
women in their stiff Tudor snoods and wimples, we feel that the
troubles which beset them, the issues they faced and the decisions
on which they acted are as outworn as their headgear. Let us admit
that Thomas More was a great man and a saint, but how can this be
relevant *now* in times so different from his own?

In fact, however, the startling thing about Thomas More's career
is the extent to which his life, both public and private, belongs as
much to our times as to his. This is in part to say that the deepest
experiences of mankind are timeless. More's enchanting household at
Chelsea belongs to every age in which men and women love each

other and bring up their children in peace, affection and loving discipline. The fact that More gave his daughters the same education—in Greek, Latin, logic, philosophy, theology, mathematics and astronomy—as to his son surprised his contemporaries more than it would us. Nor need we suppose that More knew only the joys of loving companionship and gay goodness in his family circle. He felt all the anxieties of any modern head of the house making both ends meet on an inadequate salary. Like many a man today who has gone from private to public affairs in London or Washington, More suffered a severe loss of income in giving up his private practice and City connexions and entering the King's service. He writes from Flanders that he is hard put to it to keep two households in being at once. Later, on his resignation from the Chancellorship, he refused all financial aid save his pension, and hard times and fuel shortages came to Chelsea, where his wife and grown-up family had to gather in the evenings round a single fire of peat before retiring to their cold, unheated bedrooms.

There was worse to come. We may wonder how many men in Eastern Europe today as they lie in Communist prisons are tormented most of all by the knowledge that they leave their families in desperate want and danger. More knew this quite "modern" agony and wrote to his daughter from the Tower that the "danger and great harm" in which his family were placed was "a deadly grief unto me and much more deadly than to hear of mine own death."

All this, both the joys and the sorrows, belongs to the ages, and we are not likely to be surprised at the continuity of deep and loyal family affections. The surprising fact is that it is in the sphere of public affairs, the very sphere in which we expect, our minds coloured by the romantic legends of the much-married Henry VIII, to find the greatest differences, that More's experience and our own seem most strikingly to converge. In general terms, the sixteenth and the twentieth century can both bear the name "ages of transition." The discovery of the New World then was as momentous as the mastery of the air today. The new learning of the Renaissance was as intoxicating as modern scientific advance. Men were as troubled in 1530 by the division of Christendom between Catholic and Protestant Christianity as they are now by its division between Christians of all communions and the militant force of Marxist atheism. Change, violence, division were in the air More breathed—as they are in the storms of our own day.

The resemblance is more than a general one. In politics and in economics More wrestled with dangers that are still with us, either recrudescent or never really dead. Tudor government represented a violent break with the constitutional mind of the Middle Ages. To the burgesses of the City of London, to the lawyers who had grown up after Bracton, it was a commonplace that "the King is under God and the law." In other words, the monarchy, though immensely powerful, was a monarchy limited by law, by custom and by the established rights of nobles, clergy and commons. Moreover, there was in the local state and in all Europe a plurality of power—the state representing Caesar and receiving the things that are Caesar's while the Church represented God upon earth and maintained its own independent spiritual authority.

The essence of Henry VIII's political revolution after 1529 was to destroy this double web of constitutionalism and divided power. He concentrated all power, secular and spiritual, in his own hands; he overrode all traditional rights and safeguards and judicially murdered those who sought to keep his will within limits. In fact, he and his creature Thomas Cromwell were students of Machiavelli, who taught that a prince must not ask what he *should* do but what he *can* do. Henry accepted the counsel, and not until the English Civil War was fought a century later could the threat of arbitrary despotism be razed from English society.

The Machiavellian dispensation prevailed, too, in foreign affairs. Far from pursuing the unity of Europe, threatened mortally in the early sixteenth century by the advance of the Turks, Henry and his first Chancellor, Wolsey, deliberately plunged England into a series of wasteful and useless European wars. The attacks on France were in part launched in support of the Papacy, which under the worst of Popes—the dissolute Alexander and the warlike Julius— was risking the loss of spiritual power by appearing more and more in the guise of a mere secular Italian principality. But personal ambitions—Henry's desire to rule in France and Wolsey's desire to be Pope—played their part in a policy which tore up the garment of European unity and ruined England in the process. Such was the political background to More's public life—the struggle against totalitarian power within the state and against the pursuit of nationalist ambitions of aggrandisement abroad.

He had to face as lawless a revolution in economics. In the Middle Ages, men's love of wealth and acquisitiveness had been to some extent checked by the ideal of voluntary poverty, by the traditional rights of the peasants to common lands and open field, by the extent of monastic wealth used in part on hospitals and charity, and by an infinite number of bequests and charities to schools and hospitals administered by the Church—such, for instance, were the four great hospitals of London. If, however, the prince—Henry VIII—might now do what he could and not what he should, the existence of so much wealth was tempting indeed, and there were men behind Henry very ready to share in the temptation and the plunder. Abuses in the Church provided the excuse, but the real aim was private acquisition. The peasants' lands and the Church's charities vanished together into the greedy hands of Henry and his followers in the violent, unrestrained beginnings of modern capitalism.

All these revolutions—in despotic government, in international lawlessness and in economic upheaval—came to a head in the years of More's Chancellorship, and it is the measure of his greatness that he alone, with one saintly bishop, of all the leading men of the time, saw the drift of these revolutions and was prepared to die rather than to conform to them.

We need not suppose that their meaning was easy to discern. Like most great upheavals, they came masked in a mass of irrelevances and cross purposes. On the face of it, More died for refusing to accept Henry's divorce from Katherine of Aragon and remarriage with Anne Boleyn and also for rejecting Henry's claim to supremacy of the Church in England. The argument turned on the Papacy, since the Pope would not declare Henry's first marriage null and void and since the Pope, not the King, was in More's eyes the spiritual head of the English church.

Yet the Papacy was making itself a dubious enough force in More's day. He had resisted for twenty years Henry's addiction to European war in the wake of warlike Popes, seeking to preserve their papal states. Why should he now defend the Papacy when he had actually warned Henry against its secular policies only a few years before?

The same ambiguity hung over Henry's economic "reforms." They were done in the name of abuses in the administration of the Church charities—abuses which More admitted and himself denounced. Here was a maze of good and evil intermingled. Certainly it bemused most other English minds.

The supreme value of More's resistance was his perception of principle under the tangle of politics and conflicting interests. He saw that the King in claiming his divorce was putting the will of the prince above the moral law. If there, why not elsewhere? The shadow of future totalitarianism lay over this return to despotism. More saw, too, that Henry in breaking the spiritual link with Rome was undermining Western unity—with the Turks at the gate—just as the Popes, by their wars, had earlier risked the same calamity. He foresaw the result. The intransigence of the King and the bellicosity of the Popes would destroy all trace of European unity and hasten the coming of the lawless, selfish sovereignty of the new nation-state.

Equally, More could see through the cynicism of an economic revolution which, in the name of reforming abuses, was grabbing the poor man's patrimony. He saw "a conspiracy of rich men procuring their own commodities under the name and title of the Commonwealth," while destitution spread and labourers were turned from home and land "whom no man will set to work, though they never so willingly offer themselves thereto."

We must be honest and admit that these evils—of despotism, of international lawlessness, of economic injustice—are with us to this day. They appear now in the aggravated threat of totalitarianism—in the Communist claim to total conformity, in the cynical opportunism and ruthless self-interest of Soviet foreign policy, even in the deceit of "Soviet full employment" which masks the millions labouring in Arctic slave camps.

Nor can we forget our own part in the totalitarian development. In the West, we have kept faith with constitutionalism and with the division of power. More, today, would applaud our rule of law and the parliamentary institutions for which, as Speaker in 1523, he was the first to demand complete freedom of speech. But arrogant national interest wrecked Europe again and again before Bolshevism was heard of, and even today, the Western powers have yet to find ways of creating lasting unity before the threat from the East.

In economic life, too, Western industrial capitalism for a time was fully as ruthless as its Tudor origins, and too many of the poor and the workless—whom More in his day longed to help and employ—turned to Communism in default of Western aid. Even now, in spite of many generous reforms, we still fall far short of the corporate and neighbourly responsibility which More looked for, with the common work and property of the monastery as his ideal.

In the development of ideas, four centuries is only a little space. Today, facing Soviet totalitarianism, seeking for a unity that still eludes us, compassed about with problems of economic justice— we in the West stand at the end of a revolution at whose terrifying beginnings More assisted. The issues have not changed, but we with all our hindsight still lack his prophetic clarity.

Will anyone now maintain that St. Thomas More has no relevance to our day? He lived in the middle of secular affairs— a lawyer like numbers of our own contemporaries, like them going first into Parliament—or Congress—and like them rising higher and higher in public life until the greatest issues of foreign and domestic policy are in his hands. And these issues are our issues, the issues of liberty and the rule of the law, the issue of totalitarianism, of unity and honesty in foreign policy, of justice and brotherhood in economic life. It is hard to picture a man more fully contemporary with ourselves or a man whose life and death are more relevant to our own struggles.

But, the critic will say, what has all this to do with sanctity? You have spoken of the layman, the father of a family, lawyer, statesman, martyr for liberty, prophetic interpreter of the modern age. But has all this any bearing on the fact that he is called a saint? You have shown him immersed in secular affairs and deciding great secular issues. You have not shown that his sanctity was relevant to either.

In fact, More made the stand he did because he was the man he was. We have always to remember that in his protest against arbitrary power and the abrogation of the moral law he was almost alone. There were many men of equal learning and brilliance to face the issues raised by Henry's despotism. We cannot understand the difference between More's clearsightedness and their lack of ability— or of desire—to understand the principles at stake unless we know what manner of man he was and what were the sources of his insight and his strength.

He was, first of all, a character of complete integrity. Even at his trial when no effort was spared in the attempt to defame him, nothing could be found in his record, as lawyer and statesman, save absolute honesty, endless generosity and complete discretion. In such matters the popular legend left behind by a man usually does not err. In his beloved city of London, a century of anti-Catholic propaganda could not wipe out the people's memory of More as a just, great and merciful judge. In the fragment of the Elizabethan play *Sir Thomas More* of which Shakespeare is part author, we see him as London saw him—"the best friend that the poor e'er had."

Londoners were shrewd in their tradition. If one thing more than another distinguishes More, it is his capacity for friendship and affection. We have seen him already, the devoted father of a brilliant family, with sons- and daughters-in-law who love him with filial warmth and indeed follow him—one to death, many to prison, all in exile. But this inner family circle had around it a group of friends which included the finest minds in Europe. For Erasmus, after a friendship of thirty-six years, it seemed that "in More's death, I . . . have died myself; we had but one soul between us." Vives, another great humanist, was his guest at Chelsea. The great Holbein found his first patron in More. Nor was More's love only for the talented and the notable. He was indeed "the best friend the poor e'er had." As a young lawyer, he handled all poor men's suits for nothing, and it was in the Court of Requests—the poor man's court—that he gladly served when he first joined the King's Council. Love for the poor stirred him to bitter anxiety over the fate of the labourers turned from their homes and lands, a change which others were welcoming in the name of progress. We know that in his own house, the poor of the neighbourhood were regularly feasted, and Margaret, his daughter, had special charge of the almshouse he had built. And we have a letter from More to his wife, Dame Alice, after a fire had destroyed one of their barns, telling her to pay full compensation to anyone who might have suffered as a result, "for as I should not leave myself a spoon, there shall no poor neighbour of mine bear no loss by any chance happened in my house."

Integrity, affection, friendship, intense personal love for the poor —these are great qualities, yet other men had them in More's day and still they did not see the issues clear. These admirable natural virtues take us no further than the outworks of More's character. Whatever it was that gave him his keener vision and his deeper understanding must lie beyond.

One of the great difficulties in finding one's way to the inner citadel of a man's being is that, if we already know his life, we assume that it was quite inevitable that it would always have developed in just such a way. It is well with More to realize that quite the opposite is the truth. If there is inevitability in human affairs, then inevitably More should have ended not on the scaffold but as Duke of Chelsea, and no doubt Grand Old Man of the Elizabethan settlement.

He was born to be spoilt. He had all the gifts most likely to commend him to a vivid, intellectual, pleasure-loving Court. He had a legendary wit, he was extremely attractive in appearance—indeed, in his youth young women had thrown themselves at his head. His learning was unequalled, and he had in addition the warm, loving personality which drew all to him. Moreover, he was not rich. He had his way to make in the world. Can one picture any combination of circumstances more likely to catch a young man by the throat with ambition and lead him into the scramble for wealth and honour which a vast majority of his fellow courtiers were pursuing successfully all round him?

We know that the King's good yet terrible Grace, Henry, conceived the warmest love for More. For weeks on end he would detain his friend at Greenwich to keep him company after the royal supper. Henry would delight in arriving unexpectedly at Chelsea, and one evening he walked for an hour beside More with his royal arm round his friend's neck.

Yet after this touching proof of royal favour More remarked to his son-in-law: "Howbeit, son Roper, I may tell thee I have no cause to be proud thereof, for, if my head would win him a castle in France, it should not fail to go." And we have Erasmus's evidence that More struggled as strongly to keep away from Court as most men to go there.

He was not spoilt—in the most spoiling of ages. He was not ambitious—in a most striving and ambitious time. He could still distinguish between the King's will and the moral law—when most courtiers had forgotten the distinction. Why?

There is no secret about it. More was from his first youth a man of prayer. While he studied at Lincoln's Inn he lived a life of complete austerity with the Carthusians, working and praying nineteen hours a day and sleeping on a board with a log for a pillow. Even when he found his vocation in marriage, the prayer and the austerity continued. He rose at two in the morning and worked and prayed until seven. He wore a hair-shirt all his life and took the discipline. Should we think this a commonplace of those rougher days? On the contrary, his wife was so horrified that she tried to have the hair-shirt banned by his confessor, and his merry little daughter-in-law, seeing a corner of the shirt sticking out as he sat at dinner without his ruff, had an uncontrollable fit of laughter. To live in such austerity was as unusual at Henry's luxurious court as it would be today.

Here, then, is the source of More's discernment. Ambition, the grab for wealth and power, meant nothing to a man whose life was steeped in prayer and austerity and whose ideal remained—as we see in *Utopia*—the simplicity and common life of the Franciscans or the Carthusians. As he said to his children: "We may not look at our pleasure to go to Heaven in feather beds." Not all the power and glory Henry could offer—and he offered much—corrupted a man who looked to follow his Master in the way of suffering. "To aim at honour in this world," said More grimly, "is to set a coat of arms on a prison gate."

So it was with his death. Once again we have to think away our idea of his martyrdom as inevitable. More knew what he believed to be his weakness—there was never a more humble soul. He saw good and learned clerics like Dr. Wilson and Bishop Tunstall hesitate before the final threat of death. He feared to the end that, confronted with torture or the traitor's death of disembowelling, he might falter. So, in his prison, he turned to the contemplation of One who, faced with agony and death, sweated blood and prayed that the Cup might pass. In his Treatise on the Passion, More wrote: "He that is strong-hearted may find a thousand glorious valiant martyrs whose example he may right joyously follow. But thou now, O timorous and weak, silly sheep, think it sufficient for thee only to walk after Me which am thy Shepherd and Governor and so mistrust thyself and put thy trust in Me."

Here is the inner citadel of St. Thomas More. Throughout a life set in the hubbub of law and public service, among the temptations of courts and princes, surrounded by men straining after new honours and new wealth, he walked with God, and to all his earthly occupations brought the vision and insight of eternal things. He is timeless because he lived timelessly in his prayer. He served the moral law, and the interests of peace and unity and love and compassion because he lived these things all the day in his soul. And because his

whole life was centred on God, he could distinguish the things of
God from the things of Caesar and could die at last on the scaffold

"the King's good servant, but God's first."

For Discussion:

1. Barbara Ward states that people today find it difficult to believe in
   the relevance of the saints. Why does this difficulty exist? Would it
   be better to reconstruct the idea of a saint?
2. In what ways do the facts of Thomas More's life fail to coincide with
   our idea of sanctity?
3. "Thomas More's . . . life, both public and private, belongs as much
   to our times as to his." What parallels are drawn between the events
   of More's public and private life and those of our own times?
4. Do you agree with Miss Ward that More's greatness lay in his
   willingness to die rather than to conform to the ideas of his time?
   In what way does this stand constitute his sanctity?
5. More made the stand he did because he was the man he was. What
   personal characteristics enabled him to take and to hold to his firm
   position?
6. What is the meaning of: "More should have ended not on the
   scaffold but as the Duke of Chelsea, and no doubt Grand Old Man
   of the Elizabethan settlement"? How did More protect himself from
   coming to this end?

For Composition: Make an outline of this essay. Begin with Barbara
Ward's theme: Thomas More is a saint for our times because . . .

Modern Drama

With the arrival of television, the drama has come to be one of the most popular forms of entertainment. Its history proves, however, that since ancient Greek times, it has always enjoyed prestige among the arts. In the sixteenth century, Shakespeare brought playwriting to its highest form with his great tragedies and comedies. In the nineteenth century, Henrik Ibsen, the Norwegian dramatist, made the play a powerful medium for expressing ideas about social justice and moral reform.

Ibsen's plays gradually gained admirers in England and America because of their fresh, realistic portrayal of ordinary people in everyday life. The person who did the most to have Ibsen known and accepted was George Bernard Shaw, one of the distinguished English playwrights of this century. Shaw himself imitated Ibsen in his biting portrayal of moral and social evils in modern civilization.

A further stimulus to the popularity of the drama came with the founding of the Abbey Theater in Dublin in 1904, which encouraged new playwrights and new interest in the drama at home and abroad. A notable feature of the vital use of the play as a vehicle for expressing new ideas was the introduction of the highly condensed one-act play. Such writers as John Millington Synge, Lady Gregory, John Galsworthy, and James M. Barrie often found the one-act play the most effective form for their dramas. Based on everyday human experience, these short plays have captured audiences everywhere..

The modern drama has taken many forms. Some plays have been realistic in their approach. Others have been more experimental and introduced new innovations in staging and in the presenting of characters and plot. Recently, the poetic drama has brought a new and exciting element into the modern theater. Championed by T. S. Eliot and Christopher Fry in England, these writers have combined the drama and poetry in their plays, often in a modern setting.

Today, through the medium of television, more and more people have seen not only famous plays of the past and present, but also original dramas, some of which have later been made into plays for the stage. The drama has become part of people's everyday lives.

Riders to the Sea

JOHN MILLINGTON SYNGE

Like his close friend Yeats, John Millington Synge (1871–1909) was a native of Ireland, although he studied in Germany. and Italy and settled for a while to write in Paris. It was at Yeats' suggestion that Synge returned to Ireland and began writing plays about the Irish peasants and their primitive life in prose so beautifully fashioned that it approached poetry. He also became a member of the original Abbey Theater group in Dublin, which encouraged the development of the one-act play, one of the important contributions to world literature. Thus Synge became part of the literary movement early in the twentieth century, striving for the recognition of Ireland's culture and tradition.

Among his most famous works is his three-act play, *The Playboy of the Western World,* a comedy which was almost hissed off the stage at its first performance in Dublin. This is a satire on Irish superstition, and has been performed many times with great success both in England and America.

Synge's realistic portrayal of the hard, coarse life of the Irish peasants is best seen, perhaps, in his one-act play *Riders to the Sea.* Here his concern is with the isolated men and women "fisher-folk" and their struggle with the sea. On the stage, this play creates an overwhelming mood of doom and tragedy.

Characters

> MAURYA, *an old woman*
> BARTLEY, *her son*
> CATHLEEN, *her daughter*
> NORA, *a younger daughter*
> MEN AND WOMEN

SCENE. *An island off the coast of Ireland. Cottage kitchen, with nets, oilskins, spinning wheel, some new boards standing by the wall, etc.* CATHLEEN, *a girl of about twenty, finishes kneading cake, and puts it down in the pot oven by the fire; then wipes her hands, and begins to spin at the wheel.* NORA, *a young girl, puts her head in at the door.*

NORA (*in a low voice*). Where is she?

CATHLEEN. She's lying down, God help her, and maybe sleeping, if she's able.

(NORA *comes in softly, and takes a bundle from under her shawl.*)

CATHLEEN (*spinning the wheel rapidly*). What is it you have?

NORA. The young priest is after bringing them. It's a shirt and a plain stocking were got off a drowned man in Donegal.

(CATHLEEN *stops her wheel with a sudden movement, and leans out to listen.*)

NORA. We're to find out if it's Michael's they are; sometime herself will be down looking by the sea.

CATHLEEN. How would they be Michael's, Nora? How would he go the length of that way to the far north?

NORA. The young priest says he's known the like of it. "If it's Michael's they are," says he, "you can tell herself he's got a clean burial by the grace of God, and if they're not his, let no one say a word about them, for she'll be getting her death," says he, "with crying and lamenting."

(*The door which* NORA *half closed is blown open by a gust of wind.*)

CATHLEEN (*looking out anxiously*). Did you ask him would he stop Bartley going this day with the horses to the Galway fair?

NORA. "I won't stop him," says he, "but let you not be afraid. Herself does be saying prayers half through the night, and the Almighty God won't leave her destitute," says he, "with no son living."

CATHLEEN. Is the sea bad by the white rocks, Nora?

NORA. Middling bad, God help us. There's a great roaring in the west, and it's worse it'll be getting when the tide's turned to the wind.

(*She goes over to the table with the bundle.*)

Shall I open it now?

CATHLEEN. Maybe she'd wake up on us, and come in before we'd done. (*Coming to the table*) It's a long time we'll be, and the two of us crying.

NORA (*goes to the inner door and listens*). She's moving about on the bed. She'll be coming in a minute.

CATHLEEN. Give me the ladder, and I'll put them up in the turf loft, the way she won't know of them at all, and maybe when the tide turns she'll be going down to see would he be floating from the east.

(*They put the ladder against the gable of the chimney;* CATHLEEN *goes up a few steps and hides the bundle in the turf loft.* MAURYA *comes from the inner room.*)

MAURYA (*looking up at* CATHLEEN *and speaking querulously*). Isn't it turf enough you have for this day and evening?

CATHLEEN. There's a cake baking at the fire for a short space (*throwing down the turf*) and Bartley will want it when the tide turns if he goes to Connemara.

(NORA *picks up the turf and puts it round the pot oven.*)

MAURYA (*sitting down on a stool at the fire*). He won't go this day with the wind rising from the south and west. He won't go this day, for the young priest will stop him surely.

NORA. He'll not stop him, Mother, and I heard Eamon Simon and Stephen Pheety and Colum Shawn saying he would go.

MAURYA. Where is he itself?

NORA. He went down to see would there be another boat sailing in the week, and I'm thinking it won't be long till he's here now, for the tide's turning at the green head, and the hooker's tacking from the east.

CATHLEEN. I hear someone passing the big stones.

NORA (*looking out*). He's coming now, and he in a hurry.

BARTLEY (*comes in and looks round the room; speaking sadly and quietly*). Where is the bit of new rope, Cathleen, was bought in Connemara?

CATHLEEN (*coming down*). Give it to him, Nora; it's on a nail by the white boards. I hung it up this morning, for the pig with the black feet was eating it.

NORA (*giving him a rope*). Is that it, Bartley?

MAURYA. You'd do right to leave that rope, Bartley, hanging by the boards. (BARTLEY *takes the rope.*) It will be wanting in this place, I'm telling you, if Michael is washed up tomorrow morning, or the next morning, or any morning in the week, for it's a deep grave we'll make him by the grace of God.

BARTLEY (*beginning to work with the rope*). I've no halter the way I can ride down on the mare, and I must go now quickly. This is the one boat going for two weeks or beyond it, and the fair will be a good fair for horses, I heard them saying below.

MAURYA. It's a hard thing they'll be saying below if the body is washed-up and there's no man in it to make the coffin, and I after giving a big price for the finest white boards you'd find in Connemara.

(*She looks round at the boards.*)

BARTLEY. How would it be washed up, and we after looking each day for nine days, and a strong wind blowing a while back from the west and south?

MAURYA. If it wasn't found itself, that wind is raising the sea, and there was a star up against the moon, and it rising in the night. If it was a hundred horses, or a thousand horses you had itself, what is the price of a thousand horses against a son where there is one son only?

BARTLEY (*working at the halter, to* CATHLEEN). Let you go down each day, and see the sheep aren't jumping in on the rye, and if the jobber comes you can sell the pig with the black feet if there is a good price going.

MAURYA. How would the like of her get a good price for a pig?

BARTLEY (*to* CATHLEEN). If the west wind holds with the last bit of the moon let you and Nora get up weed enough for another cock for the kelp.* It's hard set we'll be from this day with no one in it but one man to work.

MAURYA. It's hard set we'll be surely the day you're drownd'd with the rest. What way will I live and the girls with me, and I an old woman looking for the grave?

(BARTLEY *lays down the halter, takes off his old coat, and puts on a newer one of the same flannel.*)

BARTLEY (*to* NORA). Is she coming to the pier?

NORA (*looking out*). She's passing the green head and letting fall her sails.

BARTLEY (*getting his purse and tobacco*). I'll have half an hour to go down, and you'll see me coming again in two days, or in three days, or maybe in four days if the wind is bad.

MAURYA (*turning round to the fire, and putting her shawl over her head*). Isn't it a hard and cruel man won't hear a word from an old woman, and she holding him from the sea?

CATHLEEN. It's the life of a young man to be going on the sea, and who would listen to an old woman with one thing and she saying it over?

BARTLEY (*taking the halter*). I must go now quickly. I'll ride down on the red mare, and the gray pony'll run behind me. The blessing of God on you.

(*He goes out.*)

MAURYA (*crying out as he is in the door*). He's gone now, God

another cock for the kelp: another pile of seaweed

spare us, and we'll not see him again. He's gone now, and when the black night is falling I'll have no son left me in the world.

CATHLEEN. Why wouldn't you give him your blessing and he looking round in the door? Isn't it sorrow enough is on everyone in this house without your sending him out with an unlucky word behind him, and a hard word in his ear?

(MAURYA *takes up the tongs and begins raking the fire aimlessly without looking round.*)

NORA (*turning toward her*). You're taking away the turf from the cake.

CATHLEEN (*crying out*). The Son of God forgive us, Nora, we're after forgetting his bit of bread.

(*She comes over to the fire.*)

NORA. And it's destroyed he'll be going till dark night, and he after eating nothing since the sun went up.

CATHLEEN (*turning the cake out of the oven*). It's destroyed he'll be, surely. There's no sense left on any person in a house where an old woman will be talking forever.

(MAURYA *sways herself on her stool.*)

CATHLEEN (*cutting off some of the bread and rolling it in a cloth, to* MAURYA). Let you go down now to the spring-well and give him this and he passing. You'll see him then and the dark word will be broken, and you can say, "God speed you," the way he'll be easy in his mind.

MAURYA (*taking the bread*). Will I be in it as soon as himself?

CATHLEEN. If you go now quickly.

MAURYA (*standing up unsteadily*). It's hard set I am to walk.

CATHLEEN (*looking at her anxiously*). Give her the stick, Nora, or maybe she'll slip on the big stones.

NORA. What stick?

CATHLEEN. The stick Michael brought from Connemara.

MAURYA (*taking a stick* NORA *gives her*). In the big world the old people do be leaving things after them for their sons and children, but in this place it is the young men do be leaving things behind for them that do be old.

(*She goes out slowly.* NORA *goes over to the ladder.*)

CATHLEEN. Wait, Nora, maybe she'd turn back quickly. She's that sorry, God help her, you wouldn't know the thing she'd do.

NORA. Is she gone round by the bush?

CATHLEEN (*looking out*). She's gone now. Throw it down quickly, for the Lord knows when she'll be out of it again.

NORA (*getting the bundle from the loft*). The young priest said he'd be passing tomorrow, and we might go down and speak to him below if it's Michael's they are surely.

CATHLEEN (*taking the bundle*). Did he say what way they were found?

NORA (*coming down*). "There were two men," says he, "and they rowing round with poteen * before the cocks crowed, and the oar of one of them caught the body, and they passing the black cliffs of the north."

CATHLEEN (*trying to open the bundle*). Give me a knife, Nora; the string's perished with the salt water, and there's a black knot on it you wouldn't loosen in a week.

NORA (*giving her a knife*). I've heard tell it was a long way to Donegal.

CATHLEEN (*cutting the string*). It is surely. There was a man in here a while ago—the man sold us that knife—and he said if you set off walking from the rocks beyond it, it would be seven days you'd be in Donegal.

NORA. And what time would a man take, and he floating?

(CATHLEEN *opens the bundle and takes out a bit of a stocking. They look at them eagerly.*)

CATHLEEN (*in a low voice*). The Lord spare us, Nora! isn't it a queer hard thing to say if it's his they are surely?

NORA. I'll get his shirt off the hook the way we can put the one flannel on the other. (*She looks through some clothes hanging in the corner.*) It's not with them, Cathleen, and where will it be?

CATHLEEN. I'm thinking Bartley put it on him in the morning, for his own shirt was heavy with the salt in it. (*Pointing to the corner*) There's a bit of a sleeve was of the same stuff. Give me that and it will do.

(NORA *brings it to her and they compare the flannel.*)

CATHLEEN. It's the same stuff, Nora; but if it is itself, aren't there great rolls of it in the shops of Galway, and isn't it many another man may have a shirt of it as well as Michael himself?

poteen: illegal whiskey

NORA (*who has taken up the stocking and counted the stitches, crying out*). It's Michael, Cathleen, it's Michael; God spare his soul, and what will herself say when she hears this story, and Bartley on the sea?

CATHLEEN (*taking the stocking*). It's a plain stocking.

NORA. It's the second one of the third pair I knitted, and I put up threescore stitches, and I dropped four of them.

CATHLEEN (*counts the stitches*). It's that number is in it. (*Crying out*) Ah, Nora, isn't it a bitter thing to think of him floating that way to the far north, and no one to keen * him but the black hags that do be flying on the sea?

NORA (*swinging herself round, and throwing out her arms on the clothes*). And isn't it a pitiful thing when there is nothing left of a man who was a great rower and fisher, but a bit of an old shirt and a plain stocking?

CATHLEEN (*after an instant*). Tell me is herself coming, Nora? I hear a little sound on the path.

NORA (*looking out*). She is, Cathleen. She's coming up to the door.

CATHLEEN. Put these things away before she'll come in. Maybe it's easier she'll be after giving her blessing to Bartley, and we won't let on we've heard anything the time he's on the sea.

NORA (*helping* CATHLEEN *to close the bundle*). We'll put them here in the corner.

(*They put them into a hole in the chimney corner.* CATHLEEN *goes back to the spinning wheel.*)

NORA. Will she see it was crying I was?

CATHLEEN. Keep your back to the door the way the light'll not be on you.

(NORA *sits down at the chimney corner, with her back to the door.* MAURYA *comes in very slowly, without looking at the girls, and goes over to the stool at the other side of the fire. The cloth with the bread is still in her hand. The girls look at each other, and* NORA *points to the bundle of bread.*)

CATHLEEN (*after spinning for a moment*). You didn't give him his bit of bread?

(MAURYA *begins to keen softly, without turning round.*)

keen: to mourn by wailing

CATHLEEN. Did you see him riding down?

(MAURYA *goes on keening.*)

CATHLEEN (*a little impatiently*). God forgive you; isn't it a better thing to raise your voice and tell what you seen, than to be making lamentation for a thing that's done? Did you see Bartley, I'm saying to you.

MAURYA (*with a weak voice*). My heart's broken from this day.

CATHLEEN (*as before*). Did you see Bartley?

MAURYA. I seen the fearfulest thing.

CATHLEEN (*leaves her wheel and looks out*). God forgive you; he's riding the mare now over the green head, and the gray pony behind him.

MAURYA (*starts, so that her shawl falls back from her head and shows her white tossed hair; with a frightened voice*). The gray pony behind him.

CATHLEEN (*coming to the fire*). What is it ails you, at all?

MAURYA (*speaking very slowly*). I've seen the fearfulest thing any person has seen, since the day Bride Dara seen the dead man with the child in his arms.

CATHLEEN AND NORA. Uah.

(*They crouch down in front of the old woman at the fire.*)

NORA. Tell us what it is you seen.

MAURYA. I went down to the spring-well, and I stood there saying a prayer to myself. Then Bartley came along, and he riding on the red mare with the gray pony behind him. (*She puts up her hands, as if to hide something from her eyes.*) The Son of God spare us, Nora!

CATHLEEN. What is it you seen?

MAURYA. I seen Michael himself.

CATHLEEN (*speaking softly*). You did not, Mother; it wasn't Michael you seen, for his body is after being found in the far north, and he's got a clean burial by the grace of God.

MAURYA (*a little defiantly*). I'm after seeing him this day, and he riding and galloping. Bartley came first on the red mare; and I tried to say "God speed you," but something choked the words in my throat. He went by quickly; and, "The blessing of God on you," says he, and I could say nothing. I looked up then, and I crying, at the gray pony, and there was Michael upon it—with fine clothes on him, and new shoes on his feet.

CATHLEEN (*begins to keen*). It's destroyed we are from this day. It's destroyed, surely.

NORA. Didn't the young priest say the Almighty God wouldn't leave her destitute with no son living?

MAURYA (*in a low voice, but clearly*). It's little the like of him knows of the sea. . . . Bartley will be lost now, and let you call in Eamon to make me a good coffin out of the white boards, for I won't live after them. I've had a husband, and a husband's father, and six sons in this house—six fine men, though it was a hard birth I had with every one of them and they coming to the world—and some of them were found and some of them were not found, but they're gone now, the lot of them. . . . There were Stephen, and Shawn, were lost in the great wind, and found after in the Bay of Gregory of the Golden Mouth, and carried up the two of them on the one plank, and in by that door.

(*She pauses for a moment, the girls start as if they heard something through the door that is half open behind them.*)

NORA (*in a whisper*). Did you hear that, Cathleen? Did you hear a noise in the northeast?

CATHLEEN (*in a whisper*). There's someone after crying out by the seashore.

MAURYA (*continues without hearing anything*). There was Sheamus and his father, and his own father again, were lost in a dark night, and not a stick or sign was seen of them when the sun went up. There was Patch after was drowned out of a currach * that turned over. I was sitting here with Bartley, and he a baby, lying on my two knees, and I seen two women, and three women, and four women coming in, and they crossing themselves, and not saying a word. I looked out then, and there were men coming after them, and they holding a thing in the half of a red sail, and water dripping out of it—it was a dry day, Nora—and leaving a track to the door.

(*She pauses again with her hand stretched out toward the door. It opens softly and old women begin to come in, crossing themselves on the threshold, and kneeling down in front of the stage with red petticoats over their heads.*)

MAURYA (*half in a dream, to* CATHLEEN). Is it Patch, or Michael, or what is it at all?

currach: a small boat

CATHLEEN. Michael is after being found in the far north, and
when he is found there how could he be here in this place?

MAURYA. There does be a power of young men floating round in
the sea, and what way would they know if it was Michael they had,
or another man like him, for when a man is nine days in the sea, and
the wind blowing, it's hard set his own mother would be to say what
man was it.

CATHLEEN. It's Michael, God spare him, for they're after sending
us a bit of his clothes from the far north.

(*She reaches out and hands* MAURYA *the clothes that belonged to*
MICHAEL. MAURYA *stands up slowly, and takes them in her hands.*
NORA *looks out.*)

NORA. They're carrying a thing among them and there's water
dripping out of it and leaving a track by the big stones.

CATHLEEN (*in a whisper to the women who have come in*). Is it
Bartley it is?

ONE OF THE WOMEN. It is surely, God rest his soul.

(*Two younger women come in and pull out the table. Then men
carry in the body of* BARTLEY, *laid on a plank, with a bit of a sail
over it, and lay it on the table.*)

CATHLEEN (*to the women, as they are doing so*). What way was
he drowned?

ONE OF THE WOMEN. The gray pony knocked him into the sea,
and he was washed out where there is a great surf on the white rocks.

(MAURYA *has gone over and knelt down at the head of the table.
The women are keening softly and swaying themselves with a slow
movement.* CATHLEEN *and* NORA *kneel at the other end of the table.
The men kneel near the door.*)

MAURYA (*raising her head and speaking as if she did not see the
people around her*). They're all gone now, and there isn't anything
more the sea can do to me. . . . I'll have no call now to be up crying and praying when the wind breaks from the south, and you can
hear the surf is in the east, and the surf is in the west, making a great
stir with the two noises, and they hitting one on the other. I'll have
no call now to be going down and getting holy water in the dark
nights after Samhain,* and I won't care what way the sea is when

Samhain: a Celtic feast

the other women will be keening. (*To* NORA) Give me the holy water, Nora; there's a small cup still on the dresser.

(NORA *gives it to her.*)

MAURYA (*drops* MICHAEL'S *clothes across* BARTLEY'S *feet, and sprinkles the holy water over him*). It isn't that I haven't prayed for you, Bartley, to the Almighty God. It isn't that I haven't said prayers in the dark night till you wouldn't know what I'd be saying; but it's a great rest I'll have now, and it's time surely. It's a great rest I'll have now, and great sleeping in the long nights after Samhain, if it's only a bit of wet flour we do have to eat, and maybe a fish that would be stinking.

(*She kneels down again, crossing herself, and saying prayers under her breath.*)

CATHLEEN (*to an old man*). Maybe yourself and Eamon would make a coffin when the sun rises. We have fine white boards herself bought, God help her, thinking Michael would be found, and I have a new cake you can eat while you'll be working.

THE OLD MAN (*looking at the boards*). Are there nails with them?

CATHLEEN. There are not, Colum; we didn't think of the nails.

ANOTHER MAN. It's a great wonder she wouldn't think of the nails, and all the coffins she's seen made already.

CATHLEEN .It's getting old she is, and broken.

(MAURYA *stands up again very slowly and spreads out the pieces of* MICHAEL'S *clothes beside the body, sprinkling them with the last of the holy water.*)

NORA (*in a whisper to* CATHLEEN). She's quiet now and easy; but the day Michael was drowned you could hear her crying out from this to the spring-well. It's fonder she was of Michael, and would anyone have thought that?

CATHLEEN (*slowly and clearly*). An old woman will be soon tired with anything she will do, and isn't it nine days herself is after crying and keening, and making great sorrow in the house?

MAURYA (*puts the empty cup mouth downward on the table, and lays her hands together on* BARTLEY'S *feet*). They're all together this time, and the end is come. May the Almighty God have mercy on Bartley's soul, and on Michael's soul, and on the souls of Sheamus and Patch, and Stephen and Shawn (*bending her head*); and may He have mercy on my soul, Nora, and on the soul of everyone is left living in the world.

(*She pauses, and the keen rises a little more loudly from the women, then sinks away.*)

MAURYA (*continuing*). Michael has a clean burial in the far north, by the grace of the Almighty God. Bartley will have a fine coffin out of the white boards, and a deep grave surely. What more can we want than that? No man at all can be living forever, and we must be satisfied.

(*She kneels down again, and the curtain falls slowly.*)

CURTAIN

For Discussion

Riders to the Sea

1. The playwright is bound to follow standards in his art, just as the poet and novelist are. In Aristotle's *Poetics*, there are these rules for playwriting:
   (a) A well-constructed plot must neither begin nor end haphazardly . . . (for) a whole is that which has a beginning, a middle, and an end.
   (b) The effect of pity and terror is best produced when the events come on us by surprise.
   (c) The "tragedy" endeavors, as far as possible, to confine itself to a single revolution of the sun.
   Discuss the structure of *Riders to the Sea* in reference to these standards. Observe that the play opens at the "middle." What do you learn of the "beginning"? How and by whom do you learn it?
2. Why are Kathleen and Nora more concerned about Maurya's reactions, rather than about their brother's death? Show how the unfolding events prove the struggle to be Maurya's, not her children's.
3. Why does Maurya withold her blessing on Bartley's departure? Why are the two girls so concerned about this? Does Bartley's ensuing death seem to corroborate their fears? Would you explain their concern as an example of genuine faith, or as ingrained superstition? Discuss.
4. The fusion of heathen and Christian elements in the play is at times so complete that it is difficult to distinguish one from the other. In several instances, faith and fate are present simultaneously. Give examples and discuss. For example, find lines in which Maurya's faith is really a kind of fatalism which stems from her long experience with the sea.

5. Coupled with a kind of mysticism pervading the play, is the stark realism of daily life on the treeless Aran Islands where these characters live. Discuss their dress, customs, manners, and means of livelihood, indicating lines to prove your answers. For example, how was the bundle of clothes proved to be Michael's?

6. How does the dialogue add to the atmosphere? To the mood? What is the prevailing tone throughout the play?

7. Do you think Maurya will really be having "a great rest" and "a great sleeping in the long nights"? Why or why not? Is her outward resignation completely natural or is it simply a sort of calm before the full import of her situation is borne in upon her?

The Old Lady Shows Her Medals

JAMES M. BARRIE

James M. Barrie (1860–1937) was born in Scotland and educated there. At first he wrote stories and novels, the best-known being *The Little Minister* and *Peter Pan*. Eventually, however, Barrie turned to the writing of plays.

Popularly known for their quiet humor, mild satire and pathos, Barrie's delightful comedies have become perennial favorites with college and high school actors. Among them, *The Admirable Crichton*, *Dear Brutus*, and *A Kiss for Cinderella*, hold leading positions.

Unlike his contemporaries, Barrie was not much concerned with sociological themes. While the problem of class distinction often appears in his plays, he is more interested in the drama of ideas than in the drama of opinion. All his works have an authentic ring, with their true-to-life characters and dialogue, which frequently includes authentic dialect. In the one-act play that follows, Barrie's charm, humor, and pathos are particularly evident.

Characters

MRS. DOWEY

MRS. TWYMLEY

MRS. HAGGERTY

MRS. MICKLEHAM

THE REVEREND MR. WILLINGS

PRIVATE K. DOWEY

Three nice old ladies and a criminal, who is even nicer, are discussing the war over a cup of tea. The criminal, who is the hostess, calls it a dish of tea, which shows that she comes from Caledonia; * *but that is not her crime.*

They are all London charwomen, but three of them, including the hostess, are what are called professionally "charwomen and" or simply "ands." An "and" is also a caretaker when required; her name is entered as such in ink in a registry book, financial transactions take place across a counter between her and the registrar, and altogether she is of a very different social status from one who, like MRS. HAG-

Caledonia: Scotland

GERTY, *is a charwoman but nothing else.* MRS. HAGGERTY, *though present, is not at the party by invitation; having seen* MRS. DOWEY *buying the winkles,* she followed her downstairs—and so has shuffled into the play and sat down in it against our wish. We would remove her by force, or at least print her name in small letters, were it not that she takes offense very readily and says that nobody respects her. So, as you have slipped in, you can sit there,* MRS. HAGGERTY; *but keep quiet.*

There is nothing doing at present in the caretaking way for MRS. DOWEY, our hostess; but this does not damp her, caretaking being only to such as she an extra financially and a halo socially. If she had the honor of being served with an income-tax paper she would probably fill in one of the nasty little compartments with the words "Trade— charring. Profession (if any)—caretaking." This home of hers (from which, to look after your house, she makes, occasionally, temporary departures in great style, escorting a barrow) is in one of those what-care-I streets that you discover only when you have lost your way; on discovering them your duty is to report them to the authorities, who immediately add them to the map of London. That is why we are now reporting Friday Street. We shall call it, in the rough sketch drawn for tomorrow's press, "Street in which the criminal resided"; and you will find MRS. DOWEY's home therein marked with an X.

Her abode really consists of one room, but she maintains that there are two; so, rather than argue, let us say that there are two. The other one has no window, and she could not swish her old skirts in it without knocking something over; its grandest display is of tin pans and crockery on top of a dresser which has a lid to it; you have but to whip off the utensils and raise the lid, and, behold, a bath with hot and cold. MRS. DOWEY is very proud of this possession, and when she shows it off, as she does perhaps too frequently, she first signs to you with closed fist (funny old thing that she is) to approach softly. She then tiptoes to the dresser and pops off the lid, as if to take the bath unawares. Then she sucks her lips, and is modest if you have the grace to do the exclamations.

In the real room is a bed, though that is putting the matter too briefly. The fair way to begin, if you love MRS. DOWEY, is to say to her that it is a pity she has no bed. If she is in her best form she will chuckle, and agree that the want of a bed tries her sore; she will keep you on the hooks, so to speak, as long as she can; and then, with that

winkles: small shellfish

mouselike movement again, she will suddenly spring the bed on you. You thought it was a wardrobe, but she brings it down from the wall, and, lo, a bed. There is nothing else in her abode (which we now see to contain four rooms—kitchen, pantry, bedroom, and bathroom) that is absolutely a surprise; but it is full of "bits," every one of which has been paid ready money for and gloated over and tended until it has become part of its owner. Genuine Doweys, the dealers might call them, though there is probably nothing in the place except the bed that would fetch half a crown.

Her home is in the basement, so that the view is restricted to the lower half of persons passing overhead beyond the area stairs. Here at the window MRS. DOWEY *sometimes sits of a summer evening gazing, not sentimentally at a flowerpot which contains one poor bulb, nor yearningly at some tiny speck of sky, but with unholy relish at holes in stockings, and the like, which are revealed to her from her point of vantage. You, gentle reader, may flaunt by, thinking that your finery awes the street; but* MRS. DOWEY *can tell (and does) that your soles are in need of neat repair.*

Also, lower parts being as expressive as the face to those whose view is thus limited, she could swear to scores of the passers-by in a court of law.

These four lively old codgers are having a good time at the tea table, and wit is flowing free. As you can see by their everyday garments, and by their pails and mops (which are having a little tea party by themselves in the corner), it is not a gathering by invitations stretching away into yesterday. It is a purely informal affair, so much more attractive—don't you think?—than banquets elaborately prearranged. You know how they come about, especially in wartime. Very likely MRS. DOWEY *met* MRS. TWYMLEY *and* MRS. MICKLEHAM *quite casually in the street, and meant to do no more than pass the time of day; then, naturally enough, the word camouflage was mentioned and they got heated, but in the end* MRS. TWYMLEY *apologized; then, in the odd way in which one thing leads to another, the winkleman appeared, and* MRS. DOWEY *remembered that she had that pot of jam and that* MRS. MICKLEHAM *had stood treat last time; and soon they were all three descending the areas stairs, followed cringingly by the* HAGGERTY WOMAN.

They have been extremely merry, and never were four hard-worked old ladies who deserved it better. All a woman can do in wartime they do daily and cheerfully, just as their menfolk are doing it at the

Front; and now, with the mops and pails laid aside, they sprawl grace-fully at ease. There is no intention on their part to consider peace terms until a decisive victory has been gained in the field (Sarah Ann Dowey), until the Kaiser is put to the rightabout (Emma Mickle-ham) and singing very small (Amelia Twymley).

At this tea party the lady who is to play the part of MRS. DOWEY *is sure to want to suggest that our heroine has a secret sorrow; namely, the crime. But you should see us knocking that idea out of her head!* MRS. DOWEY *knows she is a criminal, but, unlike the actress, she does not know that she is about to be found out; and she is, to put it bluntly in her own Scotch way, the merriest of the whole clamjam-fry. She presses more tea on her guests, but they wave her away from them in the pretty manner of ladies who know that they have already had more than enough.*

MRS. DOWEY. Just one more winkle, Mrs. Mickleham?

(*Indeed there is only one more. But* MRS. MICKLEHAM *indicates po-litely that if she took this one it would have to swim for it. The* HAGGERTY WOMAN *takes it long afterward when she thinks, errone-ously, that no one is looking.* MRS. TWYMLEY *is sulking. Evidently someone has contradicted her. Probably the* HAGGERTY WOMAN.

MRS. TWYMLEY. I say it is so.

THE HAGGERTY WOMAN. I say it may be so.

MRS. TWYMLEY. I suppose I ought to know: me that has a son a prisoner in Germany. (*She has so obviously scored that all good feel-ing seems to call upon her to end here. But she continues, rather shab-bily.*) Being the only lady present that has that proud misfortune.

(*The others are stung.*)

MRS. DOWEY. My son is fighting in France.

MRS. MICKLEHAM. Mine is wounded in two places.

THE HAGGERTY WOMAN. Mine is at Salonaiky.*

(*The absurd pronunciation of this uneducated person moves the others to mirth.*)

MRS. DOWEY. You'll excuse us, Mrs. Haggerty, but the correct pro-nunciation is Salonikky.

THE HAGGERTY WOMAN (*to cover her confusion*). I don't think. (*She feels that even this does not prove her case.*) And I speak as one that has War Savings Certificates.

Salonaiky: mispronunciation of Salonika, the scene of a World War I naval battle

MRS. TWYMLEY. We all have them.

(*The* HAGGERTY WOMAN *whimpers, and the other guests regard her with unfeeling disdain.*)

MRS. DOWEY (*to restore cheerfulness*). Oh, it's a terrible war.

ALL (*brightening*). It is. You may say so.

MRS. DOWEY (*encouraged*). What I say is, the men is splendid; but I'm none so easy about the staff. That's your weak point, Mrs. Mickleham.

MRS. MICKLEHAM (*on the defense, but determined to reveal nothing that might be of use to the enemy*). You may take it from me, the staff's all right.

MRS. DOWEY. And very relieved I am to hear you say it.

(*It is here that the* HAGGERTY WOMAN *has the remaining winkle.*)

MRS. MICKLEHAM. You don't understand properly about trench warfare. If I had a map—

MRS. DOWEY (*wetting her finger to draw lines on the table*). That's the river Sommy.* Now, if we had barrages here—

MRS. TWYMLEY. Very soon you would be enfiladed. Where's your supports, my lady?

(MRS. DOWEY *is damped.*)

MRS. MICKLEHAM. What none of you grasps is that this is a artillery war—

THE HAGGERTY WOMAN (*strengthened by the winkle*). I say that the word is Salonaiky.

(*The others purse their lips.*)

MRS. TWYMLEY (*with terrible meaning*). We'll change the subject. Have you seen this week's *Fashion Chat?* (*She has evidently seen and devoured it herself, and even licked up the crumbs.*) The gabardine with accordion pleats has quite gone out.

MRS. DOWEY (*her old face sparkling*). My sakes! You tell me?

MRS. TWYMLEY (*with the touch of haughtiness that comes of great topics*). The plain smock has come in again, with silk lacing, giving that charming chic effect.

MRS. DOWEY. Oho!

MRS. MICKLEHAM. I must say I was always partial to the straight line (*thoughtfully regarding the want of line in* MRS. TWYMLEY'S *person*) though trying to them as is of too friendly a figure.

Sommy: her mispronunciation of the French river Somme

(*It is here that the* HAGGERTY WOMAN's *fingers close unostentatiously upon a piece of sugar.*)

MRS. TWYMLEY (*sailing into the empyrean **). Lady Dolly Kanister was seen conversing across the railings in a dainty *de jou.**

MRS. DOWEY. Fine would I have liked to see her.

MRS. TWYMLEY. She is equally popular as maid, wife, and munition worker. Her two children is inset. Lady Pops Babington was married in a tight tulle.

MRS. MICKLEHAM. What was her going-away dress?

MRS. TWYMLEY. A champagny cream velvet with dreamy corsage. She's married to Colonel the Honorable Chingford—"Snubs," they called him at Eton.

THE HAGGERTY WOMAN (*having disposed of the sugar*). Very likely he'll be sent to Salonaiky.

MRS. MICKLEHAM. Wherever he is sent, she'll have the same tremors as the rest of us. She'll be as keen to get the letters wrote with pencils as you or me.

MRS. TWYMLEY. Them pencil letters!

MRS. DOWEY (*in her sweet Scotch voice, timidly, afraid she may be going too far*). And women in enemy lands gets those pencil letters and then stop getting them, the same as ourselves. Let's occasionally think of that.

(*She has gone too far. Chairs are pushed back.*)

THE HAGGERTY WOMAN. I ask you!

MRS. MICKLEHAM. That's hardly language, Mrs. Dowey.

MRS. DOWEY (*scared*). Kindly excuse. I swear to death I'm none of your pacifists.

MRS. MICKLEHAM. Freely granted.

MRS. TWYMLEY. I've heard of females that have no male relations, and so they have no man-party at the wars. I've heard of them, but I don't mix with them.

MRS. MICKLEHAM. What can the likes of us have to say to them? It's not their war.

MRS. DOWEY (*wistfully*). They are to be pitied.

MRS. MICKLEHAM. But the place for them, Mrs. Dowey, is within doors with the blinds down.

MRS. DOWEY (*hurriedly*). That's the place for them.

empyrean: the heavens
de jou: a casual dress

MRS. MICKLEHAM. I saw one of them today buying a flag. I thought it was very impudent of her.

MRS. DOWEY (*meekly*). So it was.

MRS. MICKLEHAM (*trying to look modest with indifferent success*). I had a letter from my son, Percy, yesterday.

MRS. TWYMLEY. Alfred sent me his photo.

THE HAGGERTY WOMAN. Letters from Salonaiky is less common.

(*Three bosoms heave, but not, alas,* MRS. DOWEY'S. *Nevertheless she doggedly knits her lips.*)

MRS. DOWEY (*the criminal*). Kenneth writes to me every week. (*There are exclamations. The dauntless old thing holds aloft a packet of letters.*) Look at this. All his.

(*The* HAGGERTY WOMAN *whimpers.*)

MRS. TWYMLEY. Alfred has little time for writing, being a bombadier.

MRS. DOWEY (*relentlessly*). Do your letters begin "Dear mother"?

MRS. TWYMLEY. Generally.

MRS. MICKLEHAM. Invariable.

THE HAGGERTY WOMAN. Every time.

MRS. DOWEY (*delivering the knockout blow*). Kenneth's begin "Dearest mother."

(*No one can think of the right reply.*)

MRS. TWYMLEY (*doing her best*). A short man, I should say, judging by yourself. (*She ought to have left it alone.*)

MRS. DOWEY. Six feet two—and a half.

(*The gloom deepens.*)

MRS. MICKLEHAM (*against her better judgment*). A kilty, did you tell me?

MRS. DOWEY. Most certainly. He's in the famous Black Watch.*

THE HAGGERTY WOMAN (*producing her handkerchief*). The Surrey Rifles * is the famousest.

MRS. MICKLEHAM. There you and the King disagrees, Mrs. Haggerty. His choice is the Buffs, same as my Percy's.

MRS. TWYMLEY (*magnanimously*). Give me the R.H.A. and you can keep all the rest.

MRS. DOWEY. I'm sure I have nothing to say against the Surreys

Black Watch and **Surrey Rifles**: British regiments

and the R.H.A. and Buffs; but they are just breeches regiments, I understand.

THE HAGGERTY WOMAN. We can't all be kilties.

MRS. DOWEY (*crushingly*). That's very true.

MRS. TWYMLEY (*it is foolish of her, but she can't help saying it*). Has your Kenneth great hairy legs?

MRS. DOWEY. Tremendous.

(*The wicked woman, but let us also say "Poor Sarah Ann Dowey." For, at this moment, enter Nemesis.* In other words, the less important part of a clergyman appears upon the stair.*)

MRS. MICKLEHAM. It's the reverent gent!

MRS. DOWEY (*little knowing what he is bringing her*). I see he has had his boots heeled.

(*It may be said of* MR. WILLINGS *that his happy smile always walks in front of him. This smile makes music of his life; it means that once again he has been chosen, in his opinion, as the central figure in romance. No one can well have led a more drab existence, but he will never know it; he will always think of himself, humbly though elatedly, as the chosen of the gods. Of him must it have been originally written that adventures are for the adventurous. He meets them at every street corner. For instance, he assists an old lady off a bus and asks her if he can be of any further help. She tells him that she wants to know the way to Maddox the butcher's. Then comes the kind, triumphant smile; it always comes first, followed by its explanation, "I was there yesterday!" This is the merest sample of the adventures that keep* MR. WILLINGS *up to the mark.*)

(*Since the war broke out, his zest for life has become almost terrible. He can scarcely lift a newspaper and read of a hero without remembering that he knows someone of the same name. The Soldiers' Rest he is connected with was once a china emporium, and —mark my words—he had bought his tea service at it. Such is life when you are in the thick of it. Sometimes he feels that he is part of a gigantic spy drama. In the course of his extraordinary comings and goings he meets with Great Personages, of course, and is the confidential recipient of secret news. Before imparting the news he does not, as you might expect, first smile expansively; on the contrary, there comes over his face an awful solemnity, which,*)

Nemesis: Greek goddess of vengeance

*however, means the same thing. When divulging the names of the
personages, he first looks around to make sure that no suspicious
character is about, and then, lowering his voice, tells you, "I had
that from Mr. Farthing himself—he is the secretary of the Bethnal
Green Branch—H'sh . . ."*

(*There is a commotion about finding a worthy chair for "the reverent," and there is also some furtive pulling down of sleeves; but
he stands surveying the ladies through his triumphant smile. This
amazing man knows that he is about to score again.*)

MR. WILLINGS (*waving aside the chairs*). I thank you. But not at
all. Friends, I have news.

MRS. MICKLEHAM. News?

THE HAGGERTY WOMAN. From the Front?

MRS. TWYMLEY. My Alfred, sir?

(*They are all grown suddenly anxious—all except the hostess, who
knows that there can never be any news from the Front for her.*)

MR. WILLINGS. I tell you at once that all is well. The news is for
Mrs. Dowey.

MRS. DOWEY (*she stares*). News for me?

MR. WILLINGS. Your son, Mrs. Dowey—he has got five days' leave.

(*She shakes her head slightly, or perhaps it only trembles a little on
its stem.*)

Now, now, good news doesn't kill.

MRS. TWYMLEY. We're glad, Mrs. Dowey.

MRS. DOWEY. You're sure?

MR. WILLINGS. Quite sure. He has arrived.

MRS. DOWEY. He is in London?

MR. WILLINGS. He is. I have spoken to him.

MRS. MICKLEHAM. You lucky woman.

(*They might see that she is not looking lucky, but experience has
told them how differently these things take people.*)

MR. WILLINGS (*marvelling more and more as he unfolds his tale*).
Ladies, it is quite a romance. I was in the . . . (*He looks around
cautiously, but he knows that they are all to be trusted.*) . . . in the
Church Army quarters in Central Street, trying to get on the track
of one or two of our missing men. Suddenly my eyes—I can't account
for it—but suddenly my eyes alighted on a Highlander seated rather
drearily on a bench, with his kit at his feet.

THE HAGGERTY WOMAN. A big man?

MR. WILLINGS. A great brawny fellow.

(*The* HAGGERTY WOMAN *groans.*)

"My friend," I said at once, "welcome back to Blighty." * I make a point of calling it Blighty. "I wonder," I said, "if there is anything I can do for you?" He shook his head. "What regiment?" I asked. (*Here* MR. WILLINGS *very properly lowers his voice to a whisper.*) "Black Watch, 5th Battalion," he said. "Name?" I asked. "Dowey," he said.

MRS. MICKLEHAM. I declare. I do declare.

MR. WILLINGS (*showing how the thing was done, with the help of a chair*). I put my hand on his shoulder as it might be thus. "Kenneth Dowey," I said, "I know your mother."

MRS. DOWEY (*wetting her lips*). What did he say to that?

MR. WILLINGS. He was incredulous. Indeed, he seemed to think I was balmy. But I offered to bring him straight to you. I told him how much you had talked to me about him.

MRS. DOWEY. Bring him here!

MRS. MICKLEHAM. I wonder he needed to be brought.

MR. WILLINGS. He had just arrived, and was bewildered by the great city. He listened to me in the taciturn Scotch way, and then he gave a curious laugh.

MRS. TWYMLEY. Laugh?

MR. WILLINGS (*whose wild life has brought him into contact with the strangest people*). The Scotch, Mrs. Twymley, express their emotions differently from us. With them tears signify a rollicking mood, while merriment denotes that they are plunged in gloom. When I had finished he said at once, "Let us go and see the old lady."

MRS. DOWEY (*backing, which is the first movement she has made since he began his tale*). Is he—coming?

MR. WILLINGS (*gloriously*). He has come. He is up there. I told him I thought I had better break the joyful news to you.

(*Three women rush to the window.* MRS. DOWEY *looks at her pantry door, but perhaps she remembers that it does not lock on the inside. She stands rigid, though her face has gone very gray.*)

MRS. DOWEY. Kindly get them to go away.

MR. WILLINGS. Ladies, I think this happy occasion scarcely re-

Blighty: British slang for home

quires you. (*He is not the man to ask of woman a sacrifice that he is not prepared to make himself.*) I also am going instantly.

(*They all survey* MRS. DOWEY, *and understand—or think they understand.*)

MRS. TWYMLEY (*pail and mop in hand*). I would thank none for their company if my Alfred was at the door.

MRS. MICKLEHAM (*similarly burdened*). The same from me. Shall I send him down, Mrs. Dowey?

(*The old lady does not hear her. She is listening, terrified, for a step on the stairs.*)

Look at the poor, joyous thing, sir. She has his letters in her hand.

(*The three women go.* MR. WILLINGS *puts a kind hand on* MRS. DOWEY'S *shoulder. He thinks he so thoroughly understands the situation.*)

MR. WILLINGS. A good son, Mrs. Dowey, to have written to you so often.

(*Our old criminal quakes, but she grips the letters more tightly.* PRIVATE DOWEY *descends.*)

Dowey, my friend, there she is, waiting for you, with your letters in her hand.

DOWEY. (*grimly*). That's great.

(MR. WILLINGS *ascends the stair without one backward glance, like the good gentleman he is; and the* DOWEYS *are left together, with nearly the whole room between them. He is a great rough chunk of Scotland, howked out of her not so much neatly as liberally; and in his Black Watch uniform, all caked with mud, his kit and nearly all his worldly possessions on his back, he is an apparition scarcely less fearsome (but so much less ragged) than those ancestors of his who trotted with Prince Charlie to Derby. He stands silent, scowling at the old lady, daring her to raise her head; and she would like very much to do it, for she longs to have a first glimpse of her son. When he does speak, it is to jeer at her.*)

DOWEY. Do you recognize your loving son, missis?

("*Oh, the fine Scotch tang of him,*" *she thinks.*)

MRS. DOWEY (*trembling*). I'm pleased you wrote so often. ("*Oh, but he's* raised," *she thinks.*)

(*He strides toward her, and seizes the letters roughly.*)

DOWEY. Let's see them.

(*There is a string round the package and he unties it, and examines the letters at his leisure with much curiosity. The envelopes are in order, all addressed in pencil to* MRS. DOWEY, *with the proud words "Opened by Censor" on them. But the letter paper inside contains not a word of writing.*)

DOWEY. Nothing but blank paper! Is this your writing in pencil on the envelope? (*She nods, and he gives the matter further consideration.*) The covey * told me you were a charwoman. So I suppose you picked the envelopes out of wastepaper baskets, or such like, and then changed the addresses?

(*She nods again; still she dare not look up, but she is admiring his legs. When, however, he would cast the letters into the fire, she flames up with sudden spirit. She clutches them.*)

MRS. DOWEY. Don't burn them letters, mister.

DOWEY. They're not real letters.

MRS. DOWEY. They're all I have.

DOWEY (*returning to irony*). I thought you had a son?

MRS. DOWEY. I never had a man nor a son nor anything. I just call myself Missis to give me a standing.

DOWEY. Well, it's past my seeing through.

(*He turns to look for some explanation from the walls. She gets a peep at him at last. Oh, what a grandly set-up man! Oh, the stride of him. Oh, the noble rage of him. Oh, Samson had been like this before that woman took him in hand.*)

DOWEY (*whirling round on her*). What made you do it?

MRS. DOWEY. It was everybody's war, mister, except mine. (*She beats her arms.*) I wanted it to be my war too.

DOWEY. You'll need to be plainer. And yet I'm d—d if I care to hear you, you lying old trickster.

(*The words are merely what were to be expected, and so are endurable; but he has moved toward the door.*)

MRS. DOWEY. You're not going already, mister?

DOWEY. Yes, I just came to give you an ugly piece of my mind.

MRS. DOWEY (*holding out her arms longingly*). You haven't gave it to me yet.

covey: a small group of people

DOWEY. You have a cheek!

MRS. DOWEY (*giving further proof of it*). You wouldn't drink some tea?

DOWEY. Me! I tell you I came here for the one purpose of blazing away at you.

(*It is such a roaring negative that it blows her into a chair. But she is up again in a moment, is this spirited old lady.*)

MRS. DOWEY. You could drink the tea while you was blazing away. There's winkles.

DOWEY. Is there? (*He turns interestedly toward the table, but his proud Scots character checks him—which is just as well, for what she should have said was that there had been winkles.*) Not me. You're just a common rogue. (*He seats himself far from the table.*) Now, then, out with it. Sit down! (*She sits meekly; there is nothing she would not do for him.*) As you char, I suppose you are on your feet all day.

MRS. DOWEY. I'm more on my knees.

DOWEY. That's where you should be to me.

MRS. DOWEY. Oh, mister, I'm willing.

DOWEY. Stop it. Go on, you accomplished liar.

MRS. DOWEY. It's true that my name is Dowey.

DOWEY. It's enough to make me change mine.

MRS. DOWEY. I've been charring and charring and charring as far back as I mind. I've been in London this twenty years.

DOWEY. We'll skip your early days. I have an appointment.

MRS. DOWEY. And then when I was old the war broke out.

DOWEY. How could it affect you?

MRS. DOWEY. Oh, mister, that's the thing. It didn't affect me. It affected everybody but me. The neighbors looked down on me. Even the posters, on the walls, of the woman saying "Go, my boy," leered at me. I sometimes cried by myself in the dark. You won't have a cup of tea?

DOWEY. No.

MRS. DOWEY. Suddenlike the idea came to me to pretend I had a son.

DOWEY. You depraved old limmer! * But what in the name of Old Nick made you choose me out of the whole British Army?

MRS. DOWEY (*giggling*).Maybe, mister, it was because I liked you best.

limmer: rascal

DOWEY. Now, now, woman.

MRS. DOWEY. I read one day in the papers, "In which he was assisted by Private K. Dowey, 5th Battalion, Black Watch."

DOWEY (*flattered*). Did you, now! Well, I expect that's the only time I was ever in the papers.

MRS. DOWEY (*trying it on again*). I didn't choose you for that alone. I read a history of the Black Watch first, to make sure it was the best regiment in the world.

DOWEY. Anybody could have told you that. (*He is moving about now in better humor, and, meeting the loaf in his stride, he cuts a slice from it. He is hardly aware of this, but MRS. DOWEY knows.*) I like the Scotch voice of you, woman. It drumbles on like a hill burn.*

MRS. DOWEY. Prosen Water runs by where I was born. Maybe it teached me to speak, mister.

DOWEY. Canny, woman, canny.

MRS. DOWEY. I read about the Black Watch's ghostly piper that plays proudly when the men of the Black Watch do well, and prouder when they fall.

DOWEY. There's some foolish story of that kind. (*He has another careless slice off the loaf.*) But you couldn't have been living here at that time or they would have guessed. I suppose you flitted?

MRS. DOWEY. Yes, it cost me eleven and sixpence.

DOWEY. How did you guess the K in my name stood for Kenneth?

MRS. DOWEY. Does it?

DOWEY. Umpha.

MRS. DOWEY. An angel whispered it to me in my sleep.

DOWEY. Well, that's the only angel in the whole black business. (*He chuckles.*) You little thought I would turn up! (*Wheeling suddenly on her*) Or did you?

MRS. DOWEY. I was beginning to weary for a sight of you, Kenneth.

DOWEY. What word was that?

MRS. DOWEY. Mister.

(*He helps himself to butter, and she holds out the jam pot to him; but he haughtily rejects it. Do you think she gives in now? Not a bit of it. He returns to sarcasm.*)

DOWEY. I hope you're pleased with me now you see me.

MRS. DOWEY. I'm very pleased. Does your folk live in Scotland?

DOWEY. Glasgow.

MRS. DOWEY. Both living?

burn: brook or stream

DOWEY. Ay.

MRS. DOWEY. Is your mother terrible proud of you?

DOWEY. Naturally

MRS. DOWEY. You'll be going to them?

DOWEY. After I've had a skite * in London first.

MRS. DOWEY. (*sniffing*). So she is in London!

DOWEY. Who?

MRS. DOWEY. Your young lady.

DOWEY. Are you jealyous?

MRS. DOWEY. Not me.

DOWEY. You needna be. She's a young thing.

MRS. DOWEY. You surprises me. A beauty, no doubt?

DOWEY. You may be sure. (*He tries the jam.*) She's a titled person. She is equally popular as maid, wife, and munition worker.

(MRS. DOWEY *remembers Lady Dolly Kanister, so familiar to readers of fashionable gossip, and a very leery expression indeed comes into her face.*)

MRS. DOWEY. Tell me more about her, man.

DOWEY. She has sent me a lot of things, especially cakes, and a worsted waistcoat, with a loving message on the enclosed card.

(*The old lady is now in a quiver of excitement. She loses control of her arms, which jump excitedly this way and that.*)

MRS. DOWEY. You'll try one of my cakes, mister?

DOWEY. Not me.

MRS. DOWEY. They're of my own making.

DOWEY. No, I thank you.

(*But with a funny little run she is in the pantry and back again. She pushes a cake before him, at sight of which he gapes.*)

MRS. DOWEY. What's the matter? Tell me, oh, tell me, mister!

DOWEY. That's exactly the kind of cake that her ladyship sends me.

(MRS. DOWEY *is now a very glorious old character indeed.*)

MRS. DOWEY. Is the waistcoat right, mister? I hope the Black Watch colors pleased you.

DOWEY. What-at! Was it you?

MRS. DOWEY. I daredna give my own name, you see, and I was always reading hers in the papers.

(*The badgered man looms over her, terrible for the last time.*)

skite: a fling or spree

DOWEY. Woman, is there no getting rid of you!

MRS. DOWEY. Are you angry?

(*He sits down with a groan.*)

DOWEY. Oh, hell! Give me some tea.

(*She rushes about preparing a meal for him, every bit of her wanting to cry out to every other bit, "Oh, glory, glory, glory!" For a moment she hovers behind his chair. "Kenneth!" she murmurs. "What?" he asks, no longer aware that she is taking a liberty. "Nothing," she says. "Just Kenneth," and is off gleefully for the tea caddy. But when his tea is poured out, and he has drunk a saucerful, the instinct of self-preservation returns to him between two bites.*)

DOWEY. Don't you be thinking, missis, for one minute that you have got me.

MRS. DOWEY. No, no.

(*On that understanding he unbends.*)

DOWEY. I have a theater tonight, followed by a randy-dandy.*

MRS. DOWEY. Oho! Kenneth, this is a queer first meeting!

DOWEY. It is, woman—oh, it is—(*guardedly*)—and it's also a last meeting.

MRS. DOWEY. Yes, yes.

DOWEY. So here's to you—you old mop and pail. *Ave atque vale.*

MRS. DOWEY. What's that?

DOWEY. That means Hail and Farewell.

MRS. DOWEY. Are you a scholar?

DOWEY. Being Scotch, there's almost nothing I don't know.

MRS. DOWEY. What was you to trade?

DOWEY. Carter, glazier, orraman,* any rough jobs.

MRS. DOWEY. You're a proper man to look at.

DOWEY. I'm generally admired.

MRS. DOWEY. She's an enviable woman.

DOWEY. Who?

MRS. DOWEY. Your mother.

DOWEY. Eh? Oh, that was just protecting myself from you. I have neither father nor mother nor wife nor grandmama. (*Bitterly*) This party never even knew who his proud parents were.

MRS. DOWEY. Is that—(*gleaming*)—is that true?

randy-dandy: a party
orraman: a man who does odd jobs

DOWEY. It's gospel.

MRS. DOWEY. Heaven be praised!

DOWEY. Eh? None of that! I was a fool to tell you. But don't think you can take advantage of it. Pass the cake.

MRS. DOWEY. I daresay it's true we'll never meet again, Kenneth, but—but if we do, I wonder where it will be?

DOWEY. Not in this world.

MRS. DOWEY. There's no telling—(*leering ingratiatingly*)—it might be at Berlin.

DOWEY. Tod, if I ever get to Berlin, I believe I'll find you there waiting for me!

MRS. DOWEY. With a cup of tea for you in my hand.

DOWEY. Yes, and (*heartily*) very good tea too.

(*He has partaken heavily; he is now in high good humor.*)

MRS. DOWEY. Kenneth, we could come back by Paris!

DOWEY. All the ladies likes to go to Paris.

MRS. DOWEY. Ah, Kenneth, Kenneth, if just once before I die I could be fitted for a Paris gown with dreamy corsage!

DOWEY. You're all alike, old covey. We have a song about it. (*He sings*):

> Mrs. Gill is very ill,
>   Nothing can improve her
> But to see the Tuileries *
>   And waddle through the Louvre.*

(*No song ever had a greater success.* MRS. DOWEY *is doubled up with mirth. When she comes to—when they both come to, for they are a pair of them—she cries:*)

MRS. DOWEY. You must learn me that (*and off she goes in song also*):

> Mrs. Dowey's very ill,
>   Nothing can improve her.

DOWEY. Stop!

> But dressed up in a Paris gown
>   To waddle through the Louvre.

(*They fling back their heads. She points at him; he points at her.*)

MRS. DOWEY (*ecstatically.*) Hairy legs!

Tuileries: a former royal palace in Paris
Louvre: famous art gallery in Paris

(A *mad remark, which brings him to his senses; he remembers who
and what she is.*)

DOWEY. Mind your manners! (*Rising*) Well, thank you for my
tea. I must be stepping.

(*Poor* MRS. DOWEY, *he is putting on his kit.*)

MRS. DOWEY. Where are you living?

DOWEY. (*He sighs.*) That's the question. But there's a place called
The Hut, where some of the 2nd Battalion are. They'll take me in.
Beggars—(*bitterly*)—can't be choosers.

MRS. DOWEY. Beggars?

DOWEY. I've never been here before. If you knew (*a shadow comes
over him*) what it is to be in such a place without a friend. I was
crazy with glee, when I got my leave, at the thought of seeing
London at last; but after wandering its streets for four hours, I would
almost have been glad to be back in the trenches.

(*"If you knew," he has said, but indeed the old lady knows.*)

MRS. DOWEY. That's my quandorum too, Kenneth.

(*He nods sympathetically.*)

DOWEY. I'm sorry for you, you poor old body (*shouldering his
kit*) but I see no way out for either of us.

MRS. DOWEY (*cooing*). Do you not?

DOWEY. Are you at it again!

(*She knows that it must be now or never. She has left her biggest
guns for the end. In her excitement she is rising up and down
on her toes.*)

MRS. DOWEY. Kenneth, I've heard that the thing a man on leave
longs for more than anything else is a bed with sheets, and a bath.

DOWEY. You never heard anything truer.

MRS. DOWEY. Go into that pantry, Kenneth Dowey, and lift
the dresser top, and tell me what you see.

(*He goes. There is an awful stillness. He returns, impressed.*)

DOWEY. It's a kind of a bath!

MRS. DOWEY. You could do yourself there pretty, half at a time.

DOWEY. Me?

MRS. DOWEY. There's a woman through the wall that would be
very willing to give me a shakedown till your leave is up.

DOWEY. (*He snorts.*) Oh, is there!

(*She has not got him yet, but there is still one more gun.*)

MRS. DOWEY. Kenneth, look!

(*With these simple words she lets down the bed. She says no more; an effect like this would be spoilt by language. Fortunately he is not made of stone. He thrills.*)

DOWEY. Gosh! That's the dodge we need in the trenches.

MRS. DOWEY. That's your bed, Kenneth.

DOWEY. Mine? (*He grins at her.*) You queer old divert.* What can make you so keen to be burdened by a lump like me?

MRS. DOWEY. He! he! he! he!

DOWEY. I tell you, I'm the commonest kind of man.

MRS. DOWEY. I'm just the commonest kind of old wifie myself.

DOWEY. I've been a kick-about all my life, and I'm no great shakes at the war.

MRS. DOWEY. Yes, you are. How many Germans have you killed?

DOWEY. Just two for certain, and there was no glory in it. It was just because they wanted my shirt.

MRS. DOWEY. Your shirt?

DOWEY. Well, they said it was their shirt.

MRS. DOWEY. Have you took prisoners?

DOWEY. I once took half a dozen, but that was a poor affair too.

MRS. DOWEY. How could one man take half a dozen?

DOWEY. Just in the usual way. I surrounded them.

MRS. DOWEY. Kenneth, you're just my ideal.

DOWEY. You're easily pleased. (*He turns again to the bed.*) Let's see how the thing works. .(*He kneads the mattress with his fist, and the result is so satisfactory that he puts down his kit.*) Old lady, if you really want me, I'll bide.

MRS. DOWEY. Oh! oh! oh! oh!

(*Her joy is so demonstrative that he has to drop a word of warning.*)

DOWEY. But, mind you, I don't accept you as a relation. For your personal glory you can go on pretending to the neighbors, but the best I can say for you is that you're on your probation. I'm a cautious character, and we must see how you'll turn out.

MRS. DOWEY. Yes, Kenneth.

DOWEY. And now, I think, for that bath. My theater begins at six-thirty. A cove I met on a bus is going with me.

divert: slang for an odd person

MRS. DOWEY. (*She is a little alarmed.*) You're sure you'll come back?

DOWEY. Yes, yes. (*Handsomely*) I leave my kit in pledge.

MRS. DOWEY. You won't liquor up too freely, Kenneth?

DOWEY. You're the first (*chuckling*) to care whether I do or not.

(*Nothing she has said has pleased the lonely man so much as this.*) I promise. Tod, I'm beginning to look forward to being wakened in the morning by hearing you cry, "Get up, you lazy swine." I've kind of envied men that had womenfolk with the right to say that.

(*He is passing to the bathroom when a diverting notion strikes him.*)

MRS. DOWEY. What is it, Kenneth?

DOWEY. The theater. It would be showier if I took a lady.

(MRS. DOWEY *feels a thumping at her breast.*)

MRS. DOWEY. Kenneth, tell me this instant what you mean. Don't keep me on the dumps.

(*He turns her around.*)

DOWEY. No, it couldn't be done.

MRS. DOWEY. Was it me you were thinking of?

DOWEY. Just for the moment (*regretfully*) but you have no style.

(*She catches hold of him by the sleeve.*)

MRS. DOWEY. Not in this, of course. But, oh, Kenneth, if you saw me in my merino! It's laced up the back in the very latest.

DOWEY. Hum (*doubtfully*) but let's see it.

(*It is produced from a drawer, to which the old lady runs with almost indecent haste. The connoisseur examines it critically.*)

DOWEY. Looks none so bad. Have you a bit of chiffon for the neck? It's not bombs nor Kaisers nor Tipperary that men in the trenches think of; it's chiffon.

MRS. DOWEY. I swear I have, Kenneth. And I have a bangle, and a muff, and gloves.

DOWEY. Ay, ay. (*He considers.*) Do you think you could give your face less of a homely look?

MRS. DOWEY. I'm sure I could.

DOWEY. Then you can have a try. But, mind you, I promise nothing. All will depend on the effect.

(*He goes into the pantry, and the old lady is left alone. Not alone, for she is ringed round by entrancing hopes and dreadful fears.*

*They beam on her and jeer at her; they pull her this way and that.
With difficulty she breaks through them and rushes to her pail,
hot water, soap, and a looking glass.*

(*Our last glimpse of her for this evening shows her staring—not dis-
contentedly—at her soft old face, licking her palm, and pressing
it to her hair. Her eyes are sparkling.*)

(*One evening a few days later* MRS. TWYMLEY *and* MRS. MICKLEHAM
are in MRS. DOWEY'S *house, awaiting that lady's return from some
fashionable dissipation. They have undoubtedly been discussing
the war, for the first words we catch are:*)

MRS. MICKLEHAM. I tell you flat, Amelia, I bows no knee to junkerdom.*

MRS. TWYMLEY. Sitting here by the fire, you and me, as one to
another, what do you think will happen after the war? Are we to go
back to being as we were?

MRS. MICKLEHAM. Speaking for myself, Amelia, not me. The war
has wakened me up to a understanding of my own importance that
is really astonishing.

MRS. TWYMLEY. Same here. Instead of being the poor worms the
like of you and me thought we was, we turns out to be visible de-
partments of a great and haughty empire.

(*They are well under way, and with a little luck we might now hear
their views on various passing problems of the day, such as the
neglect of science in our public schools. But in comes the* HAG-
GERTY WOMAN, *and spoils everything. She is attired, like them, in
her best; but the effect of her is that her clothes have gone out
for a walk, leaving her at home.*)

MRS. MICKLEHAM (*with deep distaste.*) Here's that submarine
again.

(*The* HAGGERTY WOMAN *cringes to them, but gets no encouragement.*)

THE HAGGERTY WOMAN. It's a terrible war.

MRS. TWYMLEY. Is that so?

THE HAGGERTY WOMAN. I wonder what will happen when it ends?

MRS. MICKLEHAM. I have no idea.

(*The intruder produces her handkerchief, but does not use it. After
all, she is in her best.*)

THE HAGGERTY WOMAN. Are they not back yet?

junkerdom: German nobility and power

(Perfect ladies must reply to a direct question.)

MRS. MICKLEHAM. No. *(Icily)* We have been waiting this half-hour. They are at the theater again.

THE HAGGERTY WOMAN. You tell me! I just popped in with an insignificant present for him, as his leave is up.

MRS. TWYMLEY. The same errand brought us.

THE HAGGERTY WOMAN. My present is cigarettes.

(They have no intention of telling her what their presents are, but the secret leaps from them.)

MRS. MICKLEHAM. So is mine.

MRS. TWYMLEY. Mine too.

(Triumph of the HAGGERTY WOMAN. *But it is short-lived.)*

MRS. MICKLEHAM. Mine has gold tips.

MRS. TWYMLEY. So has mine.

THE HAGGERTY WOMAN *(need not say a word. You have only to look at her to know that her cigarettes are not gold-tipped. She tries to brazen it out, which is so often a mistake)*. What care I? Mine is Exquisytos.

(No wonder they titter.)

MRS. MICKLEHAM. Excuse us, Mrs. Haggerty—if that's your name —but the word is Exquiseetos.

THE HAGGERTY WOMAN. Much obliged! *(Weeps.)*

MRS. MICKLEHAM. I think I heard a taxi.

MRS. TWYMLEY. It will be her third this week.

(They peer through the blind. They are so excited that rank is forgotten.)

MRS. MICKLEHAM. A new astrakhan jacket he gave her, with Venus sleeves.

THE HAGGERTY WOMAN. Has she sold her gabardine coat?

MRS. MICKLEHAM. Not her! She has them both at the theater, warm night though it is. She's wearing the astrakhan—and carrying the gabardine, flung carelesslike over her arm.

THE HAGGERTY WOMAN. I saw her strutting about with him yesterday, looking as if she thought the two of them made a procession.

MRS. TWYMLEY. Hsh! *(Peeping)* Strike me dead—if she's not coming mincing down the stair, hooked on his arm!

(Indeed it is thus that MRS. DOWEY *enters. Perhaps she had seen*

shadows lurking on the blind, and at once hooked on to KENNETH *to impress the visitors. She is quite capable of it.*

(*Now we see what* KENNETH *saw that afternoon five days ago when he emerged from the bathroom and found the old trembler awaiting his inspection. Here are the muff and the gloves and the chiffon, and such a kind old bonnet that it makes you laugh at once. I don't know how to describe it; but it is trimmed with a kiss, as bonnets should be when the wearer is old and frail. We must take the merino for granted until she steps out of the astrakhan. She is dressed up to the nines; there is no doubt about it. Yes, but is her face less homely? Above all, has she style? The answer is in a stout affirmative. Ask* KENNETH. *He knows. Many a time he has had to go behind a door to roar hilariously at the old lady. He has thought of her as a lark to tell his mates about by and by; but for some reason that he cannot fathom, he knows now that he will never do that.*)

MRS. DOWEY (*affecting surprise*). Kenneth, we have visitors!
DOWEY. Your servant, ladies.

(*He is no longer mud-caked and dour. A very smart figure is this Private Dowey; and he winks engagingly at the visitors, like one who knows that for jolly company you cannot easily beat charwomen. The pleasantries that he and they have exchanged this week! The sauce he has given them. The wit of* MRS. MICKLEHAM'S *retorts. The badinage of* MRS. TWYMLEY. *The neat giggles of the* HAGGERTY WOMAN. *There has been nothing like it since you took the countess in to dinner.*)

MRS. TWYMLEY. We should apologize. We're not meaning to stay.
MRS. DOWEY. You are very welcome. Just wait (*the ostentation of this!*) till I get out of my astrakhan—and my muff—and my gloves—and (*It is the bonnet's turn now*) my Excelsior.

(*At last we see her in the merino—a triumph.*)

MRS. MICKLEHAM. You've given her a glory time, Mr. Dowey.
DOWEY. It's her that has given it to me, missis.
MRS. DOWEY. Hey! hey! hey! hey! He just pampers me. (*Waggling her fists*) The Lord forgive us, but this being the last night, we had a sit-down supper at a restaurant! (*Vehemently*) I swear by God that we had champagny wine. (*There is a dead stillness, and she knows very well what it means; she has even prepared for it.*) And to

them as doubts my word—here's the cork. (*She places the cork, in its lovely gold drapery, upon the table.*)

MRS. MICKLEHAM. I'm sure!

MRS. TWYMLEY. I would thank you, Mrs. Dowey, not to say a word against my Alfred.

MRS. DOWEY. Me!

DOWEY. Come, come, ladies! (*In the masterful way that is so hard for women to resist*) If you say another word, I'll kiss the lot of you.

(*There is a moment of pleased confusion.*)

MRS. MICKLEHAM. Really, them sodgers!

THE HAGGERTY WOMAN. The kilties is the worst!

MRS. TWYMLEY (*heartily*). I'm sure we don't grudge you your treats, Mrs. Dowey; and sorry we are that this is the end.

DOWEY. Yes, it's the end. (*With a troubled look at his old lady*) I must be off in ten minutes.

(*The little soul is too gallant to break down in company. She hurries into the pantry and shuts the door.*)

MRS. MICKLEHAM. Poor thing! But we must run, for you'll be having some last words to say to her.

DOWEY. I kept her out long on purpose so as to have less time to say them in. (*He more than half wishes that he could make a bolt to a public house.*)

MRS. TWYMLEY. It's the best way. (*In the important affairs of life there is not much that anyone can teach a charwoman.*) Just a mere nothing—to wish you well, Mr. Dowey.

(*All three present him with the cigarettes.*)

MRS. MICKLEHAM. A scraping, as one might say.

THE HAGGERTY WOMAN (*enigmatically*). The heart is warm, though it may not be gold-tipped.

DOWEY. You bricks!

THE LADIES. Good luck, cocky.

DOWEY. The same to you. And if you see a sodger man up there in a kilt, he is one that is going back with me. Tell him not to come down, but—but to give me till the last minute, and then to whistle.

(*It is quite a grave man who is left alone, thinking what to do next. He tries a horse laugh, but that proves of no help. He says "Hell!" to himself, but it is equally ineffective. Then he opens the pantry door and calls.*)

DOWEY. Old lady.

(*She comes timidly to the door, her hand up as if to ward off a blow.*)

MRS. DOWEY. Is it time?

(*An encouraging voice answers her.*)

DOWEY. No, no, not yet. I've left word for Dixon to whistle when go I must.

MRS. DOWEY. All is ended.

DOWEY. Now, then, you promised to be gay. We were to help one another.

MRS. DOWEY. Yes, Kenneth.

DOWEY. It's bad for me, but it's worse for you.

MRS. DOWEY. The men have medals to win, you see.

DOWEY. The women have their medals, too. (*He knows she likes him to order her about, so he tries it again.*) Come here. No, I'll come to you. (*He stands gaping at her wonderingly. He has no power of words, nor does he quite know what he would like to say.*) God!

MRS. DOWEY. What is it, Kenneth?

DOWEY. You're a woman.

MRS. DOWEY. I had near forgot it.

(*He wishes he was at the station with Dixon. Dixon is sure to have a bottle in his pocket. They will be roaring a song presently. But in the meantime—there is that son business. Blethers,* the whole thing, of course—or mostly blethers. But it's the way to please her.*)

DOWEY. Have you noticed you have never called me son?

MRS. DOWEY. Have I noticed it! I was feared, Kenneth. You said I was on probation.

DOWEY. And so you were. Well, the probation's ended. (*He laughs uncomfortably.*) The like of me! But if you want me you can have me.

MRS. DOWEY. Kenneth, will I do?

DOWEY (*artfully gay*). Woman, don't be so forward. Wait till I have proposed.

MRS. DOWEY. Propose for a mother?

DOWEY. What for no? (*In the grand style*) Mrs. Dowey, you queer

blethers: nonsense

carl,* you spunky tiddy, have I your permission to ask you the most important question a neglected orphan can ask of an old lady?

(*She bubbles with mirth. Who could help it, the man has such a way with him!*)

MRS. DOWEY. None of your sauce, Kenneth.

DOWEY. For a long time, Mrs. Dowey, you cannot have been unaware of my sonnish feelings for you.

MRS. DOWEY. Wait till I get my mop to you—

DOWEY. And if you're not willing to be my mother, I swear I'll never ask another. (*The old divert pulls him down to her and strokes his hair*). Was I a well-behaved infant, Mother?

MRS. DOWEY. Not you, sonny—you were a rampaging rogue.

DOWEY. Was I slow in learning to walk?

MRS. DOWEY. The quickest in our street. He! he! he! (*She starts up.*) Was that the whistle?

DOWEY. No, no. See here. In taking me over you have, in a manner of speaking, joined the Black Watch.

MRS. DOWEY. I like to think that, Kenneth.

DOWEY. Then you must behave so that the ghost piper can be proud of you. 'Tion! (*She stands bravely at attention.*) That's the style. Now listen. I've sent in your name as being my nearest of kin, and your allowance will be coming to you weekly in the usual way.

MRS. DOWEY. Hey! hey! hey! Is it wicked, Kenneth?

DOWEY. I'll take the responsibility for it in both worlds. You see, I want you to be safeguarded in case anything hap—

MRS. DOWEY. Kenneth!

DOWEY. 'Tion! Have no fear. I'll come back, covered with mud and medals. Mind you have that cup of tea waiting for me.

(*He is listening for the whistle. He pulls her onto his knee.*)

MRS. DOWEY. Hey! hey! hey! hey!

DOWEY. What fun we'll have writing to one another! Real letters this time!

MRS. DOWEY. Yes.

DOWEY. It would be a a good plan if you began the first letter as soon as I've gone.

MRS. DOWEY. I will.

DOWEY. I hope Lady Dolly will go on sending me cakes.

MRS. DOWEY. You may be sure.

carl: ill-mannered fellow

(*He ties his scarf round her neck.*)

DOWEY. You must have been a bonny thing when you were young.

MRS. DOWEY. Away with you!

DOWEY. That scarf sets you fine.

MRS. DOWEY. Blue was always my color.

(*The whistle sounds.*)

DOWEY. Old lady, you are what Blighty means to me now.

(*She hides in the pantry again. She is out of sight of us, but she does something that makes* PRIVATE DOWEY *take off his bonnet. Then he shoulders his equipment and departs. That is he laughing coarsely with Dixon.*)

We have one last glimpse of the old lady—a month or two after Kenneth's death in action. It would be rosemary to us to see her in her black dress, of which she is very proud; but let us rather peep at her in the familiar garments that make a third to her mop and pail. It is early morning, and she is having a look at her medals before setting off on the daily round. They are in a drawer with the scarf covering them, and on the scarf a piece of lavender. First the black frock, which she carries in her arms like a baby. Then her War Savings Certificates, Kenneth's bonnet, a thin packet of real letters, and the famous champagne cork. She kisses the letters, but she does not blub over them. She strokes the dress, and waggles her head over the certificates and presses the bonnet to her cheeks, and rubs the tinsel of the cork carefully with her apron. She is a tremulous old 'un; yet she exults, for she owns all these things and also the penny flag on her breast. She puts them away in the drawer, the scarf over them, the lavender on the scarf. Her air of triumph well becomes her. She lifts the pail and the mop, and slouches off gamely to the day's toil.

CURTAIN

For Discussion

The Old Lady Shows Her Medals

1. One critic has noted that *courage* is the theme of all Barrie's plays. Trace this theme in *The Old Lady Shows Her Medals,* keeping in mind the background of World War I. Discuss it in detail with reference to the charwoman, Mrs. Dowey, and Kenneth.
2. The play deals with the problem of social status, and shows how the

charwomen seek to preserve social distinction. What does this tell you about social attitudes prevailing in England at that time?

3. Like her fellow charwomen in London, Mrs. Dowey takes pride in three things. Name them. Show how this proves that war is no respecter of persons.

4. One of the demands made by drama is that the dialogue must give clues to the characters. Show how Mrs. Dowey reveals herself to be a rather complex character in her dialogue with Kenneth. (For example, her ingenuity in contriving so clever a plan to "get" him before he actually comes to Blighty is all brought out in their first conversation.) In contrast, Kenneth seems a very simple person. Discuss this, using specific lines for reference.

5. In a play, the contrast in characters must be "dramatic," that is, there must be some conflict. What is the conflict in this play?

6. In a drama, the main character must change and show some development. How is this true in this play? Discuss.

7. Although Kenneth will never return, do you feel that the basement home has been, in a sense, "transfigured" by this experience? Discuss.

8. What role, imposed on Mrs. Dowey by her "son," will continue to prompt her brave acceptance of life? What, precisely, are the medals she has won in her own private conquest?

9. In the last scene, how would you depict the time lapse? Would some conversation be necessary? Do you think, in general, that the author's stage directions are a sufficient help to the actors? Why or why not? Would they be a help to the director? To the reader? Discuss.

10. The play as a whole points up the experience of war and its effects upon people. Discuss in detail.

The Barretts of Wimpole Street

RUDOLF BESIER

Rudolf Besier (1878–1942), a contemporary of Barrie, had a distinctive career. Born in Java and educated in Germany, he finally married and settled in London as a man of letters. Here he collaborated with such famous authors as H. G. Wells, Hugh Walpole, and the novelist May Edington in the work of adapting their novels to the stage.

Besier's most famous play, *The Barretts of Wimpole Street*, has its own rather unique career. After being declined by two London producers and 27 New York producers, it was finally produced with Katherine Cornell as its star, and enthusiastically received. Since then the play has been produced over 700 times, and Miss Cornell took it overseas during World War II to the delight of thousands of American soldiers.

The play is based on the true story of Elizabeth Barrett and Robert Browning, both leading poets in English literature. It is a drama which will seem more like fiction with its suspense and humor and its dramatic climax. Yet it all actually happened. The playwright has faithfully captured the spirit of this famous love story of Victorian times and presented it in dialogue that is polished and alive.

Characters

DOCTOR CHAMBERS

ELIZABETH BARRETT MOULTON-BARRETT

WILSON

HENRIETTA MOULTON-BARRETT

ARABEL MOULTON-BARRETT

OCTAVIUS MOULTON-BARRETT

SEPTIMUS MOULTON-BARRETT

ALFRED MOULTON-BARRETT

CHARLES MOULTON-BARRETT

HENRY MOULTON-BARRETT

GEORGE MOULTON-BARRETT

EDWARD MOULTON-BARRETT

BELLA HEDLEY

HENRY BEVAN

ROBERT BROWNING

DOCTOR FORD-WATERLOW

CAPTAIN SURTEES COOK

FLUSH

SCENE

The scene is the bed-sitting room of Elizabeth Barrett at 50 Wimpole Street, in London, in 1845.

ACT I

SCENE 1: The evening of the 19th of May.
SCENE 2: The afternoon of the following day.

ACT II

Three months later.

ACT III

SCENE 1: Some weeks later.
SCENE 2: The following week.
(During Scene 2 the lights will be lowered to denote the passing of a few hours.)

ACT I

Scene 1

Elizabeth Barrett's bed-sitting room, in Wimpole Street, London. It is a large square room, comfortably furnished in the English furniture of the period. There is a wide door to the right, with massive iron lock on its inner side, and with brass doorknobs, and large brass key in the lock. A large fireplace with a marble mantel is opposite. At back, the wall is somewhat bowed outward to form a large bay, in which are spaced equally three large, recessed windows, with double-hung, square-paned sash, and panelling in the recesses below the windows. Through door at left is seen the hall with stairway leading up toward back. Through windows at back are seen the small iron balcony railings outside each one of them, and the flowers in the boxes just outside the sills. In the distance can be seen the upper stories of the houses on the opposite sides of the street, and a corner of the outer brick wall of this house, vines are seen climbing up outside the windows. A large wardrobe cabinet with mirror door is against wall at right. A small square tea-table is against back wall. On it are books and pamphlets. The windows at back are fitted with shades, long lace curtains, sash curtains on lower sash, and long drapes with pull cords. At back is a small open-shelved secretary desk filled with books, and with desk top also littered with books and pamphlets. Between windows, before this desk, is a straight walnut chair with upholstered seat. Before the window is a fine mahogany dressing table with swinging oval back. There is a fine mahogany dressing table with swinging oval mirror, on which are a lace cover, and some few pomade jars, toilet bottles, glass tray, tumblers, etc. Against back wall is a round low dog basket on floor with old cushion inside. Beside it a stack of books, also on floor. Against side wall is a large secretary desk with glass doors, filled with books. On mantel are a couple of brass candlesticks and candles in glass chimneys, and a small white marble statuette of a half-open shell. A round gold-framed mirror in black shadow box is on wall above. In fireplace below is a built-in black iron grate with andirons, and low brass fender rail. A brass stand with tongs, shovel, and poker stands above it, and black, brass-mounted scuttle of coal is below. Also above is a small square tabourette or stand of mahogany. A tapestry bell-pull hangs from ceiling below fireplace. To the left is a carved leg stool, with round tapestry-upholstered seat. A walnut straight chair with upholstered seat is before dressing table. On back wall over small desk hangs a square tapestry in gold frame. Over drop-leaf table is a pair of hanging book-shelves filled with books, and on wall beneath them hangs a small plaster plaque of a man's head. Over stool is a duplicate pair of hanging book-shelves with books, and a framed plaster plaque on wall beneath them. On top of wardrobe cabinet, and on top of large desk, are two plaster busts of male heads. A large table desk stands up and down stage at right of center with a green-figured upholstered bench at right of it. In front of this table is a large upholstered armchair, and a little at left of this table is another armchair with carved arms and upholstered seat and back with cushion in it. A large duplicate armchair to that in front of table is at center angled towards couch. Table top is littered with piles of books, a copy of newspaper, large portfolio of leather, with paper and envelopes, a large leather-covered inkwell, green feather quill pen, and a black sand-shaker. There is a large upholstered couch, with low straight back, and sharply upturned head and foot. On this are a number of pillows and couch covers and shawls. In hall to the right is seen a small oblong table against wall, on which is a lighted candle in glass stand with red tinted glass shade, an old portrait of woman's head in old gold frame is on wall above, and a straight rush-bottom chair with yellow flowered cushion is at either end above and below.

TIME: *Evening, about 8:30 P. M.*

AT RISE: *Shade on window is down, and drapes on all windows are closely drawn. The books from tea table have been piled on floor. Tea table is in front of couch. On it is a tray with the remains of a light meal, and a glass full of porter. The stand or tabourette near fire-place has been brought forward to head of couch, and on it is a lighted candle in lamp, of painted china with bronze base, and rough globe-shaped blue tinted glass chimney. There are discovered Elizabeth's dog, Flush, a tiny cocker-spaniel, in basket; Elizabeth, reclining on couch amidst cushions and covers, and Dr. Chambers, who is standing behind couch, watch in hand, taking her pulse.*

CHAMBERS. (*Dropping her wrist and pocketing watch, behind couch.*) H-m-m! Yes! It's this increasingly low vitality of yours that worries me. No life in you—none. What are we going to do about it?

ELIZABETH. (*Reclining on couch.*) Well, Doctor, if you shut a person up in one room for years on end, you can't very well expect to find her bursting with life and vigor. Why not prescribe something really exciting for a change?

CHAMBERS. Exciting, eh?

ELIZABETH. A gallop three times around the Park every morning—dumbbell exercises—a long sea-voyage.

CHAMBERS. How I wish I could, my dear!

ELIZABETH. It's funny to think of it now, but you know, Doctor, as a child I was a regular tomboy.

CHAMBERS. Yes, I've heard all about that—and mentally you're a tomboy still! To tell you the truth, my dear Miss Elizabeth, I'm not at all sure that brain of yours isn't altogether too active. Still hard at Greek?

ELIZABETH. Oh, not more than two or three hours a day.

CHAMBERS. Are you engaged in any literary work at the moment?

ELIZABETH. Only a few articles for the "Athenaeum," and other papers.

CHAMBERS. The "Athenaeum"—dear, dear! Now, why not give all these heavy labors a rest, and turn your mind to something light and easy for a bit? Poetry? You're not neglecting your poetry, I hope?

ELIZABETH. (*On couch.*) Meaning something light and easy?

(*Laughs.*) Oh, Doctor, I shudder to think what my life would be like if I hadn't a turn for scribbling and study.

CHAMBERS. H-m—yes. Quite so. Yes. And this isn't the liveliest house for anyone to live in—let alone an invalid.

ELIZABETH. No, I suppose not. I wish Papa were a happier man! It would make such a world of difference to all of us.

CHAMBERS. Happier, eh? It's no business of mine, but when a man has good health, plenty of money, and a jolly family, I can't see why he should make life a burden to himself and others. Well, as I said, it's no concern of mine. But *you are*, my dear, and a very worrying concern too. Of course the winter has been abominable, and these spring months are always trying. The fact is, you oughtn't to live in England at all. Italy's the place for you.

ELIZABETH. *Italy!* Oh, Doctor, what a heavenly dream!

CHAMBERS. But if only I could prescribe some sort of change for you—something—anything to get you out of these dismal surroundings for a time. Tell me now, Miss Elizabeth, have you ventured on your feet at all lately?

ELIZABETH. No, hardly at all. I rather lost my nerve after that fall I had last Christmas. Papa, or one of my brothers, carries me from my bed to the sofa. Sometimes when I'm feeling venturesome, my maid supports me across the room.

CHAMBERS. (*Rising.*) Feeling venturesome at the moment?

ELIZABETH. (*Reclining on couch.*) Not particularly.

CHAMBERS. All the same, I think we'll try a step or two. (*Crossing to her, takes both her hands.*) Quietly now—slowly—there's no hurry. (*With his help she gets to her feet.*) There we are. (*She sways a little; he supports her.*) Feeling giddy, eh?

ELIZABETH. A little——

CHAMBERS. Close your eyes and lean against me—it will pass in a minute. (*After a moment she raises her head.*) Better?

ELIZABETH. Yes—oh, yes——

CHAMBERS. Take your time now, and step carefully. Don't be nervous—I won't let go your hand. (*She takes a few faltering steps as he walks backward before her, holding her hands.*) No—don't look at the floor. Look straight ahead. That's first rate—that's fine—splendid—splendid—— (*After taking half a dozen steps she falters and sways.*)

ELIZABETH. Oh, Doctor! (*He quickly catches her in his arms, and carries her back, placing her on sofa again.*)

CHAMBERS. Feeling faint?

ELIZABETH. No, it's just my knees—they don't seem able to—to support me.

CHAMBERS. (*Replacing covers.*) Well, if they can't do that, they're a pretty useless pair! (*Walks around back of sofa, pats her shoulder.*) Why, there's no more to you than to a five-year-old. How's your appetite? Just peck at your food, I suppose?

ELIZABETH. (*Reclining on sofa.*) I always try to eat what I'm given, but I'm never very hungry. (*With sudden animation, half sitting up.*) Oh, Doctor, that reminds me! Do you remember Papa suggesting that a kind of beer called porter might do me good?

CHAMBERS. Yes—and an excellent suggestion, too.

ELIZABETH. Oh, but forgive me—it was nothing of the kind! I have to drink it twice a day, out of a pewter tankard, and my life in consequence has become one long misery.

CHAMBERS. God bless my soul!

ELIZABETH. I am not exaggerating—*one long misery!*

CHAMBERS. But, my dear child——! There's nothing I enjoy more than a pint of porter with my steak or chops at breakfast.

ELIZABETH. With your breakfast! All I can say is that to me porter is entirely horrible! Horrible to look at—more horrible to smell—and most horrible to drink! Surely, something one abominates so intensely can't possibly do one any good! It's no use my appealing to Papa—especially as the dreadful idea originated with him. But if *you*, dear, dear Doctor Chambers, were to suggest to him that something else—anything—I don't mind what it is—might be equally efficacious——?

CHAMBERS. (*Laughing.*) You poor little lady! But of course I will!

ELIZABETH. Oh, thank you, a thousand times!

CHAMBERS. (*Seated on sofa.*) What do you say to a couple of glasses of hot milk as a substitute?

ELIZABETH. (*On sofa.*) I dislike milk, but I'll drink it all day long—if only you'll rescue me from porter! (*There is a knock at door.*) Come in! (*Wilson, Elizabeth's maid, enters, leaving door open.*) Yes, Wilson?

WILSON. Begging your pardon, Miss—— (*Turning to Chambers.*) But the Master wishes most particularly to see you before you leave, sir.

CHAMBERS. Of course—of course. (*Rising, looking at watch.*) And high time I were off—is your Master in his study?

WILSON. Yes, sir. (*Crosses to door, waits there for Chambers.*)

CHAMBERS. (*Crossing to Elizabeth.*) Well, good-bye, my dear Miss Elizabeth, good-bye. (*Takes her hand.*)

ELIZABETH. Good-bye, doctor. (*In a low voice.*) And you won't forget?

CHAMBERS. Eh?

ELIZABETH. (*Spelling.*) P-O-R-T-E-R!

CHAMBERS. (*Laughing.*) No—no. I'll speak to him about it now.

ELIZABETH. (*On sofa.*) Thank you—thank you!

CHAMBERS. (*Laughing.*) Good night—— (*To Wilson as he crosses to door.*) You needn't see me downstairs—I know my way.

WILSON. Thank you, sir. (*Chambers exits, leaving door open.*) I am just going to post your letter, Miss Ba—shall I take Flush with me?

ELIZABETH. (*Excitedly, ignoring question, points at glass of porter.*) Quick, Wilson—away with it!

WILSON. What, Miss?

ELIZABETH. I hadn't the courage to drink it at dinner. I have been putting off the dreadful moment as long as I could.

WILSON. (*Turning to look at porter, then back at Elizabeth.*) Your porter, Miss?

ELIZABETH. And now dear Doctor Chambers says I needn't drink it at all. Take it away. Quick! Quick! And never mention the word porter to me again!

WILSON. (*Crossing to her.*) Lor, Miss—very good, Miss. But since you 'aven't 'ad your porter, won't you——?

ELIZABETH. (*Covering her ears.*) I told you never to mention the word again! Take it away, please. Please.

WILSON. (*A little alarmed, picks up Flush, puts him out of door.*) Very good, Miss Ba. Come, Flush. (*Elizabeth starts laughing, as Henrietta Moulton-Barrett runs quickly in. Wilson crosses with Flush.*)

HENRIETTA. What are you laughing at, Ba?

ELIZABETH. (*On sofa.*) Wilson thinks I've gone mad.

WILSON. (*Re-entering.*) Mad, Miss? What things you do say!

ELIZABETH. (*Still laughing.*) Will you, or won't you, take away that—that black beer?

WILSON. Very good, Miss Ba. (*Crosses, gets tray, exits with it, closing door.*)

HENRIETTA. (*Crosses toward Elizabeth, stands by chair.*) I don't know why you're laughing, Ba, and you needn't tell me. Only don't stop. Go on laughing till midnight. I'll tickle you if you think you can't keep it up without being helped. Oh, Ba, dinner was awful—awful! (*Sits on foot of sofa facing her.*)

ELIZABETH. Was Papa——?

HENRIETTA. Yes, he was. He was in one of his moods—the worst kind. The nagging mood is bad enough, the shouting mood is worse, but don't you think the dumb mood is the worst of all?

ELIZABETH. Yes, perhaps—but they all frighten me.

HENRIETTA. I don't believe there were more than a dozen remarks all through dinner—and most of them were frozen off at the tips. Papa would just turn his glassy eyes on the speaker. You know? For the last twenty minutes or so the only sound in the room was the discreet clatter of knives and forks. Directly dinner was over he ordered the port to be taken to his study, and thank Heaven he followed it almost at once.

ELIZABETH. Doctor Chambers is with him now.

HENRIETTA. Oh, Ba, I do hope for all our sakes his report of you isn't too good.

ELIZABETH. But, Henrietta——!

HENRIETTA. (*All contrition, moves and sits on sofa with Elizabeth and takes her hand.*) Forgive me, dearest—it was odious of me to say that. You know I didn't mean it, don't you?

ELIZABETH. Of course I do, you silly child. But what you said makes Papa an inhuman monster. And that's wickedly untrue. In his own way he cares for all his children.

HENRIETTA. (*Rises.*) In his own way! No, dear, what I meant was that good news of any kind would be sure to aggravate him in his present mood. (*Sits on sofa again.*) I don't know why it should, but it does. (*Arabel Moulton-Barrett enters, closing door.*)

ARABEL. Oh, you're here, Henrietta. I've been looking for you everywhere. Papa has just sent you this note from his study.

HENRIETTA. Me? Oh, dear! When he starts sending notes from his study, look out for squalls! (*Opens note, reads. Arabel sits in chair.*) "I have heard this morning that your Aunt and Uncle Hedley, and your cousin Bella have arrived in London earlier than was expected. They are staying at Fenton's Hotel. Your cousin Bella and her fiancé, Mr. Bevan, propose to call on you tomorrow at three o'clock. You and Arabel will, of course, be here to receive them, and if Elizabeth is well enough you will bring them upstairs to see her. I have written to invite your Uncle and Aunt and Cousin to dinner next Thursday—Papa." Well!

ARABEL. I understand now why Papa seemed so—so displeased at dinner.

HENRIETTA. Vile-tempered, you mean!

ARABEL. Is it necessary always to use the ugliest word?

HENRIETTA. Yes, Arabel—when you're describing the ugliest thing! (*To Elizabeth.*) Oh, but Papa is quite impossible! He got this letter from the Hedleys at breakfast. Why couldn't he have spoken then? Why couldn't he have spoken at dinner? Heaven knows he had time enough!

ARABEL. I'm afraid he was displeased.

HENRIETTA. Displeased! Oh, of course we all know that he hates being ordinarily polite to anyone, and now he's simply bound to show some kind of hospitality to the Hedleys. No wonder he was—displeased! (*Rising.*) What enrages me is that I was expecting a friend tomorrow at three, and now I shall have to put him off somehow. (*Crosses to Arabel.*)

ARABEL. (*Archly, stopping her.*) Why?

HENRIETTA. (*Turning to Arabel.*) Why what?

ARABEL. Why must you put your friend off? Bella and her fiancé won't eat your friend.

HENRIETTA. What—what business is that of yours?

ARABEL. But, Henrietta——

HENRIETTA. (*Rising.*) I hate people prying into my affairs! (*Exits, slamming door.*)

ARABEL. (*Distressed, takes a couple of steps after her, then turns back toward Elizabeth.*) Oh dear! Oh dear! What can be the matter with her tonight? Usually she quite enjoys being quizzed about Captain Surtees Cook.

ELIZABETH. Perhaps she may have begun to take his attentions seriously.

ARABEL. Oh, Ba, I hope not! (*Sits.*) You remember when young Mr. Palfrey wanted to marry her two years ago—those dreadful scenes with Papa?

ELIZABETH. I should rather forget them.

ARABEL. Oh, why can't Henrietta realize that if there's one thing Papa will never permit, it's marriage in the family! It doesn't worry me at all, as gentlemen never attracted me in that way. Nor you, dear.

ELIZABETH. (*With a laugh.*) Me?

ARABEL. (*Rising, goes to her.*) Oh, of course, today, anything of that kind is quite out of the question, my poor darling—Papa or no Papa. But even when you were younger and stronger, I don't ever remember your having had little affairs with gentlemen.

ELIZABETH. Perhaps the gentlemen never gave me the chance!

ARABEL. Oh, but you were quite pretty as a young girl.

ELIZABETH. What is Captain Surtees Cook like? Is he nice?

ARABEL. Yes, I think so. Yes, quite nice. But he never says much. He just sits and looks at Henrietta.

ELIZABETH. She's very lovely.

ARABEL. But Papa would never countenance any kind of under-standing between them. You know that as well as I do.

ELIZABETH. Poor Henrietta—— (*Henrietta re-enters, closing door, crosses quickly to Arabel and kisses her.*)

HENRIETTA. I'm sorry.

ARABEL. Oh, my dear, I never meant to annoy you. (*Rising, going to meet her.*)

HENRIETTA. You didn't—(*They kiss, then with a laugh.*)—you *displeased* me. Oh, I'm Papa's daughter, all right!

ELIZABETH. Henrietta, when Bella and her fiancé call tomorrow, Arabel will bring them up here to see me, and you can entertain Captain Cook in the drawing-room. (*Arabel looks distressed.*)

HENRIETTA. What a lovely thing it is to be a genius! You darling!

ELIZABETH. But I must have the room to myself at half-past three, as Mr. Robert Browning is calling then.

HENRIETTA. No!

ARABEL. (*Turns, starts to Elizabeth.*) But I ⎫ (*Together.*)
thought—— ⎭

HENRIETTA. Of course I know you've been corresponding with Mr. Browning for months. But then you write to so many literary people whom you absolutely refuse to see.

ARABEL. Has Papa given his permission?

ELIZABETH. Of course.

HENRIETTA. But why? Why have you made an exception of Mr. Browning? I've heard he's wonderfully handsome, but——

ELIZABETH. Oh, Henrietta, you're incorrigible!

ARABEL. I know he's been most anxious to call. Mr. Kenyon told me so.

HENRIETTA. But you said yourself only a short time ago that you didn't intend to receive him.

ELIZABETH. I didn't—and I don't particularly want to now.

HENRIETTA. But why?

ELIZABETH. Because, my dear, at heart I'm as vain as a peacock! You see, when people admire my work, they are very likely to picture the poetess as stately and beautiful as her verses. And it's dreadfully humiliating to disillusion them.

HENRIETTA. Don't be silly, Ba. You're very interesting and picturesque.

ELIZABETH. (*Laughing as Arabel sits down.*) Isn't that how guidebooks usually describe a ruin? As a matter of fact, Mr. Browning has been so insistent that out of sheer weariness I've given way. But I don't want an audience to witness the tragedy of his disillusionment! So mind, Arabel, Bella and her Mr. Bevan must be out of the room before he arrives. (*A knock at door.*) Come in. (*Octavius Moulton-Barrett enters, closing door after him. He stammers slightly.*) Come in, Occy.

OCTAVIUS. I've just come to see how you are, and to wish you g-good night. Doctor satisfied?

ELIZABETH. Oh, yes, I think so.

HENRIETTA. (*Handing him Papa's note.*) Read that, Octavius.

ARABEL. (*While he is reading.*) Oh dear! I quite forgot that I was to attend a meeting on the Chinese Weslyan Mission at Exeter Hall tomorrow afternoon.

OCTAVIUS. (*Flourishing letter.*) Well, you can't attend it! This is undoubtedly a Royal d-decree.

HENRIETTA. (*To Arabel.*) "Given at our study at 50 Wimpole Street on this nineteenth day of May 1845. God save Papa!"

ARABEL. (*Reprovingly.*) Henrietta, dear! (*A knock at door.*)

ELIZABETH. Come in. (*Septimus Moulton-Barrett enters. He is a year older than Octavius.*) Well, Septimus?

SEPTIMUS. (*Crossing to Elizabeth.*) How are you, Ba? (*Kisses her.*) I hope the Doctor is satisfied with you?

ELIZABETH. Oh, yes, I think so.

OCTAVIUS. I say, Septimus, the Hedleys are d-dining here in force next Thursday.

SEPTIMUS. By Jove! Not really? (*Octavius gives him letter. A knock at door.*)

ELIZABETH. Come in. (*Alfred Moulton-Barrett enters. He is older than Septimus.*) Come in, Alfred.

ALFRED. And how's our dear Ba tonight? I hope the Doctor was happy with you?

ELIZABETH. Oh, yes, I think so. (*Another knock at door.*) Come in. (*Charles Moulton-Barrett enters.*) Come in, Charles.

CHARLES. (*Enters.*) How are you feeling tonight, Ba? I hope Doctor Chambers' report was good?

ELIABETH. Oh, yes, I think so. (*Another knock at door.*) Come in. (*Henry Moulton-Barrett enters. He is slightly older than Charles.*) Come in, Henry.

HENRY. Well, Ba? How are you, my dear? (*Kisses her.*) Was the Doctor pleased with his patient?

ELIZABETH. Oh, yes, I think so.

HENRY. That's good. I must say, I think you are looking a little better. What do you say, Charles?

CHARLES. Eh? (*Septimus goes up to give Octavius the letter. Tells him in an undertone to take it to Henrietta.*)

HENRY. Looking better, don't you know. More herself, what? (*Another knock at door.*)

ELIZABETH. Come in. (*George Moulton-Barrett enters, closing door. He is slightly older than Henry.*) Come in, George.

GEORGE. Well, and how's Ba tonight? (*Kisses her.*) The Doctor's just been, hasn't he? I'm afraid he wasn't too pleased with you.

ELIZABETH. Oh, yes, I think so—I mean—why?

GEORGE. You're not looking so well. Is she, Henry?

HENRY. On the contrary, I think she's looking considerably better. So does Charles—don't you, Charles?

CHARLES. Eh?

OCTAVIUS. I say, George, the Hedleys have arrived unexpectedly in town. Bella and her swain are c-calling on the girls tomorrow afternoon, and on Thursday, she and her parents are d-dining here, in state.

HENRY. Dining *here!*
ALFRED. (*Rising.*) Not here! } (*Together.*)
SEPTIMUS. Not really!

ALFRED. Well, I hope they'll enjoy their dinner as much as we did ours tonight!

SEPTIMUS. You have met this Mr. Bevan, haven't you, Alfred?

ALFRED. I have.

SEPTIMUS. What is he like?

HENRIETTA. Yes?

ALFRED. Pompous ass. But warm—a very warm fellow. Ten thousand pounds a year, if he has a penny——

HENRIETTA. No!

ALFRED. And ten thousand more when his grandmother dies.

ARABEL. Oh!

HENRIETTA. It's grossly unfair! (*To Arabel.*) What has Bella done to deserve such luck?

OCTAVIUS. Alfred says he's a pompous ass.

HENRIETTA. Oh, that's jealousy! No man with ten thousand a year can be a pompous ass!

HENRY. I think it's just possible that you'll all be interested to hear that Papa is going to Plymouth on business next week, and—— (*Excited exclamations from all but Elizabeth.*)

HENRIETTA. Go on, Henry, and——?

HENRY. And that he's not expected to return for at least a fortnight. (*Smiles and murmurs of satisfaction.*)

HENRIETTA. (*Flings arms around George's neck, kisses him.*) Oh, George! How wonderful! How glorious! Do you polk, George?

GEORGE. Don't be childish!

HENRIETTA. Well, I polk. (*She dances the polka around room, while humming "Little Brown Jug," all the brothers join in the humming. Henry moves up to fireplace. Others look on amused, Octavius claps his hands. Door opens quietly, and Edward Moulton-Barrett enters.*)

ELIZABETH. (*Breathlessly, as she sees him.*) Papa——(*An awkward silence. Henrietta stops dead in middle of room. Barrett stands just inside room with a perfectly expressionless face. Elizabeth continues.*) Good evening, Papa. (*Without reply Barrett crosses, stands with his back to fireplace. A pause, no one moves.*)

BARRETT. (*Before fireplace, in a cold measured voice looking straight before him.*) I am most displeased! (*A pause.*) It is quite in order that you should visit your sister of an evening, and have a few quiet words with her. But I think I have pointed out, not once, but several times, that in her very precarious state of health it is most inadvisable for more than three of you to be in her room at the same time! My wishes in this matter have been disregarded —as usual! (*A pause.*) You all know very well that your sister must avoid any kind of excitement. Absolute quiet is essential, especially before she retires for the night. And yet I find you romping around her like a lot of disorderly children. I am gravely displeased. (*Henrietta gives a nervous little giggle.*) I 'am not aware that I have said anything amusing, Henrietta.

HENRIETTA. I—I beg your pardon, Papa.

BARRETT. May I ask what you were doing, as I came into the room?

HENRIETTA. I was showing Ba how to polk.

BARRETT. To—polk?

HENRIETTA. How to dance the polka.

BARRETT. I see (*Long pause.*)

OCTAVIUS. (*Nervously, starting toward Elizabeth.*) Well, B-Ba, I think I'll say g-good night, and——

BARRETT. I should be grateful if you would kindly allow me to finish speaking.

OCTAVIUS. (*Stepping back.*) Sorry, sir, I thought you'd d-done.

BARRETT. (*With frigid anger.*) Are you being insolent, sir?

OCTAVIUS. N-no, indeed, sir. I assure you——

BARRETT. Very well.

ELIZABETH. As I am really the cause of your displeasure, Papa, I ought to tell you that I like nothing better than a little noise occasionally. It's delightful having all the family here together, and can't possibly do me any harm.

BARRETT. Perhaps you will forgive my saying, Elizabeth, that you are not the best judge of what is good or bad for you. And that brings me to what I came here to speak to you about. Dr. Chambers told me just now that you had persuaded him to allow you to discontinue drinking porter with your meals.

ELIZABETH. It needed very little persuasion, Papa. I said I detested porter, and he agreed at once that I should take milk instead.

BARRETT. I questioned him closely as to the comparative strength-giving values of porter and milk, and he was forced to admit that porter came decidedly first.

ELIZABETH. That may be, Papa. But when you dislike a thing to loathing, I don't see how it *can* do you any good.

BARRETT. I said just now that you are not the best judge of what is good or bad for you, my child. May I add that self-discipline is always beneficial, and self-indulgence invariably harmful! Believe me, Elizabeth, I have nothing but your welfare at heart when I warn you that if you decide to discontinue drinking porter, you will incur my grave displeasure.

ELIZABETH. But when Dr. Chambers himself——

BARRETT. I have told you what Dr. Chambers said!

ELIZABETH. Yes, but——

BARRETT. Did you drink your porter at dinner?

ELIZABETH. No.

BARRETT. Then I hope you will do so before you go to bed.

ELIZABETH. No, Papa, that's asking too much. I can't drink the horrible stuff in cold blood.

BARRETT. Very well. Of course I have no means of coercing you. You are no longer a child. But I intend to give your better nature every chance of asserting itself. A tankard of porter will be left at your bedside, and I hope that tomorrow you will be able to tell me that you have obeyed your Father.

ELIZABETH. I am sorry, Papa—but I shan't drink it.

BARRETT. (*Taking a step forward.*) Henrietta—go down to the kitchen and fetch a tankard of porter!

HENRIETTA. (*Her voice trembling with anger and agitation.*) No, I won't!

BARRETT. I beg your pardon?

HENRIETTA. (*Desperately.*) It's—it's sheer cruelty. You know how Ba hates the stuff. The Doctor has let her off. You're just torturing her because you—like torturing!

BARRETT. I have told you to fetch a tankard of porter from the kitchen!

HENRIETTA. I won't do it!

BARRETT. Must I ask you a third time! (*Suddenly shouting.*) Obey me this instant!

ELIZABETH. (*Sharply.*) Papa! Go and fetch it, Henrietta! Go at once! I can't stand this!

HENRIETTA. No. I——

ELIZABETH. Please—please——? (*After a moment's indecision, Henrietta turns, exits, leaving door open.*)

BARRETT. (*After a pause, quietly.*) You had all better say good night to your sister.

ARABEL. (*Goes to below sofa, whispers.*) Good night, dearest. (*She kisses Elizabeth on the cheek. Elizabeth receives it impassively.*)

ELIZABETH. (*In a toneless voice.*) Good night. (*Arabel exits. Each of the boys in turn goes to Elizabeth and kisses her cheek.*)

HENRY. Good night, Ba.

ELIZABETH. Good night. (*Henry exits.*)

OCTAVIUS. Good night, Ba.

ELIZABETH. Good night. (*Octavius exits.*)

CHARLES. Good night, Ba.

ELIZABETH. Good night. (*Charles exits.*)

SEPTIMUS. Good night, Ba.

ELIZABETH. Good night. (*Septimus exits.*)

GEORGE. Good night, Ba.

ELIZABETH. Good night. (*George exits.*)

ALFRED. Good night, Ba.

ELIZABETH. Good night. (*Alfred exits. Barrett and Elizabeth stare before them with expressionless faces. Pause, then Henrietta enters with a tankard of porter. She stands at threshold glaring at Barrett and breathing quickly.*) Give it to me, please. (*Henrietta starts toward her, when Barrett suddenly but quietly intervenes.*)

BARRETT. No. (*Takes tankard, speaking to Henrietta.*) You may go. (*Henrietta makes move to approach Elizabeth, but Barrett stops her.*) You may go!

ELIZABETH. Good night. (*Henrietta, after a defiant look at Barrett, exits, closing door.*)

BARRETT. (*Places porter on mantel, then goes to sofa and stands looking down at Elizabeth. She looks up at him with wide fearful eyes. He turns and speaks in gentle voice.*) Elizabeth.

ELIZABETH. (*In a whisper.*) Yes?

BARRETT. Why do you look at me like that, child? (*Placing hand on her head and bending it slightly back.*) Are you frightened?

ELIZABETH. (*As before.*) No.

BARRETT. You're trembling, why?

ELIZABETH. I—I don't know.

BARRETT. You're not frightened of me? (*Elizabeth is about to speak, he continues quickly.*) No—no—you mustn't say it. I couldn't bear to think that. You're everything in the world to me—you know that. Without you I should be quite alone—you know that, too. And you—if you love me, you can't be afraid of me. For love casts out fear. You love me, my darling? You love your Father?

ELIZABETH. (*In a whisper.*) Yes.

BARRETT. (*Eagerly.*) And you'll prove your love by doing as I wish?

ELIZABETH. I don't understand. I was going to drink——

BARRETT. (*Quickly.*) Yes, out of fear, not love. Listen, dear. I told you just now that if you disobeyed me, you would incur my displeasure. I take that back. I shall never in any way reproach you. You shall never know by word, or deed, or hint of mine, how much you have grieved and wounded your Father by refusing to do the little thing he asked.

ELIZABETH. Oh, please, please, don't say any more. It's all so petty and sordid. Please give me the tankard.

BARRETT. You are acting of your own free will——?

ELIZABETH. Oh, Papa, let us get this over and forget it. I can't forgive myself for having made the whole house miserable over a tankard of porter. (*Crossing, he gets tankard from mantel, gives it to her. She drinks it straight off. He places tankard back on mantel and returns to above top end of sofa, looking down at her yearningly.*)

BARRETT. You're not feeling worse tonight, my darling?

ELIZABETH. (*Listlessly.*) No, Papa.

BARRETT. Just tired?

ELIZABETH. Yes—just tired.

BARRETT. I'd better leave you now. Shall I say a little prayer with you before I go?

ELIZABETH. Please, Papa. (*He kneels beside sofa, clasps hands, lifts face, shuts his eyes. Elizabeth clasps her hands but keeps her eyes open.*)

BARRETT. (*Kneeling at foot of sofa.*) Almighty and merciful God, hear me, I beseech Thee, and grant my humble prayer. In Thy inscrutable wisdom, Thou hast seen good to lay on thy daughter Elizabeth grievous and heavy affliction. For years she hath languished in sickness, and for years, unless in Thy mercy Thou take her to Thyself, she may languish on. Give her to realize the blessed word that Thou chastisest those whom Thou lovest. Give her to bear her sufferings in patience. Take her into Thy loving care tonight. Purge her mind of all selfish, and bitter, and unkind thoughts, guard her and comfort her. These things I beseech Thee, for the sake of Thy dear son, Jesus Christ. Amen.

ELIZABETH. Amen.

BARRETT. (*Rising, goes behind sofa, kisses her forehead.*) Good night, my child.

ELIZABETH. (*Receiving kiss impassively, not returning it.*) Good night, Papa. (*He crosses between chair and sofa and exits, meeting Wilson in hall as she is about to enter with Flush in her arms. Elizabeth lies motionless a moment or two staring straight before her, as Wilson enters with Flush, closing door after her.*)

WILSON. Are you ready for your bed now, Miss Ba?

ELIZABETH. Oh, Wilson, I'm so tired, tired, tired of it all. Will it never end?

WILSON. End, Miss?

ELIZABETH. This long, long, gray death in life.

WILSON. Oh, Miss Ba, you shouldn't say such things.

ELIZABETH. No, I suppose I shouldn't. Did Flush enjoy his run?

WILSON. (*Giving Flush to her.*) Oh, yes, Miss.

ELIZABETH. Is it a fine night, Wilson?

WILSON. Yes, Miss, and quite warm, and there's such a lovely moon.

ELIZABETH. (*Eagerly.*) A moon! Oh, do you think I can see it from here?

WILSON. I don't know, I'm sure.

ELIZABETH. Draw back the curtain and raise the blind. (*Wilson does so, and the moonlight, tempered by the lamplight, streams on Elizabeth's face.*)

WILSON. There you are, Miss. The moon's right above the chimneys, you can see it lovely.

ELIZABETH. (*Dreamily.*) Yes—yes. Please put out the lamp and leave me for a little——

WILSON. Very well, Miss Ba.

ELIZABETH. (*Finishing.*) I don't want to go to bed quite yet. (*Wilson extinguishes lamp behind couch, takes lamp from table desk, exits. Elizabeth is left bathed in strong moonlight. She stares for a while fixedly at the moon. Then her quickened breathing becomes audible, and one sees her whole body shaken with sobs. The only sound is her strangled weeping as curtain falls.*)

CURTAIN

Scene 2

Same as in SCENE 1, *with the following few changes. The curtains are all open and blinds up. The unlighted lamps are back in their places. The lamp and stand back of sofa have been moved back. Sofa now points somewhat up, and the casters have been removed from it. Table is back of sofa, with bowl of tulips on it. Tea table is before sofa, on it a dinner tray with an untouched sweet. The leather portfolio is on sofa, coverlet from which has been removed to desk chair. The yellow shawl has been taken away, and pewter tankard removed from mantel.*

TIME: *Mid-afternoon.*

AT RISE: *The sunshine pours into the room. There are discovered*

Flush, in his basket and Elizabeth on sofa, a cover over feet, reading with intense absorption, now and again running her fingers through her ringlets, or tossing them back from her face.

ELIZABETH. (*To herself with puzzled emphasis as she reads.*)
    "With flowers in completeness
    All petals, no prickles,
    Delicious as trickles
    Of wine poured at mass-time"——
(*A knock at door, Elizabeth, absorbed, takes no notice. She repeats, clutching her forehead.*)
    "All petals, no prickles,
    Delicious as trickles——"
(*Knock is repeated. Continuing.*)
    "Of wine——"
(*Calling.*) Come in. (*Wilson enters, crossing to sofa.*) Oh, yes, Wilson, I'm quite ready for lunch.

WILSON. (*Stolidly.*) You've 'ad your lunch, Miss Ba.

ELIZABETH. Oh, yes, of course. And I enjoyed it very much.

WILSON. You only picked at the fish, Miss Ba. An' I took away the best part of that nice chop, an' I see you 'aven't touched the pudding—cornflower blammonge, too, with raspberry jam.

ELIZABETH. (*Wonderingly regarding tray.*) Oh—anyhow it's too late now. (*Wilson takes table and tray away and then crosses to right and leaves table; puts tray on desk, then crosses to dressing table, measures out some medicine into a glass. Elizabeth, absorbed in her reading, does not notice.*)

WILSON. (*Holding glass of medicine to her.*) Your physic, Miss Ba.

ELIZABETH. (*Taking glass, eyes still fixed on book.*) Thank you. (*Glass in her hand, she continues reading.*)

WILSON. (*Noticing sunlight, crosses up to window.*) I think p'raps I'd better pull down the blind a bit. Too much sun isn't good for you, Miss. (*Half draws blind, returns to sofa.*)

ELIZABETH. (*Still holding untouched glass, eyes still on book.*) Thank you.

WILSON. But you 'aven't drunk it yet, Miss.

ELIZABETH. Oh——(*Swallows medicine, and with a little grimace hands glass to Wilson, who takes it across to tray, which she takes up and carries out to hall.*) Please open the door, Wilson. I am expecting visitors this afternoon and I want the room to be quite fresh for them. How I wish we could open the window, Wilson!

WILSON. (*Shocked, returning and crossing toward Elizabeth.*) Open the window, Miss Ba!

ELIZABETH. (*Sighing.*) Yes—I know it's strictly forbidden. Well, open the door *wide*.

WILSON. I'd best cover you well up, first of all (*Fetches shawl, covers her.*) Visitors, Miss Ba?

ELIZABETH. Yes. My cousin, Miss Bella Hedley. I haven't seen her since she was a child—such a lovely slip of a child. And now she's just become engaged.

WILSON. (*Crossing to open door wider.*) Indeed, Miss! And is she bringing her young gentleman with her?

ELIZABETH. Yes. And Mr. Robert Browning is calling later.

WILSON. (*Crossing to foot of sofa.*) Indeed, Miss? The gentleman who's always sending you such lovely boukeys?

ELIZABETH. Yes. (*Starts reading again.*)

WILSON. Sure you don't feel a draught, Miss Ba?

ELIZABETH. Quite, thanks.

WILSON. (*Arranging scarf on her shoulders.*) Hadn't you better keep your neck covered? These spring days the air is that treacherous!

ELIZABETH. (*To herself, with despairing emphasis.*) No—it's quite beyond me—I give it up.

WILSON. (*Standing above sofa.*) Beg pardon?

ELIZABETH. (*Intensely.*) Wilson?

WILSON. Yes, Miss?

ELIZABETH. Have you noticed anything—*strange* in me, today?

WILSON. Strange, Miss?

ELIZABETH. Yes, strange. I mean, dull-witted—thick-headed—stupid —idiotic?

WILSON. Lor'—no. P'raps a bit absent-minded like, but that isn't anything for *you* to worry about, Miss.

ELIZABETH. Then you don't think I'm going mad?

WILSON. Mercy on us—mad?

ELIZABETH. Very well. But now listen carefully, and tell me what you make of this. (*She reads.*)

"And after, for pastime,
　If June be refulgent
　With flowers in completeness
　All petals, no prickles

Delicious as trickles
Of wine poured at mass-time—
And choose one indulgent
To redness and sweetness;
Or if, with experience of man and of spider,
June used my June-lighting the strong insect-ridder
To stop the fresh film work—why June will consider."
(*Questioningly.*) Well?

WILSON. (*Enthusiastically.*) I call that just lovely, Miss Ba.

ELIZABETH. But do you know what it means?

WILSON. Oh, no, Miss.

ELIZABETH. Does it convey *anything* to your mind?

WILSON. Oh, no, Miss.

ELIZABETH. (*With a sigh of relief.*) Thank Heaven for that.

WILSON. But then po'try never does, Miss. Leastways, not real po'try, like what you make.

ELIZABETH. But *I* didn't write that. It's by Mr. Browning.

WILSON. He must be a clever gentleman.

ELIZABETH. (*With a laugh.*) Oh, yes, he's all that.

WILSON. (*Taking Flush from basket.*) And now, Miss Ba, if you're all nice and comfortable, I'll take Flush out for his airing.

ELIZABETH. (*Holding out her arms for the dog, which Wilson gives to her.*) Well, Flush dear, are you going to behave nicely today? I shall ask Wilson for a full report, when she gets home. (*To Wilson.*) Where are you taking him?

WILSON. Well, Miss, being so fine, I thought of a little walk in the Park.

ELIZABETH. Oh, Flush, I'd give almost anything to be going with you instead of Wilson. (*Gives Flush back to Wilson. Octavius is seen walking through hall. She continues as she sees him at door.*) Occy, dear. (*Octavius enters.*) What on earth are you doing at home at this time of day? (*Wilson exits, carrying Flush.*)

OCTAVIUS. Papa's b-bright idea. Suggested I should take a half-holiday, and help you f-feed and entertain the l-love-birds.

ELIZABETH. (*Laughing.*) But why? Henrietta and Arabel are socially quite competent. So am I.

OCTAVIUS. (*Sits on end of sofa.*) But you labor under the d-disadvantage of being all of the same sex. Papa seems to think that at least one male B-Barrett ought to show up.

ELIZABETH. I see. Occy, there's one thing you don't know, and I want you to be diplomatic. Captain Surtees Cook is calling at the same time as Bella and Mr. Bevan. He's coming to see Henrietta.

OCTAVIUS. Is he, by Jove! And won't the gallant feller rejoice when he finds himself chaperoned f-four times over!

ELIZABETH. I've arranged for Arabel to bring Bella and Mr. Bevan up here to see me. You must come with them.

OCTAVIUS. And why?

ELIZABETH. So that Henrietta may have Captain Cook to herself for a little while.

OCTAVIUS. But does it occur to you, my dear Ba, that we may be doing Henrietta an uncommonly b-bad turn by encouraging this b-budding romance?

ELIZABETH. Yes—but I think we ought to chance that. (*Octavius looks at her questioningly.*) Occy, when you six boys said good night to me yesterday, a queer thought came into my mind—you weren't alive at all—just automata.

OCTAVIUS. By Jove!

ELIZABETH. Like automata you get up at half-past seven every morning. Like automata you eat your breakfast. Like automata you go to your work. Like automata you return home. You dine like automata. You go to bed like automata.

OCTAVIUS. But, I say——

ELIZABETH. You all seem to me to have cut out of life everything that makes life worth living—excitement—adventure—change—conflict —frivolity—love——

OCTAVIUS. We haven't cut 'em out, my dear. That operation was performed by dear P-Papa.

ELIZABETH. I know, but——

OCTAVIUS. Oh, I admit we're a pretty spineless lot. But what would you? We're none of *us* particularly gifted, and we're all of us wholly dependent on Papa, and must obey or be broken. You're not c-counselling sedition?

ELIZABETH. No—but not resignation. Keep your souls alive. What frightens me is that you may become content with a life which isn't life at all. You're going that way, all of you, except Henrietta.

OCTAVIUS. And what does she get by t-trying to be herself? More kicks than ha'pence.

ELIZABETH. Yes—but being kicked keeps one alive. So don't let us do anything just for the sake of peace and quiet, to hinder her little romance.

OCTAVIUS. All very f-fine, my dear Ba—but what about you?

ELIZABETH. Me?

OCTAVIUS. Yes, you. I don't notice that you make much of a struggle against it. Where did that p-porter finally g-get to, last night?

ELIZABETH. (*With a dreary little laugh.*) I am quite out of it. You have your lives before you. My life is over. (*Henrietta enters.*)

OCTAVIUS. Rubbish!

HENRIETTA. (*As she enters.*) Why, Occy, what are you doing here?

OCTAVIUS. (*Rising, steps to meet her.*) Papa's notion. He somehow got wind that Surtees Cook was p-prowling round this afternoon, and sent me home to read the f-feller off.

ELIZABETH. Occy!

HENRIETTA. (*In breathless consternation.*) How did he hear? He couldn't have heard unless you—or Arabel——

ELIZABETH. No, dear. Occy—you idiot!

OCTAVIUS. (*Sits in chair. To Henrietta.*) Sorry—my little joke, you know!

HENRIETTA. (*Hotly.*) I hate you!

OCTAVIUS. Quite right, too. I repeat, I'm sorry. You may s-slap me if you like.

HENRIETTA. (*Half-mollified.*) I've a good mind to.

OCTAVIUS. (*Pulls her onto his lap. Elizabeth resumes reading.*) No, my che-ild, it's like this. His Majesty sent me home to represent His Majesty, at the reception. I don't intend to leave Bella's side, not even when she and her beloved come up here to em-embrace Ba. Meanwhile, you'll amuse Cook j-just as you're amusing me now. (*Kisses her.*) In fact, we may take this as a little rehearsal.

HENRIETTA. (*Jumping up.*) Occy! How can you be so vulgar? What's that? (*Runs to window.*) Oh, Ba, they've arrived. And in state. The Bevan family—barouche—powdered footmen and all. (*Octavius joins her.*) Look at Bella. What a gown—what a bonnet! Lovely! Oh, and Mr. Bevan's whiskers! (*Gestures round her chin.*) Aren't you green with envy, Occy?

OCTAVIUS. Positively verdant.

HENRIETTA. (*Pushing Octavius to door.*) Go and help Arabel receive them. Off with you—quick. I'll wait here till Captain Cook arrives. (*She pushes him off; he exits, leaving door open. Henrietta goes back up to window, looks eagerly into street.*) What's the time?

ELIZABETH. (*Smiling.*) Five minutes past three.

HENRIETTA. *Past* three?

ELIZABETH. Past three!

HENRIETTA. I don't understand—he said three——Ba—today is Thursday, isn't it?

ELIZABETH. Yes, dear.

HENRIETTA. (*With relief, turning to window.*) Oh—I wish he were able to come in his uniform. That would take the curl out of Mr. Bevan's whiskers. (*Elizabeth laughs.*) Oh, there he comes. (*She runs out of room, leaving door open.*)

ELIZABETH. Please shut the door. (*Henrietta has gone. Elizabeth smiles, shrugs, takes up book and starts reading again. After a moment, Octavius re-enters.*)

OCTAVIUS. Are you ready to receive them? (*Turns, starts to go. Voices of Bella, Arabel and Bevan are heard.*)

ELIZABETH. Yes, quite. (*Calling, as he turns to go.*) Occy! What are they like?

OCTAVIUS. (*Turning around.*) Oh, she's a dream of l-loveliness— and he isn't. (*He exits. Short pause, as voices grow nearer; then Bella Hedley flutters in, followed by Arabel, then Henry Bevan, lastly Octavius.*)

BELLA. (*Ecstatically, crossing above chair to Elizabeth above sofa.*) Cousin Elizabeth!

ELIZABETH. (*Extending hand.*) Bella, dear. (*Arabel follows Bella. Bevan crosses to foot of sofa. Octavius crosses to desk.*)

BELLA. Ba. (*Embraces Elizabeth.*) Dearest Ba. After all these years! But, oh, my poor, poor Ba, how sadly you've changed! So pale! so fwagile, so etheweal.

ELIZABETH. And you, dear Bella, are even lovelier than you promised to be as a child.

BELLA. Flatterer. (*Kisses Elizabeth's hand, and still holding it, rises.*) You hear that, Ha'wy? This is my dear, dear Ha'wy. Mr. Bevan, Miss Elizabeth Ba'wett.

BEVAN. (*Bowing.*) Delighted, Miss Barrett, charmed.

BELLA. (*Stretching her free hand to him, he takes it.*) No, no, Ha'wy, you must take her hand. (*Tenderly to Elizabeth.*) Such a lovely hand. So fwail. So spiwitual.

BEVAN. (*Takes Elizabeth's hand, bows over it.*) And the hand that penned so much that is noble and eloquent. I am honored, Miss Barrett.

ELIZABETH. Thank you. And may I congratulate you—both of you? I hope you will be very happy.

BEVAN. Thank you, Miss Barrett. I am indeed a fortunate man.

BELLA. Dear Ha'wy! Dear Ba!

ELIZABETH. But won't you sit down. (*Bella sits on couch, Arabel and Bevan sit on chairs. Octavius stands.*)

BELLA. I adore your poems, Ba—especially when dear Ha'wy weads them. He wead me "Lady Gewaldine's Courtship" the day after we became engaged. He weads so beautifully. And he too adores your poems, which ought to please you as he is so dweadfully cwitical.

BEVAN. (*Stroking his beard.*) Oh, come, come, my pet.

BELLA. Oh, but, Ha'wy, you are. He doesn't quite approve of even Mr. Alfred Tennyson's poems.

ELIZABETH. Really, Mr. Bevan?

BEVAN. I have nothing against them as poetry. No, indeed. Mr. Tennyson always writes like a gentleman. What grieves me, Miss Barrett, is that his attitude towards sacred matters is all to often an attitude tinged with doubt.

ARABEL. How sad——

BEVAN. Sad indeed, Miss Arabel, and, I grieve to say, a very prevalent attitude among the younger men of today. (*Bella exchanges glances with Octavius.*) Of course I am not alluding to Mr. Tennyson when I say this. His work is always reverent, even when expressing doubt. Now, your poems, my dear Miss Barrett, show no touch anywhere of these modern tendencies. There's not a line in one of them that I would disapprove of even dear Bella reading.

ELIZABETH. That's very satisfactory.

BELLA. Dear Ha'wy is so fwightfully earnest.

BEVAN. Oh, come, come, my pet.

OCTAVIUS. I say, Mr. Bevan, you've not yet met my Father, have you?

BEVAN. No, that pleasure is yet to come.

OCTAVIUS. I think you and he would g-get on famously together.

BEVAN. Indeed!

BELLA. Oh, yes. For dear Uncle Edward is fwightfully earnest as well. Mama has often told me so.

ELIZABETH. But now tell me, dear, when is the wedding to be? Or am I being indiscreet?

BEVAN. Not at all, dear Miss Barrett, not at all, we——

BELLA. (*To Elizabeth.*) Oh, that weminds me. Where's dear Henwietta? The wedding? Early in August. (*Looks about.*) Where's Henwietta?

OCTAVIUS. At the moment she's downstairs entertaining a friend.

BELLA. Oh, I wanted to ask her—a fwiend? Not that tall gentleman we passed in the hall?

ELIZABETH. Yes, Captain Surtees Cook.

BELLA. Oh, in the Army? How thwilling! I thought his ca'wiage was military. So he's a fwiend of dear Henwietta?

ELIZABETH. Yes. You wanted to ask Henrietta something?

BELLA. Oh, yes. Oh, Ba, I do so want her to be one of my bwidesmaids. (*Henrietta enters, is visibly distrait. Bella rises to meet her, and kisses her, taking both her hands. Bevan rises, steps back.*) Henwietta darling, I was just saying—oh, you must be one of by bwidesmaids, you simply must.

HENRIETTA. Bridesmaids? Oh, yes—at your wedding. I should love to, Bella. It's sweet of you to ask me. And of course I will, if Papa— but I'm sure he won't mind.

BELLA. Mind? Uncle Edward? Why should he mind? Isn't she funny, Ba? You're only asked to be a bwidesmaid, darling—not a bwide.

HENRIETTA. Yes, I know, but of—it's so hard to explain.

BEVAN. (*To Elizabeth.*) Perhaps Mr. Barrett looks on bridesmaids as frivolous irrelevancies at so solemn a sacrament as marriage?

HENRIETTA. No, no, Mr. Bevan, It's not that. It's—it's simply that nothing—nothing at all in this house, must happen without Papa's sanction. (*To Bevan.*) You know he once owned slaves in Jamaica, and as slavery has been abolished there, he carries it on in England.

BEVAN. Oh, come, now!

HENRIETTA. I'm quite serious—we're all his slaves here.

ARABEL. Henrietta! (*Bevan and Bella look embarrassed.*)

HENRIETTA. Well, aren't we? We haven't a soul of our own, not one of us. I tell you, Bella, it's more than likely that he'll refuse to let me be your bridesmaid, for no rhyme or reason—except that he's out of temper.

OCTAVIUS. (*Breaking in.*) I say, what about t-tea?

ARABEL. (*Rising quickly.*) Oh, yes, yes.

HENRIETTA. (*Going to window.*) Tea is quite ready. I'm sorry—I —I forgot to tell you.

OCTAVIUS. Good Heavens, let's hurry, or Captain Cook will have swallowed it all.

HENRIETTA. He's gone. (*Standing up at window, her face half averted.*)

BELLA. A wivederci, dearest Ba. (*Kisses her.*) It's been so lovely seeing you. May I come again, soon? And next time I shall want you all to myself—without Ha'wy, I mean.

ELIZABETH. Come whenever you like, dear.

BEVAN. But why must I be excluded?

BELLA. (*To Bevan.*) Because I've heaps and heaps to tell dear Ba about a certain big, big man, who might easily gwow conceited if he heard me.

BEVAN. Oh, come, come, my pet. (*Bella crosses to Arabel, and they start out. Bevan bows over Elizabeth's hand.*) Good-day, dear Miss Barrett.

ELIZABETH. Good-bye. It was nice of you to come and see me.

BEVAN. Not at all. I have long been looking forward to the honor of meeting you. Good-day.

BELLA. (*Kisses her hand to Elizabeth.*) Au wevoir, darling.

ELIZABETH. Auf wiedersehen. (*Bella and Arabel exit, Bevan follows.*)

BEVAN. (*Turns and bows at door.*) Good-day.

ELIZABETH. Good-bye. (*Bevan exits. Octavius follows, turns and bows at door in imitation of Bevan, then exits, closing door. Elizabeth smiles, glances at Henrietta, who stands with averted face at window, then takes her book, starts reading.*)

HENRIETTA. (*After pause, vehemently.*) Well, why don't you say something?

ELIZABETH. (*Coldly.*) What do you want me to say?

HENRIETTA. Nothing. Ba, don't scold me. (*Crosses to her at couch and kneels.*) I know I deserve it—I have been dreadful. But I couldn't help it. I'm so miserable.

ELIZABETH. (*Quickly.*) Miserable, dear?

HENRIETTA. Yes—and so—so—wildly happy. Surtees has just asked me to marry him.

ELIZABETH. Oh, Henrietta!

HENRIETTA. And of course I accepted him—and said that I couldn't. And I had to tell him that we must never see each other again. When he calls here tomorrow we shall have to——

ELIZABETH. You're not talking sense, child. What really has happened?

HENRIETTA. I don't know—except that we both love each other terribly. Oh, Ba, what *are* we to do? Surtees has only just enough money to keep himself decently. And I haven't a penny of my own. If only I had your four hundred a year, I might defy Papa and leave the house, and marry Surtees tomorrow.

ELIZABETH. And what earthly good is that money to me? I'd give it to you, and how gladly——

HENRIETTA. I know you would, darling. But that's utterly impossible. Think what your life would be like when Papa knew that you had made it possible for me to marry. (*With sudden urgency.*) But dear, is there anything, anything at all to be said for Papa's attitude towards marriage? Can it possibly be wrong to want a man's love desperately, and to long for babies of my own?

ELIZABETH. No. But who am I to answer a question like that? Love and babies are so utterly remote from my life——

HENRIETTA. Yes, I know, dear. You're a woman apart. But it's natural to an ordinary girl like me, and what's natural can't be wrong.

ELIZABETH. No—and yet the holiest men and women renounced these things——

HENRIETTA. I daresay. But I'm not holy—and come to that, neither is Papa—not by any means. (*A knock at door. Henrietta rises.*)

ELIZABETH. Come in. (*Wilson enters.*)

WILSON. Mr. Robert Browning has called, Miss.

ELIZABETH. (*Breathlessly.*) Mr. Browning——

WILSON. Yes, Miss.

HENRIETTA. Then I'd better be off. (*Starts to leave.*)

ELIZABETH. N-no, stay here. I can't see him. I—I don't feel up to it—I——

HENRIETTA. But, Ba, what on earth is the matter? You told me yesterday——

ELIZABETH. I know—I know. But I really don't feel that I can see him now. (*To Wilson.*) Please tell Mr. Browning I am very sorry, but I am not well enough to receive him.

HENRIETTA. But that's not true. You can't send him away like that. (*To Wilson.*) Where is Mr. Browning?

WILSON. I showed him into the library, Miss.

ELIZABETH. But I'd much—much rather not see him——

HENRIETTA. Oh, fudge! You're not a silly schoolgirl. I'll bring him up myself. (*Starts out.*) Mr. Kenyon says he's wonderfully romantic-looking, and quite the dandy. (*Runs out.*)

ELIZABETH. Is my hair tidy?

WILSON. Yes, Miss Ba.

ELIZABETH. Oh, please arrange the couvre-pied. (*Wilson does so.*) Thank you. And, Wilson—no—thank you, that will do.

WILSON. Yes, Miss. (*She goes out, closing door. A pause while Elizabeth, in strained excitement, awaits the coming of Browning. Then Henrietta enters.*)

HENRIETTA. (*As she enters, inside door.*) Mr. Robert Browning. (*Browning enters, pausing a few steps inside room. Henrietta exits again.*)

BROWNING. (*As he steps inside room.*) Miss Barrett?

ELIZABETH. (*Stretching out her hand.*) How do you do, Mr. Browning?

BROWNING. (*Crossing to sofa, takes her hand in his.*) Dear Miss Barrett—at last! (*Raising her hand to his lips.*) At last.

ELIZABETH. (*Still all nerves, and overcome by the ardor and unconventionality of his manner.*) I—I've had to put off the pleasure of meeting you much longer than I wished.

BROWNING. (*Still holding her hand.*) Would you ever have received me if I hadn't been so tiresomely insistent?

ELIZABETH. As you know from my letters, I've not been at all well during this winter, and I—— (*Realizing her hand is still in his.*) But won't you take off your cape?

BROWNING. (*Takes off cape, leaves it on chair, leaving hat and cane on desk.*) Thank you.

ELIZABETH. I—I hope you won't find this room very close, Mr. Browning?

BROWNING. No—no——

ELIZABETH. My Doctor obliges me to live in what I am afraid must be to you a hot-house temperature.

BROWNING. (*Facing windows, looking around.*) Wonderful. You may think, Miss Barrett, that this is the first time I've been here. You're quite wrong, you know.

ELIZABETH. But I——

BROWNING. I have seen this room more times than I can remember. It's as familiar to me as my own little study at home. Before I came in, I knew how your books were arranged, just how that tendril of ivy slants across the window-panes—and that bust of Homer is quite an old friend, and has looked down on me before.

ELIZABETH. But, really——

BROWNING. But I could never make out who the other fellow is, on the top of the wardrobe, and——

ELIZABETH. (*Smiling, now at her ease.*) Oh, come, Mr. Browning. I know that dear Mr. Kenyon is never tired of talking about his friends, but I can't believe that he described my poor little room to you in detail.

BROWNING. (*Moving chair to corner of sofa, and sitting.*) I dragged all the details I possibly could out of him, and my imagination supplied the rest. Directly I had read your brave and lovely verses, I was greedy for anything and everything I could get about you.

ELIZABETH. (*Smiling.*) You frighten me, Mr. Browning.

BROWNING. Why?

ELIZABETH. Well, you know how Mr. Kenyon's enthusiasm runs away with his tongue. He and I are the dearest of friends. What he told you about me I quite blush to imagine.

BROWNING. You mean, Miss Barrett, about you—you yourself?

ELIZABETH. I feel it would be hopeless for me to try to live up to his description.

BROWNING. He never told me anything about you personally that had the slightest interest for me.

ELIZABETH. (*Puzzled.*) Oh?

BROWNING. Everything he could give me about your surroundings and the circumstances of your life I snatched at with avidity, but all he said about *you* was quite beside the point, because I knew it already—and better than Mr. Kenyon, old friend of yours though he is.

ELIZABETH. But, Mr. Browning—do my poor writings give me so hopelessly away?

BROWNING. Hopelessly—utterly—entirely—to me. I can't speak for the rest of the world.

ELIZABETH. You frighten me again.

BROWNING. No?

ELIZABETH. But you do. For I'm afraid it would be quite useless my ever trying to play-act with you.

BROWNING. Quite useless.

ELIZABETH. (*Smiling.*) I shall always have to be just myself.

BROWNING. Always.

ELIZABETH. And you, too, Mr. Browning.

BROWNING. Always—just myself. But really you know, Miss Barrett, I shan't be able to take much credit for that. Being myself comes to me as easily as breathing. It's play-acting I can't manage—and the hot water I've got into in consequence. If life's to run smoothly we should all be mummers. Well, I can't mum.

ELIZABETH. I can well believe that, now I've met you. But isn't it extraordinary? When you are *writing,* you never do anything else but play-act.

BROWNING. I know——

ELIZABETH. You have never been yourself in any one of your poems. It's always somebody else speaking through you.

BROWNING. Yes, and shall I tell you why? I am a very modest man. (*Quickly.*) I am, really.

ELIZABETH. I didn't question it, Mr. Browning.

BROWNING. So modest I fully realize that if I wrote about myself —my hopes and fears, hates and loves, and the rest of it—my poems would be unutterably dull.

ELIZABETH. Well, Mr. Browning, since we are pledged to nothing but the truth, I shan't contradict that until I know you better.

BROWNING. (*Laughing.*) Bravo!

ELIZABETH. Oh, but those poems of yours, with their glad and great-hearted acceptance of life, you can't imagine what they mean to me. Here am I, shut in by four walls—the view of Wimpole Street my only glimpse of the world. And they troop into the room and round my sofa, those wonderful people of yours, out of every age and country, and all so tingling with life. No, you'll never begin to realize how much I owe you.

BROWNING. (*With emotion.*) You—you really mean that?

ELIZABETH. Why, why, Mr. Browning——

BROWNING. But, of course you do, or you wouldn't say it. And you'll believe me when I tell you that what you have just said makes up to me—oh, a thousand times over for all the cold-shouldering I've had from the public.

ELIZABETH. Oh, it infuriates me. Why can we never know an eagle for an eagle until it has spread its wings and flown away from us for good?

BROWNING. (*Lightly.*) Mind you, Miss Barrett, I've an uneasy feeling that my style is largely to blame for my unpopularity.

ELIZABETH. (*A little too eagerly.*) Oh, surely not.

BROWNING. Didn't we agree not to play-act with each other?

ELIZABETH. (*With a laugh.*) Touché! Well, perhaps there are passages in your work a little invol—well, a little too—too profound for the general reader.

BROWNING. Oh, no, it's not what I say, but how I say it. And yet to me, it's all as simple as the rule of three. And to you?

ELIZABETH. Not quite always. Sometimes there *are* passages—— (*She picks up a book.*) I have marked one or two in your "Sordello" which rather puzzled me——

BROWNING. Oh, "Sordello."

ELIZABETH. (*Opening book and handing it to him.*) Here, for instance.

BROWNING. (*Taking book.*) Somebody once called it a horror of great darkness. I've done my best to forget it. However—— (*He reads passage to himself, smiling. Then the smile fades, he passes his hand over his brow, reads it again. She watches him, covertly smiling. He mutters.*) Extraordinary—but a passage torn from its context—— (*Rises, goes to window for more light on the subject, reads passage a third time. Elizabeth has difficulty in suppressing her amusement. He turns to her with an expression of humorous chagrin.*)

ELIZABETH. Well?

BROWNING. Well, Miss Barrett, when that passage was written only God and Robert Browning understood it. Now, only God understands it. (*She laughs, he joins heartily, crossing to sofa.*) What do you say, shall we lighten this great darkness by pitching it on the fire?

ELIZABETH. (*Indignantly.*) No, indeed. We shall do nothing of the kind. Please give me back the book. (*He does so.*) Such passages are only spots on the sun. I love "Sordello."

BROWNING. (*Eagerly.*) You would. Of course you would. And shall I tell you why? Because—because it's such a colossal failure.

ELIZABETH. If by a failure you mean an attempt—yes, you're right. That's just why "Sordello" appeals to my very heart. For I too am always making colossal attempts—and always failing.

BROWNING. Isn't one such failure worth a hundred small successes?

ELIZABETH. Oh, a thousand and more.

BROWNING. (*Ardently.*) You think so, too? But of course I knew that. Miss Barrett, you smiled when I told you that Mr. Kenyon had no need to describe you, because I knew you through and through already. And what you have just said about success and failure proves to me finally how right I was. All Kenyon did was to fill in the background. I had painted the portrait with the true soul of you, ardent and lovely, looking out of it.

ELIZABETH. Ardent and lovely. And you think you know me! (*A bitter smile.*) Oh, Mr. Browning, too often impatient and rebellious!

BROWNING. Well, what of it? I've no love for perfect patience under affliction. My portrait is the portrait of a woman, not of a saint. Who has more right to be impatient and rebellious than you?

ELIZABETH. Did Mr. Kenyon paint my background with a very gloomy brush?

BROWNING. Old Rembrandt would have envied him.

ELIZABETH. (*Smilingly. Browning sits beside her.*) Poor dear Mr. Kenyon. I assure you, my afflictions worry him a great deal more than they worry me. I suppose he told you that I am a dying woman?

BROWNING. We are all of us—dying.

ELIZABETH. And that my family life was one of unrelieved gloom?

BROWNING. Yes, he hinted at something of the sort.

ELIZABETH. He really shouldn't say such things. Frankly, Mr. Browning, do you find me such a pitiable object?

BROWNING. I find you, as I expected to find you, full of courage and gaiety. And yet, in spite of what you say, I'm not at all sure that Kenyon's colors were too sombre.

ELIZABETH. But——

BROWNING. No—no—listen to me. Those colors are not yet dry. They must be scraped off. The whole background must be repainted. And if only you'll allow it, I must have a hand in that splendid task.

ELIZABETH. But, Mr. Browning——

BROWNING. No, listen, I'll dip my brush into the sunrise, and the sunset, and the rainbow. You say my verses have helped you— they're nothing. It's I—I who am going to help you now. We've come together at last, and I don't intend to let you go again.

ELIZABETH. But——

BROWNING. No, listen to me. Give me your hands. (*Bends forward, takes them.*) I've more life in me than is good for one man. It seethes and races in me. Up to now I've spent a little of that surplus energy in creating imaginary men and women. But I've still so much that I've no use for, but to give. Mayn't I give it to you? Don't you feel new life tingling and prickling up your fingers and arms right into your heart and brain?

ELIZABETH. (*Rather frightened.*) Oh, please—Mr. Browning, please let go my hands! (*He opens his hands, but she still leaves hers in his open palms for a moment, then withdraws them, and clasping her cheeks, looks at him with wide disturbing eyes.*)

BROWNING. (*Softly.*) Well?

ELIZABETH. (*A little shakily, with forced lightness.*) Well—you are really rather an overwhelming person, and in sober truth, I'm——

BROWNING. No,—don't tell me again that you are afraid of me. You're not. It's life you're afraid of—and that shouldn't be.

ELIZABETH. Life?

BROWNING. Yes.

ELIZABETH. Well, when life becomes a series of electric shocks——

BROWNING. (*Smiling.*) Was it as bad as all that?

ELIZABETH. Indeed, yes. Do you affect other people in the same way?

BROWNING. They've often told me so.

ELIZABETH. (*Lightly.*) No wonder I hesitated about meeting you, much as I wanted to. You'll laugh at me, Mr. Browning, but when my maid told me you had arrived, I was so panic-stricken that I all but sent down word that I was too unwell to receive you.

BROWNING. I think I must have been about as nervous as you, at that moment.

ELIZABETH. You, Mr. Browning?

BROWNING. Yes, yes, and I'm anything but a nervous man as a rule. But that moment was the climax of my life—up to now. Miss Barrett, do you remember the first letter I wrote to you?

ELIZABETH. Yes, indeed, it was a wonderful letter.

BROWNING. You may have thought I dashed it off in a fit of white-hot enthusiasm over your poems. I didn't. I weighed every word of every sentence—and of one sentence in particular—this sentence: "I love your books with all my heart, and I love you, too." You remember?

ELIZABETH. Yes—and I thought it charmingly impulsive of you.

BROWNING. (*Almost with irritation.*) But I tell you there was nothing impulsive about it. That sentence was as deeply felt and as anxiously thought-over as any sentence I've ever written.

ELIZABETH. I hope I may have many readers like you! It's wonderful to think I may have good friends all the world over, whom I have never seen nor heard of.

BROWNING. I am not speaking of friendship—but of love. (*Elizabeth is about to make a smiling rejoinder.*) No, it's quite useless your trying to put aside the word with a smile and a jest. I said love —and I mean love.

ELIZABETH. But, really, Mr. Browning, I must ask you——

BROWNING. I'm neither mad nor morbidly impressionable—I'm as sane and level-headed as any man alive. Yet all these months since first I read your poems, I've been haunted by you—and today you are the center of my life.

ELIZABETH. (*Very gravely.*) If I were to take you seriously, Mr. Browning, it would, of course, mean the quick finish of a friendship which promises to be very pleasant to both of us.

BROWNING. Why?

ELIZABETH. You know very well that love, in the sense you apparently use the word, has no place, and can have no place, in my life.

BROWNING. Why?

ELIZABETH. For many reasons—but let this suffice. As I told you before, I am a dying woman.

BROWNING. (*Passionately.*) I refuse to believe it. For if that were so, God would be callous and I know that He's compassionate —and life would be dark and evil, and I know that it's good. You must never say such a thing again. I forbid you to.

ELIZABETH. Forbid, Mr. Browning?

BROWNING. Yes—forbid. If you forbid me to speak of you as I feel, and I accept your orders, as I must—isn't it only fair that I should be allowed a little forbidding, as well?

ELIZABETH. Yes, but——

BROWNING. (*With sudden gaiety.*) Dear Miss Barrett, what a splendid beginning to our friendship. We have known each other a bare half hour, and we've talked intimately of art, and life, and death, and love. And we've ordered each other about, and we've almost quarrelled. Could anything be happier and more promising? Well, with your permission, I'm going now. (*Rising.*) Mr. Kenyon impressed upon me to make my first visit as short as possible, as strangers tire you. Not that I'm a stranger—still I can see that you are tired. When may I call again? (*Puts on cape, crosses to sofa.*)

ELIZABETH. (*A little dazed.*) I don't quite know——

BROWNING. Will next Wednesday suit you?

ELIZBETH. Yes, I—I think so. But perhaps it would be better——

BROWNING. Next Wednesday, then.

ELIZABETH. But——

BROWNING. At half-past three, again?

ELIZABETH. Yes—but I——

BROWNING. (*Bowing over her hand.*) Au revoir, then. (*Kisses hand.*)

ELIZABETH. Good-bye.

BROWNING. Au revoir.

ELIZABETH. Au revoir.

BROWNING. Thank you. (*Turns and exits, closing door. The moment door closes, Elizabeth sits up and clasps her face with both hands. Then slips off sofa, and unsteadily gets to her feet. With the help of a chair she manages to cross the room to window. Grasping curtains to support herself, she stands looking down into the street after the departing Browning. Her face is as alive with excitement and joy as though she were a young girl, as curtain falls.*)

CURTAIN

ACT II

SCENE: *The scene is the same, with the following changes. The sofa points down, and everything on it has been made untidy, with books, papers, etc., strewn about. The medicine, glass, spoon, and pitcher have been struck from dressing-table. Flowers placed on desk and on table.*

TIME: *The time is mid-afternoon.*

AT RISE: *The room is lighted by the bright light of day. There is discovered the dog, Flush, lying on sofa. Elizabeth, walking with firm tread to window, and back downstage again. Dr. Chambers stands by fireplace and Dr. Ford-Waterlow sits by sofa. Both Doctors are intently watching Elizabeth as she walks.*

WATERLOW. (*Standing up as Elizabeth comes down.*) Once again, if you please. (*Elizabeth walks downstage and back again with greater assurance than before. He meets her as she comes back.*) My dear Miss Barrett, I congratulate you. Now sit down.

(*Indicates sofa. She sits. To Chambers.*) When exactly was it you last called me in for consultation, Chambers? (*Taking her wrist to take pulse.*)

CHAMBERS. (*Standing back to fire.*) Three months ago—almost to a day.

WATERLOW. Yes, yes, of course—and your patient was in a very low condition at that time. Well, you've done wonders, Chambers.

CHAMBERS. Oh, mine was just the ordinary spade-work. Honesty compels me to give most of the credit to another.

WATERLOW. (*Dropping her wrist.*) Eh?

CHAMBERS. The real healer is no one but Miss Barrett herself.

ELIZABETH. But, Doctor——

CHAMBERS. I mean it, my dear—I mean it. Three months ago you seemed more than a little inclined to let life and the world slip through your pretty fingers. Then slowly the change began. Oh, believe me, I was watching you like a lynx. Life and the world became more and more worth grasping. The wish to live is better than a dozen physicians, as I think even my distinguished friend will admit.

WATERLOW. The wish to live—h'm—yes. And you are able to get about and take the air occasionally nowadays?

ELIZABETH. Oh, yes, Doctor. I have visited some of my friends and been for several delightful drives around the Park. The only bother is getting up and down stairs. I'm inclined to lose my head going down, and I'm not yet able to undertake the upward journey.

WATERLOW. Quite so—quite so. Well, now, about the future, Miss Barrett. I fully agree with Dr. Chambers that another winter in London must, if possible, be avoided. If you continue picking up strength, as you are doing, I see no reason against your traveling South by October, say.

ELIZABETH. (*With barely controlled eagerness.*) Traveling? South?

WATERLOW. To the Riviera—or better still, to Italy.

ELIZABETH. Italy! Oh, Doctor—do you really mean it?

WATERLOW. Why not? You could travel there by easy stages. I have been given to understand that you have set your heart on Italy, and there are no—er—practical difficulties in the way of your going there?

ELIZABETH. If by practical, you mean financial—none at all. I have my own little income, and——

WATERLOW. Quite so—quite so.

CHAMBERS. I've taken the liberty to tell Dr. Ford-Waterlow of the only real difficulty in the way of your wintering abroad, and he is quite prepared to deal with—him.

WATERLOW. Quite—and drastically!

ELIZABETH. Oh, I am sure that won't be necessary. Papa may not raise any kind of objection. It depends on how he is feeling at the time, and——

WATERLOW. Fiddlesticks, my dear young lady! Mr. Barrett's feelings are neither here nor there. All that matters is his daughter's health and happiness, as I intend to make clear to him. Quite clear!

ELIZABETH. Oh, you mustn't think that Papa isn't kindness and generosity itself. But gentlemen have their moods. Italy! Oh, it's hard to take in even the bare possibility of going there. My promised land, Doctor, which I never thought to see otherwise than in dreams.

WATERLOW. Well, well, let us hope realization won't bring disillusion along with it. A grossly overrated country, to my mind. Nothing but heaps of rubbish, dust, flies, stenches, and beggars. Goodbye, my dear Miss Barrett. (*Takes her hand as she starts to rise.*) No, please don't get up. I'm delighted with your improvements. Delighted. And now for a little talk with your Father. Good-bye.

ELIZABETH. Good-bye, Doctor. (*Waterlow exits.*)

CHAMBERS. (*Who has moved to sofa, patting her shoulder and taking her hand.*) Good-bye, my dear Miss Elizabeth.

ELIZABETH. Good-bye. (*Chambers exits after Waterlow, closing door after him. Elizabeth clasps both her cheeks and whispers.*) Italy—Italy—Italy! (*She picks up Flush and talks to him.*) And you're coming with us, too, Flushy. We'll see Rome together—Florence—Venice—Vesuvius—— (*Arabel enters, closing door. Elizabeth puts Flush down, jumps to her feet and embraces Arabel.*) Arabel! It's all but settled, my dear. I'm to go to Italy. He says that I shall be quite fit to travel by October. Rome! Florence! Venice! Vesuvius! ! Raphael! Dante! Sordello! Oh, I don't know what I'm saying—I'm quite off my head with excitement.

ARABEL. How wonderful for you! I'm so glad. And you think Papa will consent?

ELIZABETH. But of course he will! The Doctors are putting it before him as strongly as they can. Oh, surely he'll never have the heart to refuse when he realizes all this Italian trip means to me.

ARABEL. (*Without conviction.*) No, dear, no——

ELIZABETH. Have you seen him this afternoon?

ARABEL. Yes.

ELIZABETH. (*Quickly, taking Arabel's hands.*) What was he like?

ARABEL. (*Eagerly.*) Oh, quite sunny! He called me "Puss," and he never does that when he's in one of his moods. And afterwards, when Bella came in, he was really merry.

ELIZABETH. Thank Heaven for that.

ARABEL. Which reminds me, dear—Bella has brought the gown Henrietta is to wear as bridesmaid. They want you to see it. They're trying it on now.

ELIZABETH. Oh, I should love to. (*Pulls bell-rope.*) I need badly some distraction to help me over the suspense of waiting for Papa's decision.

ARABEL. (*Standing still.*) Somehow I felt, Ba, that it wasn't altogether wise of you to keep this Italian plan secret from Papa, and then spring it suddenly on him. (*A knock at door.*)

ELIZABETH. Come in. (*Wilson enters.*) Wilson, please tell Miss Hedley and Miss Henrietta I shall be delighted to see them now.

WILSON. Yes, Miss.

ELIZABETH. (*Going to pick up Flush from sofa.*) Oh, and, Wilson, take Flush with you. He gets so excited when there are several people in the room. (*Hands Flush to Wilson, who exits, closing door. Elizabeth sits on sofa, Arabel turns to her.*) It was Dr. Chambers himself who advised me to say nothing to Papa until both Doctors were satisfied that I was absolutely fit to travel. I quite agreed with him at the time—but now—— Oh, Arabel—(*Arabel walks toward her, she takes Arabel's hands.*) I'm not so sure now! I'm so afraid Papa may think—— (*The voices of Bella and Henrietta are heard off.*) Don't say anything about this to them. (*Arabel nods, sits on sofa beside her.*)

BELLA. (*Off*) May we come in?

ELIZABETH. (*Rising. Arabel also rises.*) Come in, dear. (*Bella flutters in, followed by Henrietta in bridesmaid's gown.*) Bella, dear! (*Elizabeth goes to meet Bella. Arabel moves behind chair. Henrietta comes to desk.*)

BELLA. (*Embracing Elizabeth.*) Darling, darling! Oh, but you weally shouldn't get up to weceive little me.

ARABEL. (*Contemplating Henrietta.*) How perfectly lovely!

ELIZABETH. (*Steps towards Henrietta.*) Delicious.

BELLA. (*As Henrietta turns about to show off gown.*) Yes, isn't it? Isn't she? I should say. Dear Henrietta will be quite the pwettiest of my bwidesmaids. Indeed I'm afwaid she'll dwaw all eyes from the little bwide. At any wate all the gentlemen's. (*Going to Elizabeth and taking both her hands.*) But, darling Ba, you weally mustn't stand about like this! (*Leads her to sofa.*)

ELIZABETH. But I'm as well able to stand as anyone nowadays.

BELLA. (*As Elizabeth submits to being led to sofa, where she sits.*) No, no. One has only to see your dear face, so twanspawent and spiwitual, to know how near you are to Heaven. You always have a look in your eyes, darling, as though you alweady saw the angels.

HENRIETTA. She's looking at me, Bella, and I'm no angel.

BELLA. No, I'm afwaid you're not—but you're vewy, vewy beautiful. And, fancy, Ba, if I hadn't spoken to Uncle Edward myself, I should never have had her for my bwidesmaid.

ELIZABETH. Yes, my dear, you certainly have a way with you.

HENRIETTA. Spoken to Papa. I like that. Why, you sat on his knee and stroked his whiskers.

ARABEL. Henrietta, dear! (*Elizabeth laughs.*)

BELLA. And why not? Isn't he my Uncle? Besides that, I think he's most fwightfully thwilling. I adore that stern and gloomy type of gentleman. It's so exciting to coax and manage them. And so easy—if you know how! And I weally think I do. What I can't understand is his extwaordinawy attitude towards love and mawwiage, and all that. And didn't he mawwy himself—and what's more, have eleven children? (*Uncomfortable silence, as sisters bow their heads.*) Oh, have I said anything vewy dweadful?

ARABEL. No, dear, but perhaps not quite nice. When God sends us children, it's not for us to inquire how and why.

BELLA. I'm so sorry. I didn't mean to be iwevewent. But I do find dear Uncle Edward's attitude extwaordinawy—and so useless. For in spite of it, and wight under his nose, and all unknown to him, his whole house is litewally seething with womance.

ABABEL. Bella!

HENRIETTA. (*Sharply.*) What one earth do you mean?

BELLA. You ought to know, darling.

HENRIETTA. I?

BELLA. (*Enthusiastically.*) I think Captain Surtees Cook is quite fwightfully thwilling. The way he looks at you, dear—and looks, and looks, and looks. If he ever looked at me like that my knees would twemble, and I'd get the loveliest shivers down my back.

ARABEL. (*Rising.*) Really, Bella!

BELLA. And then there's George. *You* may not believe it, but I'm absolutely certain he has a thwilling understanding with your little cousin Lizzie. As for poor Occy—I don't mind telling you in confidence that my dear, dear Ha'wy is fwightfully jealous of him.

ARABEL. Mr. Bevan jealous of Occy! But why?

BELLA. Why indeed? Aren't gentlemen silly?

ELIZABETH. (*Laughing.*) What an extraordinary girl you are, Bella.

BELLA. Oh, I'm a fwightfully observant little thing. F'w instance, though you hardly ever mention his name, I know that Mr. Wobert Bwowning comes here to see you at least once evewy week. But at other times he sends you flowers, and he often bwings little cakes for dear Flush. Flush! Oh, wouldn't it be fwightfully intewesting if only dear Flush could speak!

ARABEL. Good gracious—why?

BELLA. You see, dear Flush is the only witness to all that goes on at Ba's weekly tete-a-tete with the handsomest poet in England. He —Flush I mean—ought to know a wonderful lot about poetwy by this time! For when two poets are gathered together, they talk about whymes and whythms all the time. (*To Elizabeth.*) Or don't they? I'm fwightfully ignowant.

ELIZABETH. Oh, no, my dear. On the contrary, you're "fwightfully" knowing.

BELLA. Me?

HENRIETTA. I hope to goodness you won't chatter any of this outrageous nonsense in front of Papa.

BELLA. But of course I won't bweathe a word of it to Uncle Edward. I'm all on the side of womance, and the path of twue love, and all that.

ARABEL. Bella—I regret to say it, but I think you are one of the few girls I know who would have benefited entirely under Papa's system of upbringing. (*Elizabeth and Henrietta laugh.*)

BELLA. Ooh—what a thwilling thought! He was always fwightfully stwict, wasn't he? Did he whip you when you were naughty? How fwightfully exciting it would be to be whipped by Uncle Edward. (*Barrett opens door, and enters. The sisters are on the alert.*)

ELIZABETH. (*As Barrett enters, closing door after him.*) Papa!

BELLA. Oh, Uncle Edward—Uncle dear, if I had been your little girl instead of Papa's, would you have been tewibly severe with me? You wouldn't, would you? Or would you?

BARRETT. Would—wouldn't—wouldn't—would? Are you trying to pose me with some silly riddle?

BELLA. No, no, no! Sit down. (*She pushes him into chair in front of desk.*) It's like this—but why that gloomy fwown, Uncle Edward? (*Passes fingers lightly over his forehead.*) There—there, all gone. (*Sits on his knee.*) Arabel says it would have done me all the good in the world to have been brought up by you. She thinks I'm a spoilt, fwivolous little baggage, and——

ARABEL. (*Rising.*) Bella—I never said anything of the sort!

BELLA. I know you didn't, but you *do.* (*To others.*) And *you* do—and *you* do. But *you* don't, Uncle, do you?

ARABEL. Really, Bella——

BARRETT. (*Speaking to Bella, but at the others.*) If my children were as bright and affectionate and open as you are, I should be a much happier man.

BELLA. Oh, you mustn't say such things, or they'll hate me.

BARRETT. (*The two are quite withdrawn from and oblivious to the others.*) And you're a distractingly lovely little creature.

BELLA. Anything wrong in that?

BARRETT. (*Thickly.*) I didn't say so.

BELLA. Then why do you look at me so fiercely—do you want to eat me up?

BARRETT. What's that scent you have on?

BELLA. Scent? Me? (*Coyly.*) Don't you like it?

BARRETT. I abominate scent as a rule—but yours is different.

BELLA. Nice?

BARRETT. It's very delicate and subtle—still, I should prefer you not to use it.

BELLA. Why ?

BARRETT. Never mind.

BELLA. (*Triumphantly.*) I never use scent. I haven't a dwop on me! Oh, Uncle, you're a darling! You've called me bwight and open and affectionate, distwactingly lovely, and fwagwent, all within a few minutes. You may kiss me. (*He kisses her roughly on the mouth twice. Suddenly he pushes her abruptly from his knees, and rises. She looks a trifle scared.*)

BARRETT. (*Brusquely.*) There, there, child, run away now, I want to speak to Ba. (*To others.*) You can go, too. (*Crosses to window and stands looking out, his back to the room. Henrietta moves first, and exits. Arabel goes out. Bella exchanges looks with Elizabeth.*)

BELLA. (*In a rather injured voice.*) Good-bye, Uncle.

BARRETT. (*Without turning.*) Good-bye.

BELLA. Good-bye, Ba. (*With a toss of the head she exits, closing door.*)

ELIZABETH. (*As she goes.*) Good-bye, Bella. (*Pause as Elizabeth looks with nervous expectancy at Barrett: who stills stands at window, his back to the room.*)

BARRETT. (*Without turning.*) When is the wedding?

ELIZABETH. The wedding? Oh, Bella's. On the twenty-seventh.

BARRETT. (*Turning, speaking half to himself.*) Good. We are not likely to see much of her 'til then—and afterwards—well, she'll be living in the country most of the year.

ELIZABETH. But I thought you were so fond of her, Papa?

BARRETT. (*Sharply.*) Fond of her? Why not? Isn't she my niece? —She's a disturbing influence in the house. To see your brothers following her about with their eyes—Faugh! The room is still full of her! I shall be glad when she's gone. But I don't want to talk about Bella. Your Doctors have just left me.

ELIZABETH. (*Expectantly.*) Yes, Papa——?

BARRETT. (*With forced heartiness.*) Their report is excellent. Astonishing. I'm more than gratified—I'm delighted. (*Not looking at her.*) Of course, my poor child, it's unlikely that you will ever be a normal woman. Even Chambers—optimistic fool that he is—was forced to admit that. (*Looking at her.*) By the way, who is this Dr. Ford-Waterlow?

ELIZABETH. I've been told he is one of the clevest physicians in London.

BARRETT. Really? Well, he needs some amazing qualities to counterbalance his execrable manners. But even this medical phenomenon was unable to account for the sudden improvement in your health. He put it down to Chambers' ministrations—which is, of course, arrant nonsense.

ELIZABETH. Perhaps the wonderful weather we've been having has most to do with it. I always thrive in warmth and sunshine.

BARRETT. Rubbish! Last summer was sweltering, and you have never been worse than then. No—to my mind there is only One whom we have to thank—though this Doctor what's-his-name was pleased to sneer when I mentioned HIM.

ELIZABETH. HIM?

BARRETT. I mean Almighty God. It amazes me, Elizabeth, that you on whom this miracle of recovery has been worked should ascribe it to mere earthly agencies. Haven't I knelt here night after night and implored our all-loving Father to have compassion on His child? It amazes me. It grieves me unspeakably. This is all I have to say for the present. (*He crosses to door.*)

ELIZABETH. Papa. (*Barrett stops.*)

BARRETT. (*Turning.*) Well?

ELIZABETH. Didn't Dr. Ford-Waterlow speak to you about—about next winter?

BARRETT. Dr. Ford-Waterlow talked, if I may say so, a great deal of nonsense. (*He turns to go.*)

ELIZABETH. (*Stops him at door.*) But, Papa——

BARRETT. (*Testily, turning.*) What is it?

ELIZABETH. Didn't he tell you that I should avoid spending next winter in England?

BARRETT. Well?

ELIZABETH. And that he thinks I shall be fit to travel to Italy in October, if you——

BARRETT. So! It's out at last. And how long has this precious plot been hatching, may I ask?

ELIZABETH. It's now several weeks since Dr. Chambers first mentioned Italy as a real possibility.

BARRETT. And do your brothers and sisters know anything of this delightful project?

ELIZABETH. I believe I mentioned it to them.

BARRETT. You believe you mentioned it to them! And Mr. Kenyon, and Mr. Horne, and the Hedleys, and that charlatan Browning —all your friends and relations, in short—you've discussed all your plans with a lot of them, I suppose?

ELIZABETH. Oh, Papa, what does it matter? My only reason——

BARRETT. Matter? Not in the least! It's nothing at all that I alone should be shut out of my favorite daughter's confidence, treated like a cipher, ignored, insulted——

ELIZABETH. Insulted?

BARRETT. Grossly insulted. When that fellow Ford-Waterlow sprung your carefully-prepared mine on me, and I naturally expressed my astonishment and displeasure he became extremely offensive.

ELIZABETH. Believe me, Papa, my one reason for not worrying you with this Italian idea before, was——

BARRETT. The fear that I should nip it in the bud at once. Exactly, I quite understand.

ELIZABETH. But——

BARRETT. No. I beg you to spare me explanations and excuses. The whole miserable business is abundantly clear. I am cut to the heart that *you*—the only one of my children whom I trusted implicitly—should be capable of such underhand conduct.

ELIZABETH. No—no!

BARRETT. If returning health must bring with it such a sad change of character, I shall be driven to wish that you were once more lying helpless on that sofa. There is nothing more to be said. (*He once more turns to door.*)

ELIZABETH. (*With dignified and restrained passion, rises and walks toward him. He stops.*) But there is something more to be said, and I must beg you to listen to me, Papa. How many years have I lain here? (*He slowly turns to face her.*) Five? Six? It's hard to remember, as each year has been like ten. And all that time I've had nothing to look forward to, or hope for, but death.

BARRETT. (*Completing turn, and crossing to her.*) Death——?

ELIZABETH. Yes, death! I was born with a large capacity for happiness—you remember me as a young girl? And when life brought me little happiness and much pain, I was often impatient for the end.

BARRETT. You shock me! Elizabeth! (*Steps towards her.*)

ELIZABETH. And now this miracle has happened. Day by day I am better able to take and enjoy such good things as everyone has a right to—able to meet my friends—to breathe the open air, and feel the sun, and see grass and flowers growing under the sky. When Dr. Chambers first spoke to me of Italy, I put the idea away from me—it seemed too impossibly wonderful! But as I grew stronger it came over me like a blinding revelation, that Italy wasn't an impossibility at all, that nothing really stood in the way of my going, that I had every right to go.

BARRETT. Right!

ELIZABETH. Yes! Every right! If only I could get your consent.

So I set about consulting my friends, meeting all obstacles, settling every detail, so as to have a perfectly arranged plan to put before you, after the Doctors had given you their opinion. In my eagerness I may have acted stupidly, mistakenly, tactlessly. But to call my conduct underhand and deceitful is more than unkind—it's unjust, it's cruel!

BARRETT. (*More in sorrow than in anger*.) Self! Self! Self! No thought, no consideration for anyone but yourself, or for anything but *your* pleasure.

ELIZABETH. But, Papa——

BARRETT. Didn't it even once occur to you that all through those long dark, dark months you proposed to enjoy yourself in Italy, your father would be left here utterly alone.

ELIZABETH. Alone?

BARRETT. Utterly alone. Your brothers and sisters might as well be shadows for all the companionship they afford me. And you—oh, my child, don't think that I haven't noticed that even you, now that you are stronger and no longer dependent on me, are slowly drawing away from your father.

ELIZABETH. It's not true.

BARRETT. It is true, and in your heart you know it's true.

ELIZABETH. No!

BARRETT. New life, new interests, new pleasures, new friends—and little by little, I am being pushed into the background. I, who used to be your whole world—I who love you—who love you.

ELIZABETH. But Papa——

BARRETT. No. There is nothing more to be said. You want my consent for this Italian jaunt. I shall neither give it nor withhold it. To give it would be against my conscience, as encouraging selfishness and self-indulgence. To withhold it would be a futile gesture. You are at liberty to do as you wish. And if you go, I hope you will sometimes spare a thought for your father. Think of him at night stealing into this room which once held all he loved. Think of him kneeling alone beside the empty sofa, and imploring the Good Shepherd to—— (*A knock at door*.) Eh——?

ELIZABETH. (*With a start, her hand to her heart*.) Oh——

BARRETT. (*Testily*.) Who's that? Come in. (*Wilson enters*.)

WILSON. (*A little flustered*.) If you please, Miss, Mr. Browning has called.

BARRETT. (*Under his breath.*) That fellow again!

WILSON. I showed Mr. Browning into the drawing-room, Miss, seeing as you were engaged.

ELIZABETH. Wouldn't you like to meet Mr. Browning, Papa?

BARRETT. Certainly not. I should have thought you knew by this time, I never inflict myself on any of my children's friends. (*To Wilson.*) You may show Mr. Browning up.

WILSON. Very good, sir. (*She exits, closing door.*)

BARRETT. Mr. Browning appears to consider this his second home.

ELIZABETH. I have not seen him since last Wednesday.

BARRETT. Indeed. (*He exits, closing door. Elizabeth rises to await Browning's entrance.*)

WILSON. (*Opens door and steps inside, announcing.*) Mr. Browning. (*Browning enters and Wilson exits, closing door.*)

BROWNING. (*Crossing to her, taking her hands.*) Oh, but how splendid. This is the fourth time you've received me standing.

ELIZABETH. (*Her whole manner has changed, she is now all sparkle and life.*) If ever I receive you from my sofa again, you may put it down to my bad manners and nothing else.

BROWNING. I will, with all my heart, I will. Tell me quickly, I've been dithering with suspense all day? You've seen them? What did they say?

ELIZABETH. Dr. Ford-Waterlow was quite taken out of his grumpy self with astonished delight at my improvement.

BROWNING. (*Delightedly.*) Say that again.

ELIZABETH. Must I? The whole sentence?

BROWNING. (*Walking about in enthusiasm. Elizabeth sits on sofa.*) I should like to see it in letters of fire burning at me from each of these four walls. This is the best moment I've had since I got your note giving me permission to call on you! How many years ago was that?

ELIZABETH. Three months.

BROWNING. Absurd! We've always been friends. I've known you a lifetime and over! So, he was quite taken out of his grumpy self with astonished delight, was he? (*Sits.*) Splendid! Of course, I never once doubted that you would turn the corner some day. But even I little dreamt recovery would be so rapid. And Italy? Are both Doctors agreed about your wintering there?

ELIZABETH. (*With a note of reserve in her voice.*) Yes.

BROWNING. And when do they think you'll be fit for traveling?

ELIZABETH. The middle of October—unless there's a relapse.

BROWNING. Relapse? There isn't such a word! October! Extraordinary! For you know, October suits my own plans to perfection.

ELIZABETH. Your plans?

BROWNING. Don't you remember my telling you that I had thought of wintering in Italy myself? Well, now I have quite decided. You see, I have practically made up my mind to remodel "Sordello." I should never be able to grapple with the task satisfactorily in England. Impossible to get the Italian atmosphere in a land of drizzle and fog. May I call on you often in Italy? Where do you intend to stay? (*Elizabeth laughs.*) Why are you laughing?

ELIZABETH. In Italy I'm afraid you'll need seven-league boots when you call on me.

BROWNING. What do you mean?

ELIZABETH. I shall be at 50 Wimpole Street next winter.

BROWNING. Here?

ELIZABETH. Yes.

BROWNING. But didn't you tell me that both Doctors were agreed——?

ELIZABETH. Doctors may propose, but the decision rests—elsewhere.

BROWNING. Your Father?

ELIZABETH. Yes.

BROWNING. He has vetoed the plan?

ELIZABETH. No—not exactly. But I am quite sure that he—that it will be impossible for me to go.

BROWNING. But didn't the Doctors make it clear to him that this move of yours may mean all the difference between life and death?

ELIZABETH. I believe Dr. Ford-Waterlow spoke very forcibly.

BROWNING. Then, in Heaven's name——!

ELIZABETH. Oh, it's hard to explain to someone who doesn't know all the circumstances. You see, Papa is very devoted to me, and——

BROWNING. Devoted?

ELIZABETH. He's very devoted to me and depends a great deal on my companionship. He hasn't many points of contact with my brothers and sisters. If I were away for six months, he——

BROWNING. (*Visibly restraining himself, rising and going toward her.*) Miss Barrett, may I speak plainly?

ELIZABETH. Oh, do you think you'd better? I know—more or less —how you feel about this. But you see, you don't quite understand all the situation. How should you?

BROWNING. Oh, very well—then I'll say nothing. (*His control suddenly gives way, and his words pour out.*) You tell me I don't understand. You are quite right. I don't. You tell me he is devoted to you. I don't understand a devotion that demands favors as if they were rights, demands duty and respect, and obedience and love, demands all and takes all, and gives nothing in return. I don't understand a devotion that spends itself in petty tyrannies and gross bullying. I don't understand a devotion that grudges you any ray of light and glimpse of happiness, and doesn't even stop at risking your life to gratify its colossal selfishness. Devotion! Give me good sound, honest hatred, rather than devotion like that!

ELIZABETH. Mr. Browning, I must ask you——

BROWNING. Forgive me, but I won't be silent any longer. Even before I met you, I was aware that sickness wasn't the only shadow in your life. And all these months, even though you never once breathed a syllable of complaint, I felt that other shadow deepening, and I've stood by and looked on, and said nothing. I might find you tired and sick after hateful scenes I could picture only too vividly—and I must pretend to know nothing, see nothing, feel nothing? Well—I've done with pretense from today on. I refuse any longer to let myself be gagged and handcuffed. It's not just your comfort and happiness which are at stake now. It's your very life—and I forbid you to play with your life! And I have the right to forbid you!

ELIZABETH. (*Desperately.*) No—no—no—oh, please don't say any more.

BROWNING. (*With compelling ardor.*) The right—and you won't deny it—you're too utterly candid and true. At our first meeting you forbade me to speak of love—there was nothing more than friendship between us. I obeyed you, but I knew very well—we both knew —that I was to be much more than just your friend. Even before I passed that door, and our eyes first met across the room, I loved you, and I've gone on loving you—and I love you more now than words can tell—and I shall love you to the end and beyond. You know that? You've always known?

ELIZABETH. (*Brokenly.*) Yes—I've always known. And now, for pity's sake—for pity's sake—leave me. (*Rising.*)

BROWNING. (*With a firm grasp of both her hands, rises, comes to end of sofa.*) No!

ELIZABETH. Oh, please—please—let me go! Leave me. We must never see each other again.

BROWNING. (*Maintaining his grasp.*) I shall never let you go—I shall never leave you! (*Draws her into his arms.*) Elizabeth—Elizabeth!

ELIZABETH. (*Struggling feebly.*). No—no—— Oh, Robert, have mercy on me——

BROWNING. Elizabeth, my darling—— (*He kisses her, and at the touch of his lips her arms go round his neck.*)

ELIZABETH. Oh, Robert—I love you—I love you—I love you. (*They kiss again, then she sinks onto sofa. He sits, holding her hands.*)

BROWNING. And yet you ask me to take my marching orders, and go out of your life.

ELIZABETH. Yes, Robert, for what have I to give you? I have so little of all that love asks for. I have no beauty, and no health—and I'm no longer young——

BROWNING. I love you.

ELIZABETH. (*With restrained spiritual ecstasy.*) I should have refused to see you after our first meeting. For I loved you then, though I denied it even to myself. Oh, Robert, I think Eve must have felt as I did when her first dawn broke over Paradise—the terror—the wonder—the glory of it. I had no strength to put up any kind of resistance, except the pitiful pretense of mere friendship. I was paralyzed with happiness that I had never dreamt it was possible to feel. That's my only excuse—and God knows I need one—for not having sent you away from me at once.

BROWNING. I love you.

ELIZABETH. My life had reached its lowest ebb. I was worn out, and hope was dead. Then you came. Robert, do you know what you have done for me? I could have laughed when Dr. Chambers said that I had cured myself by wanting to live. He was right—oh, he was right. I wanted to live—eagerly, desperately, passionately—and all because life meant you—you—— (*He leans down to kiss her hands.*) —and the sight of your face, and the sound of your voice, and the touch of your hand. Oh, and so much more than that! Because of you the air once more was sweet to breathe, and all the world was good and green again.

BROWNING. (*Rising from kissing her hands.*) And with those words singing in my ears, I'm to turn my back on you and go?

ELIZABETH. But, Robert, can't you see how impossible——?

BROWNING. I've never yet turned my back on a friend or an enemy. Am I likely to turn it on you?

ELIZABETH. But how is it all to end? What have we to look forward to? And how——?

BROWNING. I love you, and I want you for my wife.

ELIZABETH. Robert, I can't marry you. How can I, when——?

BROWNING. Not today or tomorrow. Not this year, perhaps, or next year. Perhaps not for years to come——

ELIZABETH. I may never be able to marry you.

BROWNING. What then? If you remain to the last beyond my reach I shall die proud and happy in having spent a lifetime fighting to gain the richest prize a man was ever offered.

ELIZABETH. Oh, Robert, put aside your dream of me and look on me as I am. I love you too well to let you waste your manhood pursuing the pale ghost of a woman.

BROWNING. Do you think I'm a boy to be swept off my feet by an impulse, or a sentimental dreamer blind to reality? There's no man alive who sees things clearer than I do, or has his feet more firmly planted on the earth. And I tell you in all soberness that my need of you is as urgent as your need for me. If your weakness asks my strength for support, my abundant strength cries out for your weakness to complete my life and myself.

ELIZABETH. (*After pause.*) Robert, have you thought what your position here would be like if you went on seeing me after today?

BROWNING. Yes.

ELIZABETH. We should have to keep our love secret from everyone lest a whisper of it get to my Father's ears.

BROWNING. I know.

ELIZABETH. If he had the least suspicion that you were more than a friend, the door would be slammed in your face, my letters supervised, and my life made unbearable.

BROWNING. I know.

ELIZABETH. And you, my dear, you're as frank and open as the day. How would you enjoy coming here under false pretenses, and all the subterfuges and intrigues we'd be forced to use?

BROWNING. (*Smiling.*) I shall detest it—I shall hate it with all my heart and soul—and I thank God for that.

ELIZABETH. But Robert——

BROWNING. For it's splendid and right that I should suffer some discomfort at least for such a reward as you. The immortal garland was never won without dust and heat.

ELIZABETH. (*Bitterly.*) Immortal! Oh, Robert, fading, if not already faded. (*He is about to protest.*) No, don't speak! Don't speak! (*She rises.*) Robert, if we were to say good-bye today, we should have nothing but beautiful memories of each other to last to the end of our lives. We should be unhappy, but there are many kinds of unhappiness. Ours would be the unhappiness of those who have put love away from them for the sake of love. There would be no disillusion in it, or bitterness, or remorse.

BROWNING. (*Turning to her, in low tense voice.*) Is it *you* who are speaking?

ELIZABETH. What do you mean?

BROWNING. I don't know you. I thought yours was the courage that dared the uttermost, careless of defeat. Here's life—*life*—offering us the best that life can give, and you dare not grasp at it for fear it will turn to dust in your hands. We're to dream away the rest of our lives in tepid sadness, rather than risk utter disaster for utter happiness. I don't know you—I never thought you were a coward.

ELIZABETH. (*Proudly and indignantly.*) A coward? I? (*With a sudden change of voice.*) Yes, I am a coward, Robert, a coward through and through—but it's not for myself that. I'm afraid.

BROWNING. (*Going swiftly to her and taking her in his arms.*) I know that, my darling.

ELIZABETH. What's another disaster, great or small, to me who have known little but disaster all my life? But you're a fighter, and you were born for victory and triumph. If disaster came to you through me——

BROWNING. Yes, a fighter. But I'm sick of fighting alone. I need a comrade-at-arms to fight beside me.

ELIZABETH. Not one already wounded in the battle?

BROWNING. Wounded, but undefeated, undaunted, unbroken!

ELIZABETH. Yes, but——

BROWNING. Then what finer comrade could a man ask for?

ELIZABETH. But, Robert—— (*He bends down and kisses the protests from her lips.*)

BROWNING. No.

ELIZABETH. But, Robert——

BROWNING. No. (*Continues kissing away her protests as curtain falls.*)

CURTAIN

ACT III

Scene 1

The scene is the same. The room is the same as in Act II, with the following few changes. The sofa is now straight. A book has been placed on mantel. The desk has been tidied up. All the flowers have been removed. There are five letters recently received for Elizabeth on desk.

TIME: *The time is late afternoon.*

AT RISE: *The room is lighted by the light of the late afternoon sun. The stage is empty at rise. When curtain is well up Arabel, in outdoor clothes and carrying Flush, opens door and enters.*

ARABEL. (*Speaking as she enters.*) You had really better let Wilson help you up the last few stairs, Ba.

ELIZABETH. No! No, Wilson! I'm quite all right!

ARABEL. But, my dear—— (*Elizabeth, also in outdoor attire, enters, breathless but triumphant. Wilson follows at her heels.*)

ELIZABETH. There! All the way up and without one pause or help of any kind! And I feel splendid—just a little out of breath, that's all. (*Sways a little, and Wilson stretches out her hand to support her.*) No, don't touch me—I'm quite all right. Now, wasn't that a glorious triumph? (*Sits on sofa.*) And you know, Wilson, I got out of the carriage and walked quite two miles in the Park!

WILSON. Lor', Miss! (*Elizabeth gives bonnet to Wilson: who crosses to put them in wardrobe.*)

ARABEL. Ba, dear——!

ELIZABETH. Well, one mile then. Anyhow, that's what I'm going to tell Dr. Chambers.

ARABEL. Really, Ba——

ELIZABETH. Oh, my dear, Flush has muddied your gown disgracefully. (*To Flush.*) What a filthy state you're in, Flushy!

Wilson, you had better take him and get Jenny to bathe him. He's not been properly washed for ages.

WILSON. (*Taking Flush from Arabel.*) Very good, Miss. (*Wilson exits, carrying Flush.*)

ELIZABETH. (*Pointing to letters on desk.*) Oh, the post has come. Please give me those letters, dear?

ARABEL. (*Crosses to desk and returns, handing her letters.*) Why, that's Mr. Browning's handwriting! I'm sorry, I couldn't help seeing it. But aren't you expecting him this afternoon?

ELIZABETH. Yes—— (*Opens letter and reads it with a smile, throws envelope in fire, and stops at corner of sofa.*) Yes, dear, he should be here very soon now. This was just to wish me good night.

ARABEL. To wish you good night?

ELIZABETH. Yes, you see it was written yesterday evening.

ARABEL. Oh!

ELIZABETH. (*Running through other letters.*) Mr. Hayden—Miss Martineau—Mr. Horne—— (*With a sharp change in her voice.*) Oh! This is from Papa——

ARABEL. (*Anxiously.*) From Papa? But he's returning today.

ELIZABETH. (*Opening letter.*) Perhaps he's been detained.

ARABEL. (*Hopefully.*) Oh, do you think so?

ELIZABETH. (*Quickly scanning letter, then in consternation.*) Oh! Oh—Arabel——!

ARABEL. What is it, my dear?

ELIZABETH. We're leaving.

ARABEL. Leaving?

ELIZABETH. Yes—leaving this house. Leaving London. Listen—— (*A knock at door, and Henrietta's voice is heard.*)

HENRIETTA. May I come in, Ba?

ELIZABETH. Come in, dear. (*In a hurried whisper to Arabel.*) Don't speak of this yet. (*Henrietta enters, leaving door open.*)

HENRIETTA. (*In great excitement.*) Oh, Ba, you must see him at once! You positively must!

ELIZABETH. See *him?*

HENRIETTA. He's in his full regimentals! He's just been to St. James to receive—or whatever you call it—his adjutancy or something from Queen Victoria herself. He's wonderful! He's gorgeous! May I bring him up here for you to look at?

ELIZABETH. But——

HENRIETTA. Papa need never know. (*Elizabeth sits on sofa.*) Oh, Ba, do let me! You've never seen him yet—it's high time you met—and you couldn't see him to better advantage than now. I'm talking of Captain Cook, you know.

ELIZABETH. Yes, so I gathered. But I can't see him now, dear, as I'm expecting Mr. Browning any minute.

HENRIETTA. (*Crestfallen but resigned.*) Oh—then of course it's impossible. But I tell you what, Ba! I'll try to keep him until Mr. Browning goes. I don't think he'll mind. He likes sitting and staring at me. We can both stare at each other. He's well worth staring at today. You can keep your poet here as long as you like. (*Exits, closing door.*)

ELIZABETH. (*With a short laugh ending in a sigh, staring after her.*) Yes, she had best make the most of her soldier while she can, poor darling. (*She takes up Barrett's letter.*)

ARABEL. Oh, Ba—tell me quickly——

ELIZABETH. (*Taking up letter, reading.*) He writes from Dorking: "This is to let you know that we shall be leaving London on Monday the twenty-second of this month. I have taken a furnished house at Bookham, in Surrey, some twenty miles from London, and six miles from Leatherhead, the nearest railway station. Whether we shall eventually make it our permanent home, I have not yet decided. At any rate we shall spend the winter there. You will benefit by the country air, and the complete seclusion of your new surroundings. I have felt for some time now that your present feverish restless mode of life in London will, if continued, affect you harmfully, both physically and morally. I am writing this letter so that you may inform your brothers and sisters of my decision, and tell them that I decline absolutely to discuss it when I return home tomorrow." That's today.—"The matter is finally settled, and you and they will make such preparations as are needful for the move."

ARABEL. Oh, Ba——

ELIZABETH. (*Bitterly.*) That's not quite all. He finishes up with a characteristic touch of humor.

ARABEL. Humor?

ELIZABETH. Yes. He signs himself, "Your loving Papa."

ARABEL. The twenty-second. That gives us barely a fortnight longer here.

ELIZABETH. (*Walking to fireplace, where she crumples and throws letter into grate.*) My "feverishly restless mode of life"! A few drives—a few calls on my friends—a few visitors! I wonder he doesn't describe me as a recklessly dissipated woman! He made my going to Italy impossible and now I am to be cut off from any little pleasures I have begun to find here. (*Drops into chair.*)

ARABEL. I know, dear, I understand and I'm dreadfully sorry for you. The change won't hit me so hard. My only ties in London are my Mission work and district visiting. But you and Henrietta——

ELIZABETH. Well?

ARABEL. (*With sudden earnestness.*) Oh, Ba, don't be angry with me. We all pretend to be ignorant of each others' affairs in this house—except poor Henrietta's. It's safer so. And yet we know—we all know—that you and Mr. Browning——

ELIZABETH. Well——?

ARABEL. Oh, Ba, one has only to look at your face when you re expecting him—and again after he has left you——

ELIZABETH. (*Proudly.*) I love him and he loves me. What of it? Haven't I as much right to love and be loved as any other woman?

ARABEL. Oh, yes dear—but how is it all to end? As long as Papa's alive none of us will ever be able to marry with his consent—and to marry without it is unthinkable. And in your case it isn't only a question of Papa's consent. Of course it's—it's wonderful how much stronger and better you are. You walked upstairs splendidly just now—but—but——

ELIZABETH. But even if I can manage to walk up a few steps, it doesn't mean that I shall ever be fit to marry—is that what you're trying to say?

ARABEL. Oh, Ba, darling, it's because I love you so dearly, and don't want you to suffer, that I'm forcing myself to speak. I know very little about gentlemen—except that they all want to marry the ladies they fall in love with. I don't know Mr. Browning at all—but even great poets want to settle down in time, and have a home —of their own—and a wife—and little ones. It would be so dreadful, if——

ELIZABETH. (*Springing up, crosses to window.*) Oh, be quiet! Be quiet! Do you suppose I haven't thought of all that a thousand times already? (*She turns to window and looks out.*)

ARABEL. I am sorry—I—I didn't mean to interfere. (*Rising.*) All

I want is to save you any—— (*Notices that Elizabeth, her face transformed with joy, is no longer listening, but is waving her hand to someone in the street.*) Oh——! (*She crosses and exits quietly, closing door softly, unnoticed by Elizabeth.*)

ELIZABETH. (*Turning.*) Mr. Browning has just—— (*She realizes the empty room.*) Oh——! (*Her eyes fall on crumpled letter in grate, she picks it out, smooths it, and puts it on mantelpiece, her face emptied of joy. Knock at door. She crosses.*) Come in. (*Browning enters. They look at each other in silence for a second.*)

BROWNING. (*Crosses to her, takes her in his arms.*) My love!

ELIZABETH. Oh, Robert! (*They kiss.*)

BROWNING. (*Holding her at arms' length.*) You look tired, sweetheart. What have you been doing today?

ELIZABETH. (*With forced lightness.*) I went for a drive and a walk in the Park. And then I ran all the way upstairs without help, and without one stop——

BROWNING. Oh, but you know! Of course, dearest, it's a splendid feat and I'm proud of you! Come and sit down. (*Points to chair, she sits, he stands, facing her.*) Now, don't you think you're being a trifle too ambitious?

ELIZABETH. (*Looking aside.*) I don't think so—I'm feeling wonderfully well.

BROWNING. Look at me. (*She does so.*) What's the matter, Ba?

ELIZABETH. (*Looking away.*) Nothing——

BROWNING. Has your Father returned?

ELIZABETH. No—we expect him today.

BROWNING. Those talking eyes of yours give you hopelessly away. Something has gone wrong. What is it? You must tell me.

ELIZABETH. Read that letter on the mantelpiece, Robert.

BROWNING. (*Crossing to mantelpiece, taking Barrett's letter.*) From your Father?

ELIZABETH. Yes. (*He reads letter to himself, then looks at her, a peculiar smile on his face.*) Well?

BROWNING. (*Still smiling.*) I think, by the look of it, you crumpled up this letter furiously in your hand—and I'm quite sure you pitched it into the grate.

ELIZABETH. Yes, I did.

BROWNING. (*Replacing letter on mantel, crossing to her.*) Why?

ELIZABETH. Oh, Robert, don't you see what this means to us?

BROWNING. Yes—and perhaps a great deal better than you do.

ELIZABETH. Better than I? Oh, you mustn't deceive yourself. You don't know Papa as I do. He's grown jealous of my life here, my pleasures and my friends, and I'm slowly and surely to be parted from them. Oh, Robert, it will soon be made impossible for me to see you at all.

BROWNING. This precious letter may mean all that. But it means a great deal more that you haven't as yet been able to grasp.

ELIZABETH. A great deal more——?

BROWNING. It means that you will be in Italy before the month is out.

ELIZABETH. (*In a whisper.*) Italy?

BROWNING. Yes, and with me. It means that we must be married at once.

ELIZABETH. Do you know what you are saying?

BROWNING. Yes, I know what I'm saying—and I repeat it. We must be married at once! My darling, listen to me—— (*He is about to take her hands.*)

ELIZABETH. No! Don't touch me! What you say is madness. I can't marry you. I can never marry you.

BROWNING. You can and you shall! You'll marry me if I have to carry you out of this house and up to the altar. Do you seriously imagine I'm going to allow myself to be elbowed out of your life, now? And just to satisfy the selfish jealousy of a man whom I no longer believe to be sane? You ought to know me better by this time.

ELIZABETH. (*Quickly breaking in.*) Oh, Robert, it's not only Papa who stands between us. It's I—it's I——

BROWNING. We've been into that a hundred times already, and——

ELIZABETH. Yes—and now we shall go into it once again, and frankly, and for the last time. Robert, it's no use deceiving ourselves. However much stronger I become, I shall always remain an invalid. You tell me that you want me, sick or well. And it's wonderful of you to say this. But I—Robert, I'm not generous enough—I'm too proud, if you like. As your wife I should be haunted by the thoughts of all the glories you would have enjoyed but for me—freedom—adventure—and passionate love I could never really satisfy.

BROWNING. Oh, no, listen——

ELIZABETH. Oh, Robert, I should be haunted by the ghosts of your unborn children. When I read that letter my world seemed to fall to pieces. But now I thank God that it came while we're still free, and have the strength to say good-bye.

BROWNING. (*Matter-of-fact.*) On the whole I think this will be our best plan of campaign. The family leave here on the twenty-second. So we have barely a fortnight to get everything done in. You told me last week that Mr. Hedley had invited your sisters to picnic in Richmond Park next Saturday. So the house will be conveniently empty. We'll meet at Mary-le-Bone Church, and be married quietly some time in the morning. I'll see about the license and interview the Vicar at once.

ELIZABETH. (*Who has been staring at him in bewilderment.*) Robert——

BROWNING. It would be madness to leave England on the same day. You'll want all the rest and quiet you can get before the journey. So after the ceremony I think you had better come back here and take things easily for a week or two. You'll have six days if we leave here on Saturday week. Now—— (*Takes paper from pocket.*)

ELIZABETH. Oh, stop! I can't listen to you!

BROWNING. (*Consulting paper.*) For some time now I've kept careful note of the sailings from Southampton in case of just such an emergency as this. The Packet leaves the Royal Pier on Saturdays at nine o'clock. We must catch the five o'clock express at Vauxhall. (*Rises.*) It arrives at Southampton at eight.

ELIZABETH. (*Laughs wildly, changing to sobs.*) Oh——! And I always thought that Papa was the most overbearing man in the world——

BROWNING. (*Kneeling and smiling.*) And yet you've known me for some time now.

ELIZABETH. But I mustn't give way, Robert, I daren't.

BROWNING. There's one other thing, my darling, of the utmost importance, that we must settle at once. You can't possibly travel without a maid. You tell me Wilson is entirely devoted to you. Do you think she will be willing to come abroad with us?

ELIZABETH. (*After a pause, in a low voice.*) Robert—have you ever thought that my strength may break down on the journey?

BROWNING. Yes.

ELIZABETH. Suppose I were to die on your hands?

BROWNING. (*Quietly.*) Are you afraid, Ba?

ELIZABETH. (*Proudly, indignantly.*) Afraid? I? You know that I am not afraid. You know that I would sooner die with you beside me, than live a hundred lives without you. But how would *you* feel if I were to die like that? And what would the world say of you?

BROWNING. (*Quietly.*) I should be branded as little less than a murderer, and what I should feel I leave you to imagine——

ELIZABETH. And yet you ask me to come with you?

BROWNING. Yes. I am prepared to risk your life and much more than mine, to get you out of this dreadful house into the sunshine, and to have you for my wife.

ELIZABETH. You love me like that?

BROWNING. I love you like that. (*A long pause. Elizabeth sits motionless staring in front of her.*)

ELIZABETH. Robert—give me a little time?

BROWNING. Time is short, my dear.

ELIZABETH. (*Rising.*) Yes, I know. But I must have a little time. I can't decide now. I daren't. (*Browning rises.*) Give me a few hours. Before I sleep tonight, I'll write and tell you my decision. Please, Robert?

BROWNING. (*Following after Elizabeth.*) You promise me that?

ELIZABETH. I promise.

BROWNING. Very well.

ELIZABETH. Thank you.

BROWNING. Shall I go now?

ELIZABETH. Please—— (*He kisses her hand, goes straight out, closing door. Elizabeth stands motionless, staring at door. A slight pause, then a knock at door, another pause then a louder knock. Elizabeth starts from her reverie.*) Come in. (*Henrietta enters.*)

HENRIETTA. I saw Mr. Browning going down the stairs. May I bring him in?

ELIZABETH. Him?

HENRIETTA. He's standing on the landing outside. Wake up, Ba! I'm talking of Surtees.

ELIZABETH. Won't some other time do as well?

HENRIETTA. No—no! I told you he was in uniform. You promised to see him, Ba.

ELIZABETH. (*With a sigh.*) Very well, dear——

HENRIETTA. (*Runs to door, speaking off into passage.*) Come in, Surtees. (*Capt. Surtees Cook, arrayed in regimentals, and with his headgear under his arm, enters.*) Captain Surtees Cook, Ba—my sister, Elizabeth.

COOK. (*Bowing stiffly.*) Your servant, Miss Barrett.

ELIZABETH. How do you do. (*She sits on sofa.*)

COOK. (*Crossing to her, taking her hand and bowing over it.*) Greatly honored, upon my word I am, Miss Barrett. Understand not everyone received here.

HENRIETTA. No, indeed, Surtees! With the exception of the family very few gentlemen have ever been allowed in Ba's room.

COOK. Twice honored in one day, ye know. First by Her Majesty, now by you, Miss Barrett. Can't think what I've done to deserve it.

ELIZABETH. Oh, I had forgotten! You've just come from the Palace! I have never seen the Queen. What is she like?

COOK. Very little lady, Ma'am, but royal, every inch of her.

HENRIETTA. Surtees, you haven't got your sword on!

COOK. Not etiquette, as I told you, to wear it indoors.

HENRIETTA. Oh, bother etiquette! I want Ba to see you in full war paint. Where did you leave it?

COOK. In the hall.

HENRIETTA. I'll fetch it. (*Runs to door.*)

COOK. (*Following.*) No, but really—Miss Barrett doesn't want——

ELIZABETH. But indeed I do, Captain Cook. I don't think I've ever seen an officer in—full war paint before.

COOK. (*After short pause, steps to her.*) Indeed? Er—Miss Barrett——

ELIZABETH. Yes?

COOK. Miss Barrett——

ELIZABETH. (*Encouragingly.*) Yes, Captain Cook?

COOK. I say, Miss Barrett——

ELIZABETH. You want to tell me something about Henrietta?

COOK. (*Eagerly.*) Just so, Miss Barrett, just so. Exactly. You know, Miss Barrett, you know—— (*He is unable to go on.*)

ELIZABETH. (*Very kindly.*) Yes, Captain Cook, I know. And though I'm powerless to help, believe me you have my heartfelt sympathy. (*She gives him her hand.*)

COOK. (*As he takes her hand.*) Thank you. Thank you. More than I deserve. Thank you, Miss Barrett. Never was such a girl, y'know—Henrietta, I mean. Dunno what I've done to deserve it.

HENRIETTA. (*Re-enters with sword, closing door.*) Oh, yes, I thought he'd seize the opportunity to tell you something while I was out of the room. Did he really manage to get it out?

ELIZABETH. (*Smiling.*) Well, not quite. Did you, Captain Cook?

COOK. Well—ah—y'know—still, like most ladies—quick in the uptake.

ELIZABETH. Yes, I understand. My dear, how I wish I could do something for you both!

HENRIETTA. Well, you can't—nobody can. Surtees wants to ask Papa—for my hand and all that—quite like the conventional suitor. I can't get it into his poor old head that such things simply are not possible at 50 Wimpole Street. (*Cook sits.*)

ELIZABETH. (*Earnestly.*) Oh, believe me, Captain Cook, it would be more than useless.

COOK. Quite aware that I'm not much of a match, Miss Barrett. Poor man, y'know. Still, decent family and all that. Should be more than willing, if necessary to throw soldiering and take to some money-making business, but——

HENRIETTA. And a fine mess you'd make of it, my poor dear!

COOK. Well, I'm not so sure about that. Admit, of course, that soldiering's my special job. Haven't the brain for much else, I'm afraid. Still, you never know what a fellah can't do with a prize like Henrietta to reward his efforts.

HENRIETTA. Well, anyhow, you're not to speak to Papa, and I forbid you to give up soldiering. Now that I've seen you in your glory, do you suppose I should ever take you without your uniform? (*Rises and crosses to him.*) Get up. I want to buckle on your sword. (*She kneels.*)

COOK. Aw, I say—— (*Rises, smiling rather sheepishly.*)

HENRIETTA. (*Starting to fasten on sword.*) Ba thinks poets are the flower of manhood—a certain poet, at any rate. I mean to show her that she's mistaken——

COOK. I say, you've got it wrong. Sword hangs from the left hip, y'know.

HENRIETTA. Why?

COOK. Well—— (*Door opens and Barrett enters, taking in scene with a look of amazement, his face hardening. Henrietta rises; both girls stare in consternation. Cook stands rigid.*)

ELIZABETH. Papa—you're—you're home earlier than I expected, Papa.

BARRETT. (*Slowly and deliberately closing door.*) I don't think I have the privilege of this gentleman's acquaintance.

HENRIETTA. Captain Cook, may I introduce my Father? Papa—Captain Surtees Cook.

COOK. Your servant, Sir. (*Both men bow stiffly.*)

HENRIETTA. Captain Cook is a great friend of George and Occy's.

BARRETT. Indeed? (*To Cook.*) My sons are very rarely at home at this time of day.

COOK. Fact is—just passing the house—thought I'd look in on the off chance, y'know, sir—finding one of them in, and all that——

BARRETT. I see.

ELIZABETH. (*Breaking a pause.*) Captain Cook has just come from Buckingham Palace and Henrietta thought I should like to see him in all the splendor of his regimentals.

BARRETT. Indeed. (*Takes out his watch.*)

COOK. Nothing much to look at, of course—but ladies like a bit of color, and—er—m-m—— By Jove, must be getting late.

BARRETT. It's nineteen and a half minutes past five.

COOK. By Jove! High time I were moving—— Good-bye, Miss Barrett.

ELIZABETH. (*Giving him her hand.*) Good-bye, Captain Cook. (*Barrett crosses to door and holds it open.*)

COOK. Good-bye, Miss Henrietta.

HENRIETTA. I'll see you out. (*Cook moves to door, followed by Henrietta.*)

COOK. (*To Barrett.*) Your servant, sir. (*Barrett returns his bow in silence. Cook exits and Henrietta is about to follow. Barrett stays her with a gesture.*)

HENRIETTA. I am seeing Captain Cook to the door.

BARRETT. The servant will attend to that. (*He closes door in silence, crosses to fireplace, stands with his back to it, speaking straight before him.*) Your list of gentlemen visitors appears to be lengthening, Elizabeth.

ELIZABETH. This is the first time I have had the pleasure of meeting Captain Cook.

BARRETT. (*Turning.*) Indeed. But I infer from what I saw as I came into the room, that Henrietta's acquaintance is of somewhat longer standing? Or am I *mistaken?*

HENRIETTA. I have known Captain Cook for some time now.

BARRETT. Ah! And since when has it been your custom to buckle on his accoutrements?

HENRIETTA. I have never seen him in uniform before.

BARRETT. And I think it improbable that you will see him in uniform, or in mufti, very frequently in the future.

HENRIETTA. (*In a strained voice.*) Why?

BARRETT. (*To Elizabeth.*) You received my letter?

ELIZABETH. Yes, Papa.

BARRETT. What has just happened fully confirms me in the wisdom of my decision. This house is fast becoming a rendezvous for half London. I have neither time nor inclination to find out whether all the persons visiting here are desirable acquaintances for my children. Fortunately our new home is so far from town that your London friends are not likely to trouble us—at least during the winter.

HENRIETTA. (*Blankly.*) Our new home?

BARRETT. (*To Elizabeth.*) You have not told your sisters?

ELIZABETH. Arabel knows.

HENRIETTA. I don't understand. Are we—are we leaving Wimpole Street?

BARRETT. (*Without looking at Henrietta.*) I have taken a house at Bookham, in Surrey, and we move in on the twenty-second.

HENRIETTA. Why?

BARRETT. I am not in the habit of accounting for my actions to anyone—least of all to my children.

HENRIETTA. But one thing I have a right to ask you, Papa. If Captain Cook is to be forbidden to visit us, is it because you found him here in Ba's room, and saw me fastening on his sword?

BARRETT. I understood you to say that Captain Cook was George's friend, and Occy's?

HENRIETTA. Yes, and my friend, too.

BARRETT. Ah!!

HENRIETTA. Yes, and since it was I who suggested his seeing Ba, and I who asked him to show me how to buckle on his sword, it's unjust to penalize him for——

ELIZABETH. (*Sharply.*) Henrietta——

BARRETT. (*In a sharp low voice, advancing slowly toward Henrietta.*) Come here.

HENRIETTA. (*Takes a few steps towards him, and says somewhat breathlessly.*) Yes, Papa?

BARRETT. (*Regards her steadily, and points to the floor at his feet.*) Come here. (*She goes right up to him, breathing quickly and fearfully. He keeps his eyes on her face, then in a low ominous voice.*) What is this fellow to you?

HENRIETTA. I—I've told you—he's a friend of ours.

BARRETT. What is he to *you?*

HENRIETTA. A—a friend.

BARRETT. Is that all?

HENRIETTA. (*In a whisper.*) Yes.

BARRETT. (*Suddenly grasping her wrist, his voice like the crack of a whip.*) You liar!

ELIZABETH. (*Sharply.*) Papa!

HENRIETTA. (*Gaspingly.*) Let me go!

BARRETT. (*Tightening his grip.*) What's this man to you? Answer me! (*She tries to free herself and cries out.*) Answer me!

HENRIETTA. (*Wildly.*) Oh, Papa,—please——

BARRETT. Answer me!

HENRIETTA. (*Trying to resist.*) Oh, don't—don't——

BARRETT. Answer me!

HENRIETTA. (*In a strangled voice.*) He's—he's—— Oh, Papa, I love him.

BARRETT. (*Between his teeth, seizing her other wrist, forcing her to her knees.*) And you—you—you—— (*She gives a cry of pain.*)

ELIZABETH. (*Rising from sofa, crosses to Barrett, seizing his arm.*) Let her go, Papa! I won't have it! Let her go, at once! (*He flings Henrietta off, and she collapses in a heap on floor, her face buried in her hands, sobbing.*)

BARRETT. (*Turning to Elizabeth.*) And you—you knew of this filthiness?

ELIZABETH. I've known for some time that Henrietta loved Captain Cook, and I've given her all my sympathy.

BARRETT. You dare to tell me——

ELIZABETH. Yes—and I would have given her all my help as well, if I had had it to give.

BARRETT. I'll deal with you later. (*To Henrietta.*) Get up.

HENRIETTA. (*Suddenly clasping his knees, in a voice of passionate entreaty*) Oh, Papa, please listen to me—please! I—I'm not a bad girl—I swear to you I'm not. I know I've deceived you—and I'm sorry. I'm sorry—but I couldn't help it. I—I love him—and if you'd known, you'd have turned him from the house. Oh, can't you under-stand—won't you try to understand? He's a good man—and it can't be wrong to love him. Other women love—why must I be forbidden? I want love. Remember—remember how you loved Mama, and how she loved you—and—you'll understand and pity me——

BARRETT. (*Inexorably.*) Get up!

HENRIETTA. (*Drops to floor again from his knees. Elizabeth sits on sofa.*) Have pity on me, Papa.

BARRETT. Get up. (*She brokenly rises.*) Sit there. (*He points to chair. She sits, he crosses to her.*) How long has this been going on? (*No answer.*) Do you hear me? How long have you been carrying on with this fellow?

HENRIETTA. I—I've known him a little over a year.

BARRETT. And you've been with him often?

HENRIETTA. Yes.

BARRETT. Alone?

HENRIETTA. Yes.

BARRETT. Where?

HENRIETTA. We—I—I've met him in the Park, and—and——

BARRETT. And—here?

HENRIETTA. Yes.

BARRETT. Here! And alone? (*Henrietta is silent.*) Have you met him in this house alone?

HENRIETTA. Yes.

BARRETT. So! Furtive unchastity under my roof. (*Turning to Elizabeth.*) And abetted by one whom I believed to be wholly chaste and good——

HENRIETTA. No—no.

ELIZABETH. (*Fiercely.*) How dare you, Papa!

BARRETT. Silence! (*To Henrietta.*) Now attend to me. Something like this happened a year or two ago, and I thought I had crushed the devil in you, then. I was wrong. It needed sterner measures than I had the courage to use. But now, unless I have your solemn word that you will neither see nor have any communication with this man again, you leave this house at once, as you are, with nothing but the clothes you have on. In which case you will be your own mistress and can go to perdition any way you please. But of this you may be certain. Once outside my doors you will never again be admitted under any pretext whatever, so long as I live. I think by this time you have learnt that it's not my habit to make idle threats, and that I never go back on my word. Very well. You have your choice. Take it.

HENRIETTA. (*After an agonized mental struggle.*) Is it nothing to you that I—that I shall hate you for this to the end of my life?

BARRETT. Less than nothing.

HENRIETTA. But—but I must let Captain Cook know that——

BARRETT. No. I will deal with Captain Cook.

HENRIETTA. (*Desperately, dropping her head in her hands.*) But, Papa——

BARRETT. Will you give me your word that you will neither see nor have any communication with this man again?

HENRIETTA. (*After a pause, in a choked voice.*) I—I have no choice——

BARRETT. Give me your Bible, Elizabeth.

ELIZABETH. Why?

BARRETT. I am not prepared to accept your sister's bare promise, but I think even she would hesitate to break an oath made with her hand resting on the Word of God. Give me your Bible.

ELIZABETH. No. My Bible belonged to Mama. I can't have it used for such a purpose.

BARRETT. Give me your Bible!

ELIZABETH. No.

BARRETT. You refuse?

ELIZABETH. Yes. (*Without a word, Barrett crosses and pulls bell-rope, then stands tapping his fingers on mantel. A pause. No one speaks or moves, then Wilson enters.*)

BARRETT. I want you to go to my bedroom and fetch my Bible. (*Wilson starts to go, he stops her.*) Are your hands clean?

WILSON. (*Bewildered, looks at her hands.*) My hands, sir?

BARRETT. Are they clean?

WILSON. (*With a touch of asperity.*) Yes, sir. I've just been helping to bathe Flush.

BARRETT. You will find the Bible on the table beside my bed.

WILSON. Very good, sir. (*She turns; exits. All are silent and motionless till she returns. After a moment she re-enters with Bible.*)

BARRETT. (*Pointing to desk.*) Place it on the table. (*Wilson does so, turns and exits. Barrett crosses to desk. To Henrietta.*) Stand up! (*Henrietta rises and goes to desk.*) Place your hand upon the book. (*She does so.*) Repeat after me: "I give my solemn word that I will neither see, nor have any communication with Captain Cook again."

HENRIETTA. (*In a toneless voice.*) "I give you my solemn word that I will neither see, nor have any communication with Captain Cook again."

BARRETT. You will now go to your room and remain there until you have my permission to leave it. (*Without a word, but with head held high, Henrietta goes out. Barrett continues after a pause.*) Have you anything to say to me, Elizabeth?

ELIZABETH. (*In a dead voice.*) No.

BARRETT. Then I must leave you under my extreme displeasure. I shall not see you again. I can have nothing to do with you, until God has softened your heart, and you repent of your wickedness and ask His forgiveness—and mine. (*He picks up Bible and goes out. The moment he has closed door, Elizabeth gets up with an air of decision, crosses and pulls bell-rope. A pause, then Wilson enters.*)

ELIZABETH. Shut the door, please. (*Impulsively, as Wilson does so.*) Wilson, are you my friend?

WILSON. (*Bewildered.*) Your—friend, Miss?

ELIZABETH. Yes, my friend. I am in dire need of friendship and help at the moment.

WILSON. I—I don't quite understand, Miss Ba—but I'm that fond of you, I'd do anything to help you.

ELIZABETH. You would? And I know I can trust you?

WILSON. Yes, indeed, Miss.

ELIZABETH. Wilson, next Saturday I am going to marry Mr. Browning.

WILSON. (*With a gasp.*) Marry——

ELIZABETH. Hush! We're to be married secretly at Mary-le-Bone Church. Will you come with me?

WILSON. Me, Miss—yes, Miss—and gladly——

ELIZABETH. Directly afterwards I shall return here for a few days, and——

WILSON. (*In boundless amazement.*) Here! With Mr. Browning!

ELIZABETH. (*With a hysterical laugh.*)No—no—no! Just alone with you. Then on the following Saturday I shall join Mr. Browning, and we're going abroad. We're going to Italy. Will you come with us?

WILSON. (*In a whisper.*) To Italy——?

ELIZABETH. Yes—will you come with me?

WILSON. Well, Miss, I can't see as how I can help myself. Not that I 'old with foreign parts—I don't. But 'usband or no 'usband, you'd never get to Italy alive without me.

ELIZABETH. Then you'll come? Then you'll come! Oh, I am so glad! I'll tell Mr. Browning—(*Crosses to desk, takes out writing materials.*) I'm writing to him now. And I shall want you to take the letter to the post at once. Go and put on your things—I'll have finished by the time you're ready.

WILSON. Yes, Miss. (*Wilson goes out. Elizabeth is writing as curtain falls.*)

CURTAIN

Scene 2

The scene is the same, with the following few changes. Chair has been moved up to window. Lamp on desk has been taken away. Most of the books have been removed from small bookcase. Elizabeth's coat and hat are in wardrobe. Nine letters written by Elizabeth to members of her family are on desk.

TIME: *The time is early evening.*

AT RISE: *Elizabeth is discovered kneeling beside Flush's basket, fastening a lead to his collar. She pats his head abstractedly, rises, picks up little pile of letters from desk, runs through them, crosses and places them on mantel. Then with a shuddering sigh, she walks to window, clasping and unclasping her hands in agitation. After a moment she sighs again, crosses to mantel, picks up letters and crossing, places them one by one on desk again. After a moment Wilson enters, hurries in with two traveling rugs on her arm. Elizabeth at desk walks to upper armchair, crosses back to desk chair.*

WILSON. Ah, Miss Ba, I'm that sorry! In my flurry to get the luggage off to the railway station yesterday, I clean forgot to pack these rugs, and there was 'eaps of room in the carpet-bag.

ELIZABETH. Never mind.

WILSON. (*Putting rugs over back of chair.*) I do hope we haven't forgotten nothing else.

ELIZABETH. And if we have it won't matter much. Mr. Browning insisted that we should travel as lightly as possible. We shall be able to get all we need in Paris.

WILSON. Lor', Miss, it don't seem possible we'll be in Paris to-morrow!

ELIZABETH. No—— (*Consulting watch.*) Oh, how the time crawls. We've still an hour and a half of this dreadful waiting. You're sure, Wilson, they quite understood at the livery stables, exactly when, and where, the cab was to meet us?

WILSON. (*Taking Elizabeth's things from wardrobe.*) Oh, yes, Miss, I was most particular to see that the young man took it all down—the cab to be at the corner of Wimpole Street at ha' past three, punctual. It won't take us more than ten minutes to get to Hodgson's Library, and then Mr. Browning will 'ave us in his charge. (*Drops voice to a warm conversational tone.*) Your 'usband, Miss Ba, dear——

ELIZABETH. (*Coming to her.*) Oh, hush! Hush! Don't breathe that word here——

WILSON. But, Miss Ba——

ELIZABETH. I'm foolishly nervous, but I can't help it. The very walls seem to be listening.

WILSON. There is no one in the house except Miss Henrietta. She was putting on her bonnet as I came along the passage, so she should have gone out by now. (*Wilson gets bag and hat from wardrobe.*)

ELIZABETH. Oh, Wilson, it's impossible to believe that in a little more than an hour I shall have left this room, never in all likelihood to see it again.

WILSON. And glad you'll be to see the last of it, I'm sure, Miss Ba.

ELIZABETH. Yes—and no. I've been very miserable here, and very happy. Oh, I wish it were time to go! This waiting is killing me.

WILSON. 'ave you finished writing your letters, Miss?

ELIZABETH. (*Almost hysterically.*) Yes. Yes. I've written to them all. I've just been reading over my letter to Mr. Barrett to see if there was something I could add—something—anything. But I can't think—I can't think——

WILSON. Least said, soonest mended, Miss. (*With chuckling laugh.*) Oh, Miss Ba, I know I shouldn't say such things—but there's a lot I'd give to be here tonight when the Master reads your letter.

ELIZABETH. The very thought terrifies me. I can see his face—I can hear his voice. Thank God, we shall be miles and miles away. (*Looks at watch.*) An hour and twenty minutes still—— Will time never pass?

WILSON. Why don't you write some poetry, Miss?

ELIZABETH. (*Turns dumbfounded.*) Poetry——?

WILSON. Yes, Miss. That'll make the time pass nicely, I know.

(*Elizabeth bursts into laughter, as Henrietta in bonnet and shawl enters with letter in hand. Elizabeth looks at her frightened.*)

ELIZABETH. (*Turning her letters on their faces.*)I—I thought you had gone out.

HENRIETTA. Wilson, I want to speak to Miss Ba.

WILSON. Yes, Miss. (*Crosses, exits, closing door.*)

HENRIETTA. I was just going out when I ran into a messenger at the door. He brought this letter—it's for you.

ELIZABETH. (*Anxiously, reaching for letter.*) For me?

HENRIETTA. (*Retaining letter.*) Yes, but it's in—in *his* handwriting.

ELIZABETH. Captain Cook's?

HENRIETTA. Yes.

ELIZABETH. Open it, dear.

HENRIETTA. (*Tears open letter and reads.*) "Dear Miss Barrett, I know I am doing very wrong in drawing you once again into my and Henrietta's affairs. But the matter is so urgent I am sure you will forgive me. My regiment has been ordered to Somerset at short notice, and I must positively see Henrietta before I go. If I wrote to her directly, my letter would certainly be read by Mr. Barrett. I understand he opens all her correspondence. Hence my trespass on your kindness. Will you please give Henrietta the enclosed letter, and believe me your grateful and obedient servant, Surtees Cook." (*She lets letter drop to floor, while she opens enclosure, which she reads eagerly. Elizabeth picks up letter from floor, tears it into bits, and throws them into fireplace.*) You remember Papa threatened to turn me out of the house unless I swore on the Bible not to write to or see Surtees?

ELIZABETH. (*Turning to face her.*) Yes.

HENRIETTA. Well—I am going to break that "Bible oath" today!

ELIZABETH. (*Quietly.*) Are you, dear?

HENRIETTA. Yes—and I shall glory in breaking it! And if Papa asks where I have been, I shall go out of my way to lie to him as often and as grossly as I can.

ELIZABETH. (*Quietly.*) I see. But why do you tell me this?

HENRIETTA. (*Fiercely.*) Because I want you to say that I'm a wicked, deceitful, perjured, *loose* woman, so that I can fling the words back in your face. (*Elizabeth crosses to her, and Henrietta suddenly flings her arms round Elizabeth.*) Oh, Ba, darling, forgive me! I'm not myself these days. I am all love and hate—and I don't know which is the worst torture.

ELIZABETH. (*With passionate tenderness, arms about Henrietta.*) My dear, you think I don't understand! I do—I do. And I feel for you and pity you with all my heart. I can do nothing to help you— I daren't even advise you. But never lose hope—never lose courage —never—— (*Wilson enters quickly, in great agitation.*)

WILSON. Oh, Miss Ba—Miss Ba——! The Master! (*They stare at Wilson, Henrietta in amazement, Elizabeth in terror.*)

ELIZABETH. Shut the door!

WILSON. (*As she does so, then crosses to Elizabeth.*) He's just come in—just this minute. He must 'ave heard—someone must 'ave told him——

ELIZABETH. Be quiet. (*Wilson steps back up a little.*)

HENRIETTA. (*In amazement.*) But, Ba, what on earth is the matter?

ELIZABETH. Nothing—nothing! It's—it's only that Papa hasn't been to see me for ten days now—ever since—you remember? And— and scenes of forgiveness are always trying. (*To Wilson.*)Put away my hat and cloak quick. (*Wilson does so, in wardrobe.*)

HENRIETTA. (*Crossing to Elizabeth.*) I don't believe that's all. You're as white as a sheet. What did Wilson mean? Ba, is there anything I can——?

ELIZABETH. (*Softly, intensely.*) No—no—no! Don't speak—don't ask me anything. You know nothing—you understand? Nothing— nothing!

HERIETTA. But——

ELIZABETH. (*To Wilson.*)Those rugs——! (*Wilson picks up rugs from chair. A knock at door. Wilson gasps. Elizabeth answers in a whisper, turning towards fireplace.*) Come in. (*Clears her throat, then louder.*) Come in. (*Turning from fireplace. They are standing in tense attitudes when Barrett enters. Henrietta is watching Elizabeth, who commands her voice.*) You're home early, Papa. (*Barrett, without replying, looks at each of the three in turn, then crosses to front of fireplace. Wilson, obviously terror-stricken, exits with rugs over her arm.*)

BARRETT. (*To Elizabeth.*) What's the matter with that girl?

ELIZABETH. Wilson?

BARRETT. Yes.

ELIZABETH. Nothing, Papa——

BARRETT. (*After staring broodingly at her for a moment, crosses to Henrietta.*) Where have you been?

HENRIETTA. Nowhere.

BARRETT. Where are you going?

HENRIETTA. To tea with Aunt Hedley.

BARRETT. Is that the truth?

HENRIETTA. Yes.

BARRETT. You remember your oath?

HENRIETTA. Yes.

BARRETT. Have you kept it?

HENRIETTA. Yes.

BARRETT. Are you going to keep it?

HENRIETTA. Yes.

BARRETT. I wish to speak to your sister—you can go. (*Without a glance at either of them Henrietta crosses, exits, closing door. Elizabeth stands at fireplace. Barrett walks to armchair and turns.*) Do you know why I am back so early?

ELIZABETH. (*In a whisper.*) No, Papa.

BARRETT. (*In a low intense voice.*) Because I could bear it no longer. It's ten days since last I saw you.

ELIZABETH. Am I to blame for that, Papa?

BARRETT. You dare to ask me such a question? Weren't you a party to your sister's shameless conduct? Haven't you encouraged her? And did you expect to go scot-free of my displeasure? (*Stopping himself with a violent gesture.*) I've not come to speak about that—but to put it behind me—to forget it! I wonder, my child—have you been half so miserable these last ten days as your Father?

ELIZABETH. Miserable, Papa?

BARRETT. Do you think I can be happy when I'm bitterly estranged from all I love in the world? Do you know that night after night I had to call up all my will-power to hold me from coming here to forgive you?

ELIZABETH. Papa——

BARRETT. All my will-power, I tell you—all my sense of duty, and right, and justice. But today I could bear it no longer. The want of your face and your voice became a torment. I had to come. I am not so strong as they think me—I had to come—and I despise myself for coming, despise myself, hate myself——

ELIZABETH. (*Crossing to him on sofa, puts hands on his shoulders*) Oh, Papa, can't you see, won't you ever see, that strength may be weakness, and your sense of justice and right and duty may be mistaken and wrong?

BARRETT. (*In a tense voice, putting her hands off his shoulders.*)

Mistaken and wrong? What do you mean? (*Quickly stopping her.*) No, be silent. Don't answer me. Mistaken and wrong? You don't know what you're saying.

ELIZABETH. If you'll only listen to me, Papa, I——

BARRETT. No.

ELIZABETH. But, Papa——

BARRETT. No! (*Crosses to fireplace, stands half turned away. A pause, his voice calm as he continues.*) If there were even a vestige of truth in what you say, my whole life would be a hideous mockery. For always, through all misfortunes and miseries, I've been upheld by knowing beyond a doubt what was right, and doing it unflinchingly, however bitter the consequences. And bitter they've been—how bitter only God knows. It's been my heavy cross that those whom I was given to guide and rule have always fought against the right that I knew to be the right, and was in duty bound to impose upon them. Even you. Even your Mother.

ELIZABETH. (*In a whisper, turning to him.*) My Mother?

BARRETT. (*His back to fireplace.*) Yes, your Mother. But not at first. You—you, my eldest child, were born of love, and only love. But the others—long before they came, the rift began to open between your Mother and me. Not that she ever opposed me—never once. Or put into words what she felt. She was silent, and dutiful, and obedient. But love died out, and fear took its place——

ELIZABETH. (*A whisper.*) Oh, dear God, what she must have suffered!

BARRETT. She? She? And what of me?

ELIZABETH. You? Oh, Papa, then you loved her after her love for you had died?

BARRETT. (*Embarrassed, looking aside.*) Love? What's love? She was my wife. You—you don't understand——

ELIZABETH. (*In same horrified whisper.*) And all those children—born in fear! Oh, it's horrible—it's horrible——! (*Covers face with her hands.*)

BARRETT. (*Embarrassed, taking a couple of steps toward her.*) Ba, my dear—don't—don't. I shouldn't have spoken—I shouldn't have told you all that. Forget it, my child. (*Crosses to her.*) Take your hands from your face. (*Gently takes her wrists, she starts away from him with frightened eyes.*) Don't look at me like that. (*In a low thick voice, averting his eyes.*) You don't understand. How should you? You know nothing of the brutal tyranny of passion, and how the strongest and best are driven by it to hell. You would have abetted your sister in her——

ELIZABETH. Henrietta's love—how dare you speak of it in the same breath as——

BARRETT. Her love? You ignorant little fool! What do *you* know of love? Love! The lust of the eye—the lowest urge of the body!

ELIZABETH. (*Starting to rise.*) I won't listen to you.

BARRETT. (*Taking her hands and putting her down again.*) You must—you shall! Do you suppose I should have guarded this house like a dragon from this so-called love, if I hadn't known from my own life all it entails of cruelty and loathing, and degradation and remorse? With the help of God, and through years of tormenting abstinence, I strangled it in myself. And so long as there's breath in my body, I'll keep it away from those I was given to protect and care for. You understand me?

ELIZABETH. (*A low voice, looking him in the face.*) Yes—I understand you.

BARRETT. (*Turns away from her. She sits quite still looking straight before her.*) This has been a hateful necessity. I had to speak plainly, but we must turn over this ugly page and forget what was on it.

ELIZABETH. (*Drawing her hand from his.*) I shall never forget what you said!

BARRETT. Never—perhaps that's as well. (*With sudden urgency.*) But for God's sake, my darling, don't let this raise any further barrier between us! Your love is all I have left to me in the world.

ELIZABETH. You had Mamma's love once—you might have had the love of all your children.

BARRETT. Yes, if I'd played the coward's part, taken the easier way, shirked my duty. I'd rather be hated by the whole world than gain love like that.

ELIZABETH. Oh, Papa, you don't know how I pity you!

BARRETT. Pity? I don't want your pity, but if I should ever lose you, or if I should ever lose your love—— (*He seizes her unwilling hands.*) Ba, my darling, next week we shall have left this house. I've grown to loathe it—even this room has become hateful to me. In our new home we shall draw close to each other again. There will be little to distract you in the country—nothing and no one to come between us. (*He draws her stiffening form into his arms.*) My child, my darling, you must look up to me and depend on me, lean on me. You must share your thoughts with me, your hopes, your fears, your prayers. I want all your heart and all your soul. (*He draws her passionately close to him. She leans away from him, her face drawn with fear and pain.*)

ELIZABETH. (*Sobbingly.*) I can't bear it—I can't bear any more. Let me go, Papa—please let me go! (*He releases her, she stands aside, her arm covering her face.*)

BARRETT. Forgive me, dear—I was carried away. I'll leave you now.

ELIZABETH. (*In a whisper.*) Please——

BARRETT. (*Rising.*) Shall I see you again tonight?

ELIZABETH. (*As before.*) Not tonight.

BARRETT. I shall pray for you.

ELIZABETH. (*Half to herself.*) Pray for me? Tonight? Yes, pray for me tonight—if you will. (*He touches her forehead gently, goes out. Elizabeth sits a moment staring before her, then with frightened eyes around the room, she whispers.*) I must go at once—I must go—I must go—— (*Rises quickly, gets cloak and bonnet from wardrobe. Wilson enters stealthily and hurriedly, rugs on her arm.*)

WILSON. He's gone to the study.

ELIZABETH. (*Putting on her bonnet.*) We must go—now—at once!!

WILSON. But, Miss Ba——

ELIZABETH. At once! Help me on with my cloak.

WILSON. (*Doing so.*) But the cab won't be there yet—not for an hour. Besides——

ELIZABETH. Then we must walk the streets. I can't stay here any longer. I'm frightened—I'm frightened. Fetch your cloak and bonnet. Quick!

WILSON. Walk about the streets, Miss? You can't—you can't! Besides, the Master's at home—he may see us leaving——

ELIZABETH. (*Crossing to desk, arranging letters.*) He can't stop me. I don't belong to him any more—I belong to my husband. Papa can kill me, but he can't stop me!

WILSON. I daren't, Miss—I daren't!

ELIZABETH. Then I must go alone!

WILSON. You can't do that!

ELIZABETH. (*With compelling earnestness, turning to face Wilson.*) Wilson—things have passed between my father and me which force me to leave this house at once. Until today I've never really known him. He's not like other men—he's dreadfully different. I

—I can't say any more. If you draw back, you need never reproach yourself. But I must go now.

WILSON. I'll fetch my hat and cloak, at once, Miss. (*Elizabeth puts her arm about her neck and kisses her.*) Oh, Miss Ba—— (*Crosses, and exits quickly. Elizabeth turns, spreads out letters on desk, then from a ribbon on which it is hung she draws her wedding ring from her bosom, and slips it onto her finger. She looks at it a moment, then slowly draws on her gloves. Wilson re-enters quickly and softly in cloak and bonnet.*)

ELIZABETH. I am quite ready. You take the rugs Wilson—I had better carry Flush.

WILSON. (*Breathlessly.*) Yes, Miss. (*Gets Flush from basket and gives him to Elizabeth.*)

ELIZABETH. And now just slip downstairs and see whether the study door is shut.

WILSON. Very well, Miss. (*She exits quickly, leaving door open. Elizabeth, with an indescribable expression on her face, stands with Flush under her arm, and looks about room. Wilson re-enters speaking in a breathless whisper.*) Yes, Miss—the door is shut, and all is quiet.

ELIZABETH. Very well. (*Speaking to Flush as she goes.*) If you bark now, Flush, we're lost! (*She passes out, exits, Wilson follows, closing door softly after her. The room stands empty for a moment, then lights slowly dim down and out to darkness.*)

(*A period of darkness for thirty seconds to indicate the passage of an hour or more of time, then lights slowly come back. After lights are up, a moment's pause, then Arabel enters.*)

ARABEL. Ba dear, I want—— (*Realizes the room's emptiness, and looks bewilderedly about, exits and immediately returns with lamp which she places on desk, where she sees letters Elizabeth has left. Picks one up in agitation, and whispers.*) For me—what can it mean? (*Sits in chair by desk, tears letter open, reads it with little gasping exclamations.*) Oh—No! No! Married!—No! Oh—Oh! Married! Gone—— (*She looks up from letter, her face transformed in excitement, crosses to sofa and sits, then suddenly goes off into shrieks and peals of laughter. After a moment the voices and hurriedly approaching footsteps of George, Charles, Octavius, are heard outside, and they hurriedly enter.*)

GEORGE. Arabel! For Heaven's sake!

CHARLES. What is it?

GEORGE. Arabel! What on earth?

OCTAVIUS. High-strikes! B-by Jove! (*Arabel continues laughing.*)

GEORGE. (*Slapping one of her hands.*) Stop that, Arabel! Stop it at once!

ARABEL. (*Half gasping, half shrieking.*) Married—gone! Married—gone! (*Another wild peal of laughter.*)

GEORGE. Be quiet! (*Slaps her hand again.*) Fetch some water, someone! (*Rises, starts up.*)

OCTAVIUS. Eau-de-cologne—— (*Crosses up to dressing-table. Alfred, Henry, Septimus, two dressed, other without coat and collar, enter quickly.*)

ALFRED. What's the matter?

HENRY. Is Ba ill? Arabel!

ARABEL. (*Gaspingly.*) She's married—she's gone—married—gone—— (*Henrietta enters in cloak and bonnet. Stands a moment taking in scene, as Arabel continues.*) Married and gone—married and gone—— (*She moans and sobs. Realization begins to dawn on others.*)

CHARLES. What does she mean? Where's Ba?

ARABEL. Married and gone!

SEPTIMUS. Married and gone—she's mad!

GEORGE. (*Taking Arabel's shoulders.*) Arabel—what do you mean?

OCTAVIUS. Married!

HENRIETTA. (*Suddenly pushing them aside, seizes Arabel by shoulders, shakes her vigorously.*) Arabel—Arabel! Pull yourself together at once! Where's Ba? Answer me! Where's Ba?

ARABEL. She—she's m-m-married Mr. Robert Browning——

HENRIETTA. (*In a whisper.*) Married—— (*Consternation among others and amazed exclamations: "Married!" "Married!" "It can't be true!"—"Robert Browning." "Good God!" etc. Henrietta continues to Arabel, who is still sobbing.*) Where is she?

ARABEL. (*Indicating letters on desk.*) She—she's gone! Those letters—she's written to—to—all of us! She—she's gone—— (*Octavius crosses to desk, followed by Alfred, Henry, and Septimus. Alfred takes his letter. Henrietta gets her letter.*)

GEORGE. Yes—she was married last Saturday.

OCTAVIUS. (*From desk, holding up a letter.*) And this one is for

P-papa. (*There is a frightened silence, only Henrietta looks before her with a frightened smile on her face.*)

ARABEL. (*In a shuddering whisper.*) P-p-papa—!

SEPTIMUS. Is he in?

GEORGE. He's dressing for dinner.

OCTAVIUS. What's to be d-done?

HENRY. Someone must give him Ba's letter.

HENRIETTA. Let me—I should love to.

ARABEL. (*In a whisper.*) Oh, hush—hush——! (*She tremblingly indicates door, and all stand breathless. Footsteps are heard approaching. Barrett, in evening dress, appears on threshold as he enters.*)

BARRETT. (*Looks at assembled family in stern amazement, no one stirs.*) What is the meaning of this? (*No one stirs or replies.*) Who was making that hideous noise just now? (*Still no one stirs or replies, he continues sharply.*) Where is Elizabeth? (*A silence, he crosses to Henrietta. Arabel rises, clings to Henrietta's arm.*) Do you hear me? (*To Henrietta.*) Where is your sister?

HENRIETTA. (*Freeing herself from Arabel, hands Barrett his letter.*) She left you this letter.

BARRETT. (*Without touching it, in a low voice, his face a dreadful mask.*) Left me? What do you mean?

HENRIETTA. She left letters for all of us—this is yours. (*Arabel sits on sofa. Barrett, his eyes fixed on Henrietta's face, takes letter and is about to open it, when she suddenly springs forward and seizes his arm, continuing passionately and entreatingly.*) You must forgive her, Papa—you must forgive her—not for her sake—but for yours. I thought I hated you—but I don't. I pity you—I pity you! And if you've any pity on yourself—forgive her. (*He looks at her steadily for a moment, then pushes her aside. He opens and reads letter. No one stirs. Nothing but the fury of his quickened breathing shows his emotion. He starts as if to collapse, Henrietta and Octavius go to him; he pushes them aside. He turns and walks up to window, quite steadily, but his gait gives the impression that he is blind. He stands in front of window, his back to room, his hands tightly clasped behind him, grasping letter. The movement of his shoulders shows that he is breathing quickly and heavily. No one stirs.*)

BARRETT. (*Half to himself, turning from window.*) Yes—yes—her dog. (*An ugly smile flickers across his face.*) Yes—I'll have her dog—— Octavius!

OCTAVIUS. Sir?

BARRETT. Her dog must be destroyed! At once! (*Slightly raising his voice.*) You will take it to the vet—tonight! You understand me? Tonight! (*A pause.*) You understand me!

OCTAVIUS. (*Desperately.*) I really d-don't see what the poor little beast has d-done to——

BARRETT. (*Ominously.*) You understand me?

HENRIETTA. (*Vainly trying to control the triumph in her voice.*) In her letter to me, Ba writes that she has taken Flush with her! (*Barrett's face once more becomes a still white mask. He stands perfectly still, staring straight before him, mechanically tearing letter into little pieces which drop to his feet, as curtain falls.*)

CURTAIN

For Discussion

The Barretts of Wimpole Street

ACT I, Scene 1.

1. What do the dialogue and action at the opening of this scene reveal about Elizabeth's situation, outlook, and interests in life? Describe her personality. Is Dr. Chambers' advice about her need for a change a foreshadowing of later events in the play? Why does the playwright dwell on Elizabeth's dislike for porter? How does the playwright use this incident to show the kind of person her father is?

2. Contrast Arabel and Henrietta. How do Henrietta's remarks prepare the audience for Mr. Barrett's entrance? Why is there so little contrast in the characters of Elizabeth's brothers? Which one seems most alive? Is their outward docility exaggerated, or is it typical of the sons in a Victorian family? Discuss.

3. Compare the mood at the opening of this scene with the mood at the end of the scene. What effect does the end of Scene 1 achieve?

ACT I, Scene 2.

1. In this scene, further light is thrown on the characters and situation set up in the first scene. Elizabeth is intent on reading the poetry of Mr. Robert Browning. In her conversation with Occy, she criticizes her brothers' over-submissiveness. Lastly, there is the entrance of Mr. Browning and a scene ending in direct contrast with that of Scene 1. How does each of these major points, particularly the last, heighten the tension and further the progress of the play?

2. Point out the difference in character and attitude of both Bella and Robert Browning to the Barrett family. Does Bevan seem a suitable husband for Bella? Explain.

3. This scene is a mingling of gaiety and banter with serious overtones. Can you point out instances of this in Mr. Browning's remarks to Elizabeth? In Bevan's comments on her poetry?

ACT II

1. Observe in this scene, the parallel with the opening of the first scene: Elizabeth is once more with her physician. "The wish to live is better than a dozen physicians," says Doctor Chambers. How do you account for Elizabeth's present will to live? Is Chambers aware of the cause? (Awareness by the audience of facts unknown to a character is known as *dramatic irony*.)

2. Here again there is a strong alternation in tone and mood. Trace the change of mood through each of the climactic points in this act. How is each point related to the other? To the play as a whole?

3. What self-revelation is made by Mr. Barrett in this scene? What are the emotional effects on the audience at its close? What dramatic purpose does Bella's little conquest of her uncle serve? How is the tension relaxed after Mr. Barrett's exit?

4. Point out instances in this scene showing Elizabeth's heroic philosophy of life.

ACT III, Scene 1.

1. How does Mr. Barrett's letter add to the mounting tension? What does it reveal about his affection for his daughter?

2. Suspense is further heightened both for Elizabeth and the audience by Arabel's cautioning her sister to give up love and yield to their father's will. What does the passage disclose about Arabel's choice regarding life?

3. The climax is quickly reached with Browning's entrance. How does he interpret the father's letter? What do his well-laid plans prove regarding his feeling for Elizabeth? Do you admire his decisiveness? Why?

4. How does Mr. Barrett's treatment of Henrietta explain the family's fear of opposing him? What effect does it have on the girl? On Elizabeth? Are both these effects in the natural event of things? Discuss fully.

ACT III, Scene 2.

1. Dramatic tension is now at its peak. What effect does Henrietta's unexpected entrance have at this moment? What has Wilson just

said that made Elizabeth laugh? Can you understand why she laughed?

2. Show how Henrietta's resolution regarding Surtees Cook parallels, in a way, Elizabeth's own decision regarding Robert. Contrast their decisions in the light of each girl's attitude toward their family, their father, and life in general.

3. What is the final threat to Elizabeth's happiness? How does her father's exposition of love's "meaninglessness," together with his ironic decision to "keep it away from those I was given to protect," affect her final decision?

4. Describe the closing scene. Explain how each person's reaction is typical of his or her personality. Why is the final, triumphant line reserved for Henrietta? Is the closing effective? Discuss.

Reviewing the Play As a Whole

1. The two general aims of comedy are to gratify our love of laughter and to see the good triumph over every obstacle. Are these aims realized in this play? Discuss. Point out details of Victorian life and customs which are especially amusing. Which characters provide most cause for laughter? What obstacles prevent the "good" characters from realizing their ambitions?

2. How would you state the theme of the play in a single sentence?

3. What do you consider the climax or turning point of the play?

4. Describe the denouement of the play.

5. Does the fact that the romance is based on actual fact give weight to its plausibility and to your acceptance of it as reality?

6. An interesting follow-up to the reading of this play would be your reading Elizabeth Barrett Browning's *Sonnets from the Portuguese*, particularly her poem, "How Do I Love Thee?"; also Browning's "Prospice," written after her death.